Body and Self

Body and Self

Elements of Human Biology,
Behavior, and Health

George J. Bloch, Ph.D.

WILLIAM KAUFMANN, INC. ▪ LOS ALTOS, CALIFORNIA

LOVINGLY DEDICATED TO

My father and my mother, for their unflagging
support and their uncompromising principles.

ISBN 086576-041-1

Printed in the United States of America

Contents

CHAPTER 9: Skeletal Muscles, the Control of Movement, and Muscle Tone 191

CHAPTER 10: Reproduction, Sex Hormones, and Behavior 211

CHAPTER 11: The Chemical Nature of the Brain 245

Introduction

This book is based on over fourteen years of experience teaching college students physiological psychology and medical physiology. During these years it has become clear to me that even though a proper teaching of these subjects requires the student to learn a tremendous amount, the material should not become so detailed that one can no longer "see the forest for the trees." This problem is not easy to solve. When I first became interested in these topics over 20 years ago, it was customary for students to learn most of the material on their own. Small groups of psychologists at a few universities were intensely devoted to studying the relation between psychology and physiology, but their emphasis was much more on research than on teaching. Typically, students of psychology would have to wait until they entered graduate school before they were exposed to enough material to make firm connections between psychological processes and biological processes. In general, this method of learning was successful. Students would join a group interested in some specialized area. They would become part of a laboratory devoted to the study of learning and memory, the study of stress and avoidance behavior, sleep and dreams, sexual behavior, and so forth. Here they would gain not only technical knowledge of research techniques, but also detailed knowledge of neurophysiology and other areas of human and animal biology to "round out" their training.

Today things are different. Many people are actively seeking to understand the relationship between our psychological states and the body, and the converse—how our body's activities influence our behavior and psychological states. Some wish to pursue a career in health, others to specialize in psychosomatic medicine. Still others are interested mainly in psychology that can be applied in therapy, counselling, or in discussions with friends. Many are interested in these topics simply for themselves.

It is impossible for a person to fulfill any of these goals by taking just one class or by reading just one book. Eventually, this interdisciplinary interest must be approached from all sides. At one time this might mean a study of anatomy, at other times biochemistry—or comparative behavior, mental disease, psychotherapy, theories of personality, nutrition, or acupuncture.

For some, the enormity of the task can be very discouraging. Unfortunately, many excellent, highly motivated students begin to settle for much less than what their talents are capable of providing. *This book has been written in an attempt to provide encouragement—encouragement to continue the study of how psychology and behavior, health, and human biology interact with each other so that subsequent studies of the numerous detailed, intricate mechanisms involved will pose a wonderful challenge rather than a tedious chore.*

Over my years of teaching, I have found that encouragement lies in emphasizing three fundamental points:

1) *Physiological mechanisms are generally EXPERIENCED by us in one way or another.* Once we begin to become familiar with these experiences, the relevance of physiology to behavior and psychology ceases to be a question. The study of physiology then becomes an exciting search for self-knowledge.

2) *A general layout of important structures of the BRAIN and their function is all that is needed to instill an appreciation for body-mind interactions.* Once basic structures and functions are grasped, further study of the detailed workings involving neurophysiology and neuroanatomy is an adventure.

3) *Everything that we learn about ourselves can be connected to HEALTH in simple, obvious ways.* With this recognition, a more detailed study of health and disease becomes an extension of what we already know rather than a separate, mysterious discipline.

This book covers basic functions such as eating, drinking, breathing, and sexual behaviors, drives such as hunger, and thirst, feelings such as anger, rage, fear, and anxiety, skills such as reading, writing, and speech, and a variety of terms describing psychological function such as consciousness, attention, arousal, stress, reward, volition, addiction and dependence, sleep and dreams, satiety, and depression. In covering these topics, I will not attempt to explain the psychological bases for their existence. If you are looking for a body of knowledge that defines the precise psychological parameters that modify bodily processes and/or create disease, you will be disappointed, for no such body of knowledge exists. We are still quite ignorant of what these parameters are. A major reason for this lack is that there has not been enough focused study and research to provide the information required; we are looking at functions that are determined by a tremendous number of variables, all of which have to be carefully controlled if the answers we get are to have meaning.

Each chapter of this book does contain a considerable amount of information on what types of psychological variables are most influential in affecting the bodily processes being discussed, and, as you will discover, our knowledge of the connecting links between physiological and psychological functions has advanced considerably, even in the last decade. Because much of this knowledge has to do with the workings of the brain, its contribution constitutes a section of every chapter. The brain does not exist in isolation, however, and for this reason the function of other organs is sometimes discussed in detail so that their contribution to our psychological functioning can be appreciated.

Each chapter also contains a section on health in specific relation to the topics covered in the chapter. Although specific abnormalities and diseases are included to give the reader a good introduction to psychosomatic medicine, the main emphasis of this book is on processes that occur to all of us in our normal, day-to-day existence. A primary goal has been to show clearly that *our state of health is largely determined by physiological/psychological interactions which, for the most part quite commonplace, are very influential.*

Chapters 3 through 10 open with a brief presentation of a specific medical disorder associated with the subject to which the chapter is devoted. Again, in these "overtures," the attempt has been to make clear both the psychological and physiological contributions to disease. As you continue to read through the chapter, you will better understand these specific disorders. This format is also designed to encourage readers to regard disease in a broad body-mind framework.

Wherever possible, the attempt has been made to show how *specific physiological functions are often associated with specific experiences and thereby connected to specific psychological processes.* An appreciation of this fact is important in understanding body-mind interactions. To take this concept and put it to practical use seemed best accomplished by starting with very simple, basic functions where body-mind interactions are quite obvious—so much so, in fact, that you may think it not worthwhile to discuss them. Behind these commonplace relationships, however, lies a wealth of information about ourselves, as you will quickly discover.

For example, in discussing mechanisms of hunger and thirst (Chapters 3 and 4), you will learn that these states are not just singular experiences nor are they represented by single physiological mechanisms. In discussing breathing (Chapter 5) you will find that how we breathe has a powerful influence on the activity of our brain and, therefore, on our mental and emotional states. Conversely, you will see that our emotional states have a profound influence on our rate of breathing. When you read about the sense organs and sensory experiences (Chapter 6), it will become apparent that what we call "consciousness" is quite varied and to a large extent depends upon which mechanisms are being activated. In discussing defense mechanisms (Chapter 7), you will see that profound connections exist among stress, our emotions, and our ability to be protected from disease. Chapter 8's consideration of mechanisms of arousal and sleep will reveal that these functions not only exert a very powerful influence on our physical state but also are inseparably connected to attention, experiences of satiety, and many other functions. A look at skeletal muscle (Chapter 9) will make clear its importance as a biofeedback organ that we can use to regulate our level of arousal. Under reproductive function (Chapter 10), you will see that female/male functions are not only clearly different, but also, in many respects, identical. Finally, in the overview of the chemical nature of the brain (Chapter 11) you will discover that such variables as how we perceive a situation, our level of stress, and even what we eat can affect extremely refined chemical workings that influence all of the functions discussed in the earlier chapters. In addition, you will discover that these chemical workings are connected to drug addiction, possibly even our "bad" habits.

As we discuss these topics, we emphasize repeatedly that physiology and behavior are "inseparably interconnected." Behavior is required in order to produce many physiological responses and physiological responses are required for behavior to occur. We also emphasize the "continuity of physiology and behavior," by which we mean simply that behavior, physiology, and various psychological states make up a continuum where it is impossible to categorically state that one process has ended and another begun.

Another term you will encounter throughout is "coexistence," and by this we mean that physiological mechanisms, behavior, and psychological states occur together and at the same time. Correspondingly, the term "integration" is used to indicate that behavior, psychological states (such as arousal, reward, and satiety), and physiological processes not only occur together but often interact with each other to produce a unified response. We are *not* trying to explain why we are built this way, nor are we implying that this term somehow explains the mechanics of body-mind interactions. It is merely a term used to indicate that, in fact, these concerted actions of behavior, physiology, and psychological states are occuring all the time and that they contribute greatly to what we are, both in health and in disease.

In later chapters we indicate that our experiences and their corresponding physiology are composed of extremely refined workings, and that "consciousness," "attention," "reward," and so forth, rather than representing singular phenomena, are varied in their nature and defined by specific interactions of specific mechanisms occurring at specific times. These statements are meant to indicate that refined physiological workings are completely interconnected with refined psychological workings, and vice versa.

One final comment. For the most part, the information presented here is not new; it is knowledge that has been confirmed time and again over the years. For this reason, referencing of these findings has been held to a minimum. If the reader wishes more information, any text in human physiology, anatomy, psychology, or physiological psychology will suffice. Because many of the chapters in this book cover a variety of topics, some of the lists of books and articles recommended for reading are rather long. They are provided for the reader who wishes a broad selection of source materials from which to pursue a particular interest. They need not be regarded as necessary reading.

In writing an introductory book of this type, there is always the danger of presenting material that is controversial and making it appear as if it is well-documented dogma. I have made every attempt to avoid such a presentation. Whenever controversial or little-known material has been used, I have noted that fact and included appropriate references. All findings that are relatively recent and still being subjected to intense research are also referenced. Many of these references are research articles and, although you are encouraged to read them (particularly when the topic is of special interest to you), they are generally included for those wishing more advanced study of a topic. Overall, it is my hope that this book will give you a firm foundation for understanding the fascinating relations that comprise the links between physiology, behavior, and health, and that it will encourage you to continue studying these relations.

ACKNOWLEDGMENTS

I would like to thank all of the physicians, researchers, teachers, and students who reviewed the manuscript during its preparation and helped me to write this book. Comments by Drs. John Finley and John Canova gave me the impetus to write the "overtures," which describe specific disorders in some detail. Valuable criticism and advice furnished by Drs. Richard Thompson and Sam Singer, who read early versions of the whole book, resulted in many alterations. Dorothy Cobb (Yokum) participated in the design of many of the original figures and provided invaluable assistance. Laurel Cook was a devoted and thorough editor. My publisher, William Kaufmann and his associates (especially Mike Hamilton) were helpful throughout. Thank you all.

The Brain

Before we discuss the physiology of behavior and how behavior and psychological states influence bodily functions, let's review a few important aspects of brain function (neural impulses and neural transmission), and morphology (how the brain is organized). Then let's turn our attention to some of the common research techniques used to study the brain, and, finally, to a particular technique called "self-administered electrical stimulation." Most of the concepts that will be raised in subsequent chapters rely on your grasp of these fundamentals.

Neural Impulses and Transmission Between Nerve Cells

The human nervous system is composed of tens of billions of special cells, called **neurons** or **nerve cells**. Approximately 200 different types of these cells are all organized in a similar way to serve two basic functions: a) *The propagation of a neural impulse from one end of the neuron to the other*, and b) *The transmission of information to other neurons or, sometimes, to various organs in the body.*

The Neural Impulse. **Neural impulses—** transmissions of neural energy that are propagated by nerve cells—travel from the main part of the nerve cell, the **cell body**, along the length of its **axon**, a thin elongated extension of the cell, to a rounded swelling at the end of the cell, called the **nerve ending**. Neural impulses travel along the surface of the cell's axon at various speeds depending on the type of neuron that is involved. Some of the neurons regulating the movement of skeletal muscles propagate neural impulses at a velocity as fast as 130 meters per second (about 290 miles per hour), whereas those involved in sensations such as crude temperature or itch propagate neural impulses at a velocity as slow as 0.5 meters per second (about 1.1 miles per hour).

Nerve cells are all **polarized**, meaning that there is a difference in the electrical charge across the cell's outer membrane. In a resting neuron, the inside of the cell is negatively charged relative to the outside of the cell. When activated by the energy of light, for example, a small, localized area of the membrane of a nerve cell in the retina of the eye is altered in its functioning, causing a rapid change in polarity, or **depolarization**. This depolarization then travels along the surface of the neuron as the neural impulse. As soon as the localized area of the surface of the neuron is depolarized, there is a rapid **repolarization** of this area that restores the original charge across the membrane. In this example, neural impulses travel along neurons comprising a visual pathway as they course through the brain.

In their totality, neural impulses make up an important part of the brain's activity. These impulses serve vision, as in the example above, or they serve the other sensory modalities, such as temperature, pain, and hearing. As neural impulses are being transmitted elsewhere in the brain or to other organs such as muscles, they also regulate language functions, movement, the activities of many of the internal organs, and it is generally assumed (though not proven) that they play an important role in converting abstract thoughts and emotional states into neural activity. The neural impulse is illustrated in Figure 1-1.

The change of polarity that occurs can be measured with **electrodes**. An electrode is a thin metal wire or some other conductor used both to record electrical responses from the brain and to stimulate the brain by means of electrical current. Depending on the size, placement, and distance between the electrodes, recordings can be made of just one or large numbers of neurons. The electrical signal detected by the electrode must be amplified in order for us to pick it up. These signals are used to measure the *electrical activity of the brain*, which is really a measurement of changes in voltage caused by the depolarization and repolarization of nerve cells.

(1) Resting neuron. The electrical charge across the membrane is uniformly *polarized*, with the inside of the cell charged negatively with respect to the outside.

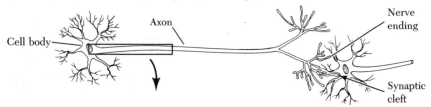

(2) Propagation of the neural impulse. The neural impulse consists of a small, localized area of *depolarization*, where the membrane is charged so that the outside of the cell is negative with respect to the inside.

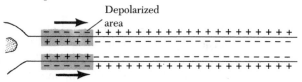

Neural impulse (indicated by the heavy arrow)
travels along the surface of the axon

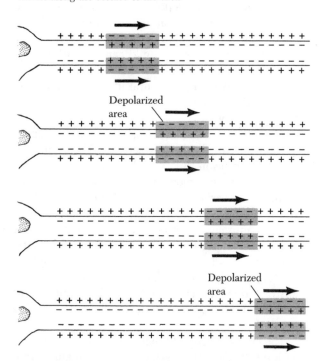

Figure 1–1. The neural impulse. The neural impulse is propagated only as far as the end of the nerve cell.

Neural Transmission. When the neural impulse reaches the end of the neuron, the depolarization initiates neural impulses in other closely connected neurons. However, the neural impulse does not directly cause the neuron next in line to depolarize. Instead, neural chemicals called **transmitter substances** are released into the junction between the two nerve cells. This junction is called the **synapse**

and the space it defines is called the **synaptic cleft**. When the neural impulse reaches the nerve ending, it causes the release of neural chemicals into the synaptic cleft.

For purposes of description, the cell that is sending the neural impulse is called the *presynaptic* neuron, and the cell destined to receive this information is called the *postsynaptic* neuron. The information received by the postsynaptic neuron causes it to become more or less activated—that is, to continue or discontinue propagating the neural impulse. Although this state of activity is partially determined by the ongoing activity of the postsynaptic neuron itself, to a large extent it appears to be determined by the effect of the transmitter substance released by the presynaptic neuron. The release of transmitter substances is illustrated in Figure 1-2.

Figure 1–2. Transmission of information among neurons. When the neural impulse reaches the end of the nerve cell, it causes the release of neural chemicals, called "transmitter substances." For neurons that end on organs rather than on other neurons, neural chemicals exert their action by affecting the activity characteristic of these organs.

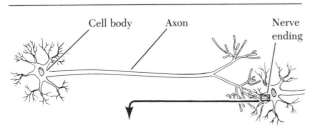

Cell body   Axon   Nerve ending

(1) Resting neuron; the endings of the nerve cell contain the chemicals it produces and stores.

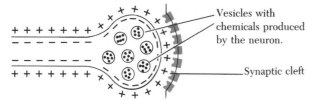

Vesicles with chemicals produced by the neuron.

Synaptic cleft

(2) Release of neural chemicals, called "transmitter substances," occurs as the result of the neural impulse (heavy arrow).

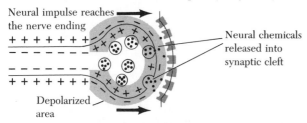

Neural impulse reaches the nerve ending

Neural chemicals released into synaptic cleft

Depolarized area

(3) The neural chemical exerts its action on another nerve cell, causing it to become either more or less excitable.

Neural chemicals interact with nerve cell across cleft

Neurons release many different types of transmitter substances. These chemicals, produced by the cells themselves, can modify the activity of other neurons by increasing or by decreasing their excitability. In other words, the neural impulse of one neuron can cause the activity of another neuron to be either increased or decreased depending upon which chemicals are released and what their chemical actions are. The actions of various neural chemicals are covered in Chapter 11, which discusses the chemical nature of the brain.

In addition to their effect on other neurons, neural chemicals influence the other organs of the body. Two chemicals that are not only released by nerve cells within the brain but also by neurons which innervate the organs are **norepinephrine** and **acetylcholine**. The actions of these chemical substances are discussed in Chapter 7 where we cover the body's mechanisms of defense.

Basic Organization of the Brain

A few general comments about the anatomy of the brain will assist you in understanding how it is organized to serve the varied functions that are discussed in subsequent chapters.

In general terms, the brain can be differentiated into three main systems: the phylogenetically "old" systems represented by the **upper spinal cord and hypothalamus**, the phylogenetically "middle-aged" **limbic system**, and the phylogenetically "young" **cerebral cortex**. These three parts of the brain are illustrated in Figure 1-3. *Phylogeny* refers to evolutionary development. In other words, to call a part of the brain phylogenetically "old" simply means that it made its appearance in the animal kingdom at an earlier time than other parts. For example, even the most primitive brains (like those of sharks) have well-developed spinal cords and an area analogous to the hypothalamus in humans. Well-developed limbic structures begin to predominate in more recently evolved animals, such as frogs, but are much more developed in early mammals like the opossum. The cerebral cortex becomes similar to ours only in very recently evolved animals, such as cats, but much more so in primates.

The **hypothalamus** and **upper spinal cord** control vital organs such as the heart, lungs and the pituitary gland, and they regulate vital processes such as body temperature, blood volume, blood pressure, and body pH, which is a measure of the concentration of hydrogen ions in the body. They also are essential for behaviors such as eating, drinking, sexual activity, and the defensive responses of rage, anger, or fear.

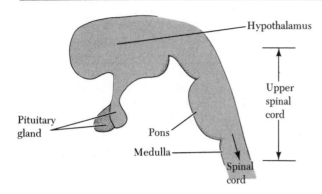

(1) **Hypothalamus and upper spinal cord:** this phylogenetically "old" part of the brain regulates many vital physiological processes in the body as well as eating, drinking, sexual, and defensive behaviors (rage, anger, or fear).

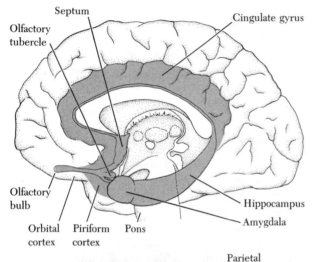

(2) **Limbic system:** this phylogenetically "middle-aged" part of the brain surrounds the "older" hypothalamus and upper spinal cord. Among its other functions, it modulates the responses integrated in lower parts of the brain, such as the hypothalamus.

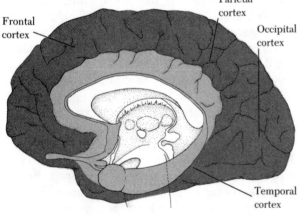

(3) **Cerebral cortex:** this phylogenetically "young" part of the brain surrounds the limbic system, which controls the movement of skeletal muscle and integrates information received through the sense organs.

Figure 1–3. 1) The upper spinal cord and hypothalamus. 2) The limbic system. 3) The cerebral cortex. These illustrations are all medial views of the brain (side views of the middle of the brain).

The **hypothalamus** and **upper spinal cord** also integrate and control the autonomic nervous system, which regulates the blood vessels and organs of the body.

The **limbic system** surrounds the hypothalamus and the upper spinal cord. The limbic system is composed of the hippocampus, amygdala, cingulate gyrus, septum, olfactory areas, and the "younger" orbitofrontal cortex and piriform cortex (see Figure 1-3, 2). These structures are all interconnected and have many connections with the hypothalamus (which is often considered to be a part of the limbic system). In general, the limbic system is believed to act as a modulator of lower structures represented by the upper spinal cord and hypothalamus. The limbic system, although involved in the various behaviors mentioned above as being essentially connected with the hypothalamus and upper spinal cord, doesn't appear to be directly in charge of enacting these behaviors. That is, if selected areas of the upper spinal cord or hypothalamus are destroyed, electrical stimulation of the limbic system will often no longer elicit such behaviors. The limbic system appears, rather, to participate in the important process of selecting whatever is the appropriate response to any given situation.

The **cerebral cortex**, which consists of the frontal, parietal, occipital, and temporal lobes, surrounds the limbic system (see Figure 1-3, 3). This "youngest" and most developed part of our brain is involved in a variety of integrative processes necessary for such functions as recognition and speech. Some areas of the cerebral cortex are highly specialized to serve the sensory processes of vision, audition (hearing) and touch, while others are specialized for controlling the movement of skeletal muscle.

The functions of these three systems of the brain are discussed in each chapter as they relate to the specific topic being considered.

Research Techniques Used to Study the Brain

There are many ways to study the workings of the brain. Some techniques are used to reveal the anatomy of the brain, some to elucidate chemical processes occurring within the brain, and some to monitor changes in neural activity by measuring electrical activity. A host of other techniques are also employed. Some of these are outlined below.

Much information has been gathered by clinicians who carefully study the **clinical symptoms** of patients suffering from brain damage or other brain disorders and attempt to cure these symptoms. The hope is to connect the disorder within the brain with symptoms unique to this disorder.

Many experiments have been performed on animals where portions of the brain are removed or destroyed, a technique called **ablation** or **brain lesion**. The purpose is to observe any subsequent impairment of functions that would not otherwise be present.

Electrical current appropriately applied to a region of the brain through an inserted electrode will elicit neural activity. This technique, called **electrical stimulation** of the brain, is used to observe effects involving the activity of that area of the brain.

Numerous **chemicals** are also used as research "tools." Such chemicals may be one of various drugs known to modify neural functions, or they may be hormones and other chemicals that are present within the brain and/or the rest of the body. These chemicals can be injected directly into selected regions of the brain or they can be injected elsewhere in the body. Again, the purpose is to deduce information about brain function by observing the effects of these chemicals.

Behavior, too, can be used. For example, as an animal goes to sleep, as it wakes up, as it eats, or as it learns a task, one can observe how these behaviors affect brain function. These techniques can be used in many different ways. For example, an electrode may be placed in one region of the brain to be used for electrical stimulation and another electrode may be implanted in a different region of the brain to record changes in electrical activity occurring as a result of the stimulation. The occurrence of such changes would indicate that the two regions are connected to each other. In this type of experiment, electrical stimulation is combined with electrical recording as a means of exploring *neural connections*.

Electrical stimulation of the brain is also used to investigate the role of the brain in regulating *physiological functions* throughout the body. In these experiments, changes in blood pressure or other physiological parameters are used as indexes that the region of the brain being stimulated might be involved in regulating one or another physiological function.

Behavioral effects can also be elicited by electrical stimulation—a leg may begin to move, sleep may be induced, eating or drinking may occur, or experimentally-evoked rage reactions may be reduced, to name a few.

It should now be apparent that the study of the brain's functions and regulatory roles involves various techniques and experimental protocols. Although it is easy to describe the research techniques commonly used, it is often very difficult to interpret the effects observed. To illustrate this point, let's return to ablation studies where specific portions of the brain are destroyed as a way of investigating the role of that region in serving behavioral and/or physiological functions. We know, for example, that destroying a certain portion of the brain will subsequently reduce or abolish an animal's normal eating responses. The obvious interpretation is that the brain area destroyed is involved in regulating eating behavior. The specific assumption is that the region destroyed contains the neurons regulating eating behavior, and that the destruction of these neurons has reduced or abolished this behavior.

However, we must be very careful in interpreting this effect. For example, has the lesion destroyed an area that contributes to sensations of hunger rather than affected the ability of the animal to eat? Is the animal only not eating or is the lack of eating behavior caused by a motor disability induced by the lesion that makes the animal unable to respond with normal muscular movement and coordination? Is the animal not eating food because of a sensory disability such as an impaired sense of smell? Is it possible that the area destroyed by ablation is merely a relay station, and that a different portion of the brain is actually responsible for regulating eating behavior? In this same reasoning, it may be that one function of the destroyed area is to inhibit other brain areas normally involved in suppressing eating behavior. In this case, the observed impairment would result more from the activity of other parts of the brain than directly from the lesion. Clearly, the number of possible interpretations is very large.

The number of interpretive possibilities can (and should) be controlled to some extent by initially designing the experiment with care. For example, animals can be tested for any impairments in smell or motor function prior to and during their inclusion in the study. In spite of such precautions, however, a diversity of interpretations of results often remains. For this reason, *it is usually necessary to combine the evidence gained from one technique with additional evidence gained from other techniques.*

Continuing our example, let us suppose that an electrode is inserted into the same area of the brain as before, but instead of destroying it we stimulate it electrically. Let's then say that, if food is available, the animal begins eating each time this area of the brain is stimulated. Again, the obvious interpretation is that this area of the brain is involved in regulating eating behavior. If we combine this finding with the previous result (that destruction of this same region abolishes eating behavior), it indeed looks as if this region is involved in regulating eating behavior.

Many other interpretations are still possible, however. The electrical stimulus used to elicit this behavior is not at all the type of stimulation that occurs in this (or any other) area of the brain under normal conditions. Our interpretation would be considerably strengthened if we could show that electrical stimulation of this area elicits eating behavior even when its connections to other regions of the brain are severed. At least we could then maintain that the changes observed in eating behavior are not due to indirect effects involving other brain areas. This type of experiment does not absolutely rule out the possibility

of indirect effects, however, because there are many ways by which one area of the brain is connected to another.

Another way to strengthen our interpretation is to design experiments that limit the possible role of hunger. Using electrical stimulation, we can test motivation. Will the animal respond to the electrical stimulation by eating when it is not hungry, or only when it is food deprived? If we find that electrical stimulation elicits eating whether or not the animal is food-deprived, we have certainly reinforced our interpretation.

As a general rule, the more clear-cut the evidence, the more likely the interpretation. In this case, such additional evidence might be provided by implanting recording electrodes within this same area of the brain and demonstrating changes in electrical activity as the animal begins to eat. Or perhaps one could show changes in electrical activity when the animal is food-deprived, or when the animal is injected with a nutrient, such as glucose.

Throughout this book we will refer to findings based on investigations and considerations similar to those just described. Needless to say, the information that will be presented has not come easily, nor is it likely that all interpretations offered will remain what they are today. Nevertheless, a great deal has been learned about the brain and this knowledge has at least given us the first steps to a more exact understanding of the relations between body and self.

Self-Administered Electrical Stimulation

In 1954, two psychologists, James Olds and Peter Milner, reported the rather remarkable finding that when a small electrode was implanted into the brain of rats and electrical current was passed through this electrode, the stimulation of nerve cells could be a **rewarding** experience—that is, the rats would "come back for more" (Olds and Milner, 1954). The experimental technique that established this phenomenon is described below in general terms.

An electrode is inserted into the animal's brain and is wired to a receptacle fixed on the skull. The rat with the implanted electrode is placed in a cage equipped with a lever that is connected to an electrical stimulator wired to turn on whenever the lever is depressed. Every time the rat presses the lever, it turns on the stimulator for a brief period of time (about half a second) and electrical current passes through the electrode into the brain (see Figure 1-4). In order to receive another burst of current, the rat must release the lever and press it again.

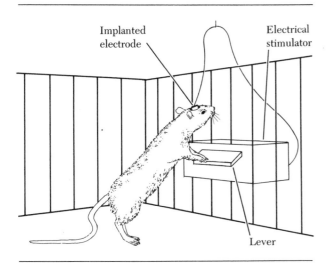

Implanted electrode

Electrical stimulator

Lever

Figure 1–4. Self-administered electrical stimulation of the brain, generally called "self-stimulation." The apparatus is designed so that when the rat presses the lever, a pulse of current travels through a wire attached to an electrode inserted into the animal's brain. If the animal presses the lever again, or repeatedly, it is assumed that the stimulation is "rewarding" in some way.

If the rat presses the lever repeatedly, it appears that the animal is seeking the resultant stimulation—i.e., that the excitation of the brain area is rewarding. How strong the reward is can be measured by how frequently the lever is pressed. If the lever is pressed many thousands of times per hour, the electrical stimulation of the brain is said to be strongly rewarding. If the rat avoids pressing the lever, or presses a second lever wired to stop the transmission of current, the electrical stimulation is regarded as *aversive*.

The phenomenon of **self-administered electrical stimulation**, sometimes referred to as **self-stimulation**, has been observed in many species, including rats, cats, chickens, dolphins, monkeys, and humans. In one way or another, the results of using this technique are touched upon in almost every chapter of this book. Again, the outcomes vary in accordance with the circumstances in which the technique is used and the areas of the brain under study.

Although the key role the brain plays in determining many relations between body and self will quickly become apparent, we must also emphasize the important role of *food* in influencing our physiology and behavior. The fundamental relationship between body and self not only involves the brain, but every part of the body. In the next chapter we will define what food is and describe the general ways that it is incorporated into the body. This will lead us to discuss solid foods, water, air, and sensory stimuli. These are the foods associated with eating and hunger, drinking and thirst, breathing, and sensory experiences.

Recommended Reading

NETTER, F. *The CIBA Collection of Medical Illustrations, volume 1, Nervous System.* Summit: CIBA Pharmaceutical Co., 1956, 168 pages. *An excellent collection of illustrations of the human nervous system; various pathologies of the brain and spinal cord are illustrated as well. This book has a special supplement on the anatomy of the hypothalamus.*

NOBACK, C., and DEMAREST, R. *The Human Nervous System.* New York: McGraw-Hill, 1981, 591 pages. *This text offers a detailed review of the physiology of the nervous system. There are many illustrations of the brain and concise statements concerning its functions. Recommended only for readers who wish detailed knowledge.*

NOBACK, C., and DEMAREST, R. *The Nervous System: Introduction and Review.* New York: McGraw-Hill, 1979, 225 pages. *This paperback is written for the beginning student who wishes a fairly comprehensive survey of the structures and functions of the brain.*

OLDS, J. "Pleasure centers in the brain." *Scientific American*, 195,4, 105-116, 1956. *This article illustrates the methodology of self-administered electrical stimulation and discusses how this procedure is applied.*

ROUTTENBERG, A. "The reward system of the brain." *Scientific American*, 239,5, 154-164, 1978. *A general discussion of reward areas of the brain, covering their anatomical distribution, chemical properties, and some relationships to learning and memory.*

STEVENS, C. "The neuron." *Scientific American*, 241,3, 54-65, 1979. *A nicely illustrated, easy to follow, article on the structure of nerve cells, the propagation of the neural impulse, and synaptic transmission.*

Food: General Comments

Our relationship with foods is very important. Not only are foods necessary for our survival, but to assimilate food correctly and in the proper amounts involves *behavior* and *experience*. How this takes place is the subject of the next four chapters. In this chapter we will simply define what food is and describe the general manner whereby foods are incorporated into the body.

Broadly defined, foods are substances taken into the body from the outside to nourish or sustain us. Notice that I do not stipulate that foods must be eaten or that they must be made up of organic molecules like proteins, carbohydrates and fats. Rather, *anything that is taken in by us as essential for maintaining or repairing our functions or for promoting natural growth is considered to be nourishing and therefore is called food.*

Solid Foods, Water, Air, and Sensory Stimuli

There are four basic types of food: **solid food**, **water**, **air**, and **sensory stimuli**. Solid foods are what we ingest when we are eating. These are often simply called "food." Solid foods consist of carbohydrates, proteins, fats, and minerals. Aside from minerals, which are made up of elements such as calcium and iron, solid foods are made up of organic molecules. Some are vitamins and some are amino acids—the basic units that make up proteins; others are sugars— the basic units that make up carbohydrates; and still others are molecules like cholesterol, which is a fat. These nutrients are considered to be solid even if they are suspended in liquids such as broth, milk, juice, and tea.

Water is a liquid food composed of just one molecule, H_2O. Water is taken in as a liquid and it is used mostly as a liquid. It is also used as a substance that vaporizes and as a source of positive and negative ions. It is the only liquid the body needs.

Air is a mixture of gases—oxygen, nitrogen, and a host of other molecules—that are contained in the atmosphere. Of these, oxygen is the most essential to ingest.

Sensory stimuli are the various and varied constituents in our environment that are used by our sense organs. Some are electromagnetic waves such as light waves that make up visible light and infrared rays that create heat, recorded by temperature and pain-sensitive cells in the skin. Others are compressional waves which travel through air and other media, such as those that strike our ear drums and cause them to move, thus producing the perception of sound. Some mechanical stimuli that activate touch, pressure, and pain receptors when applied directly to the body are also regarded to be sensory stimuli, as are numerous ingested chemicals that interact with cells in the mouth and the olfactory epithelium to produce sensations of taste and smell. Other stimuli do not originate outside of us. Rather, they originate within the body and activate, for example, pressure- and pain-sensitive receptors in the organs.

Although the foregoing description of foods is rather uncommon to physiologists or psychologists, it is entirely appropriate from the body/self point of view. In the following chapters we will see that our relation to these foods is importantly related to the fact that they are essential to our health and that they must be furnished from sources outside of ourselves.

All of these foods are essential to our existence. If any one of them were to be eliminated entirely from our diet, we would die within a short period of time or, in the case of sensory stimuli, we would be so severely disabled that we would require constant care. On the other hand, an excess of these foods can also be detrimental. In the case of sensory stimuli, for example, too much infrared radiation causes burns, or too intense a sound can damage our auditory apparatus. (Table 2-1 lists the four types of food with general comments on their effects.)

Digestive Processes

We have already mentioned that foods must be taken into the body from the outside. Unlike the other foods described, water can generally be used by the body without further treatment. Wherever it is, it immediately exerts its actions and these actions do not require any special modification of water by the body. Most other foods need to be modified and/or treated by the body in special ways before the body can use them. Proteins and most fats and carbohydrates, for example, must be broken down into smaller units before they can enter into the blood. Amino acids, vitamins, and glucose must be further converted within the body so that they can participate in forming new molecules or providing energy for the body. All sensory stimuli must have their energy converted into neural impulses before they can provide sensory input into the brain. Oxygen must attach to hemoglobin in the blood in order to be transported to

tissues in sufficiently high concentrations.

These various processes continue until the foods we ingest can finally serve their ultimate purpose of promoting the maintenance, repair, or growth of our functions. Until this end-result is achieved, foods have little or no nutrient value, although, to a certain extent, this depends on their roles. For example, oxygen is of little value until it enters cells where it acts as the final electron acceptor in an electron transport chain associated with the formation of high-energy molecules. Amino acids, on the other hand, have great value even before they enter cells. Dissolved in the blood, they help retain water as do other solutes (see Chapter 4); however, at this point they are of no value as the basic units needed to create the body's proteins. This phenomenon does not occur until they enter into cells.

The *entire* process through which foods are treated so that the body can use them is called **digestion**. Digestion comes from the Latin noun "digestio"

Table 2-1. Basic nutrients (solid foods, water, air, and sensory stimuli) and their actions.

Basic nutrient	Source	Physiological actions	Psychological correlates	Effects of deprivation
Solid foods	Plants (vegetables, grains, fruits), animals (meat), earth (minerals)	Forms molecules and the appropriate environment for energy, growth, and maintenance of the body	Experiences of hunger and satiety	Starvation, leading to death
Water	Water	Provides a special environment for bodily functions	Experiences of thirst and satiety	Dehydration, leading to death
Air	Atmosphere	Forms molecules that the body uses for energy; intimately connected with body pH	Various experiences involving breathing (e.g., slow and rapid breathing patterns)	Suffocation, leading to death
Sensory stimuli	Photons, mechanical vibration, chemicals, warmth or cold, pressure on the skin or on internal organs	Imparts sensory information	Experiences of vision, hearing, gustation (taste), olfaction (smell), touch, pressure, temperature	Sensory deprivation, leading to an impaired ability to perceive and interact with events external to oneself

which means "an orderly distribution or arrangement." The Latin verb "digero" means "to arrange, distribute, dispose of, or spread over." Thus, digestion can be looked at as a continuous, orderly process of manipulation, arrangement, and disposition of foods. As defined here, digestion refers not only to processes occurring within the stomach or intestines, but also to activities within cells and organs throughout the entire body, *including the body's behavior.* For example, the behavior of chewing is essential if we are to extract full nourishment from many solid foods, but especially corn and other plants. With corn, chewing tears apart membranes that are made up of cellulose, which does not break down to any appreciable extent within the stomach and intestines. Therefore, unchewed, most of the corn we eat will simply pass through as if we had never ingested it.

The *form* a food is in determines to a large extent what constitutes an appropriate digestive process. For example, cooked carrots will not have to be chewed as completely as raw carrots because their cell walls are weaker and therefore are broken apart more easily. Of course, although very different from chewing, cooking itself is a behavior. Also, sunlight and mechanical vibration are foods used by sense organs but they are forms that cannot be used by the stomach or lungs, which are adapted for solid foods, water and air. Here the appropriate organs are the eyes and ears. Similarly, water can be ingested by drinking, but it is a form of food that cannot be properly absorbed if we inhale too much of it and it floods our lungs. In fact, our ability to control our breathing when we are under water is an example of a digestive behavior that aids in the selection of an appropriate organ for ingesting food. In like manner, a steak is digested by placing it into the mouth, not the ears!

Table 2-2 indicates the variety of behavioral and physiological processes brought into play for the digestion of foods. Many of these processes will be discussed in the following four chapters. Chapter 3 deals with solid foods, Chapter 4 with water, and Chapters 5 and 6 with air and sensory stimuli. The food category most familiar to us, solid foods, is the topic of the next chapter.

Table 2-2. Digestive processes involved in the assimilation of food.

Basic nutrient	1. Digestive behaviors that precede food intake	2. Digestive behaviors that bring food into the body	3. Digestive assimilation of food by organs in contact with the outer environment	4. Digestive assimilation of food by internal organs
Solid foods and water	Shopping, cooking, going to a restaurant for dinner (eating); walking to a water fountain (drinking)	Eating (hands, chewing, swallowing), and drinking (hands, swallowing)	Outside → mouth → esophagus → stomach → small intestines → large intestines → anus → outside	Gastrointestinal cells → blood → liver, other organs and cells
Air		Breathing (diaphragm, intercostal muscles)	Outside → nose and mouth → trachea → bronchi → alveoli of lungs → bronchi → trachea → nose and mouth → outside	Alveolar membrane → blood → all cells
Sensory stimuli	Turning on a radio (hearing), building and igniting a fire (warmth), adding spice to food (taste), etc.	Movements associated with sensory stimuli (opening of eyelids, turning one's head)	Outside → retina, ear drum, touch receptors, taste receptors, smell receptors, etc.	Sensory receptors → sensory nerves → central nervous system

Solid Food: The Clinical Reality

Medical Disorder: Anorexia Nervosa.

Read this "overture" carefully before you read Chapter 3. The connections between the medical reality of anorexia nervosa and the basic underlying physiological and psychological processes that regulate normal eating behaviors are developed in this chapter. (For more information about anorexia nervosa, see Herzog, 1982; Russell, 1982.)

Anorexia nervosa is a disease characterized by a persistent refusal to eat that leads to extreme weight loss. Adolescent and young adult women are most prone to this disorder, which has no known medical origin. Men comprise approximately one twentieth the total number of patients. Although the disease is not very common, it can be fatal. Living with the disease is always a devastating condition for the afflicted person and her/his family.

The symptoms of anorexia nervosa are physical, emotional, and behavioral. Patients typically have a disturbed body image which is manifested in their intense fear of becoming obese. Often suffering from a distinct distaste and aversion to food, they do not maintain a minimal normal body weight (anorectics typically lose at least 25 percent of their original body weight, and sometimes 50 percent or more). They are usually hyperactive and have sleep disturbances, often not recognizing that they are fatigued. Women anorectics generally stop menstruating (and many develop an aversion to sexual behavior). Anorectics, generally, suffer from constipation, nausea and vomiting (especially if food is forced), difficulties in swallowing, and delayed gastric emptying (passing of food from the stomach to the intestines).

Patients usually refuse to acknowledge the abnormality of their eating behavior and often argue convincingly that they are not unhealthy. In fact, anorectics are often quite adept at making themselves appear better than they are. Nevertheless, the psychiatric disorders among anorectics range from neurotic overreactions to diet and obesity to schizophrenic delusions.

There is no specific cure for anorexia nervosa. Approximately 75 percent of anorectics improve or fully recover, sometimes spontaneously and sometimes following treatment; however, it is not clear to what extent their recovery can be attributed to specific treatments, which currently include medical care, nutritional counselling, and psychotherapy. Although many drugs have been reported to alleviate symptoms in one or another patient, no one drug is considered to be a cure. Individual or group psychotherapy sometimes produces good results, and family counseling is often effective.

3

Solid Food

Our involvement with food is important. Not only must we assimilate foods in order to live, but a very large part of our lives is devoted to food in one way or another. In terms of our physiology, digestive processes are continuously active and, in terms of our behavior, at least three hours a day (often four to six hours) are spent in gathering and preparing food, eating, and eliminating waste products. This is truly an enormous amount of time to be devoted to one function.

In this chapter we will begin to understand how psychological processes are interwoven with physiological processes. We will discuss the fact that physiology and behavior comprise one inseparable system—the underlying thesis of *Body and Self*. We will see the broad range of experiences—hunger, satiety, eating, and reward—that are involved in our assimilation of food. Specifically, the discussion will proceed with: a) a basic definition of solid foods and how they are used by the body; b) the mechanisms responsible for our assimilation of food (with examples to illustrate the coexistence of physiological, behavioral and psychological components), and c) some of the ways these workings relate to health.

I. SOLID FOOD AND ITS USE BY THE BODY

In the previous chapter I mentioned that solid foods come from plants, animals and the earth. From these sources we get the salts, vegetables, grains, meat, dairy products, nuts and fruits that contain all of the proteins, carbohydrates, fats, vitamins and minerals the body needs. Whether suspended in a liquid (as a broth, tea, etc.) or not (as meat, cheese, bread, vegetables, etc.), these foods are considered to be "solid."

Many minerals and vitamins are used by the body in the same form as they are in the foods we eat; that is, to be effective they do not need to be changed by the body after we have ingested them. Most proteins, fats and carbohydrates are first broken down into smaller components before they are used again. Solid foods are used in a variety of ways: a) as a source of energy, b) as a source of chemicals which are incorporated by the body into other chemicals that the body needs, and c) as a source of chemicals used by nerve cells for their functioning. These uses are discussed in turn below.

Food for Energy

The energy required by the body comes from the metabolism of solid foods. Virtually all carbohydrates, fats and proteins can be transformed either into glucose or some other compound that shares a derivation from glucose. This process is illustrated in Figure 3-1.

As shown, almost all of the amino acids (which come from proteins) can be converted into pyruvic acid. This conversion occurs mainly in the liver. Once pyruvic acid is formed, it can be further metabolized or it can be resynthesized into glucose. Fatty acids (from fats) and some amino acids are transformed into acetyl CoA. This transformation also occurs mainly in the liver. Thus, amino acids and fats are readily transformed into products that are also formed from carbohydrates.

As the chemicals course through the reactions outlined in Figure 3-1, energy is produced for the body. Although other forms can be used, by far the most important usable form of energy in the body is contained in a molecule called **adenosine triphosphate (ATP)**. ATP is present in all cells of the body and can be used for energy by all cells. The chemical structure of ATP is shown in Figure 3-2. As illustrated here, ATP is composed of three portions, two of which, adenine and ribose, are linked to form a larger molecule, adenosine. Three phosphates comprise the

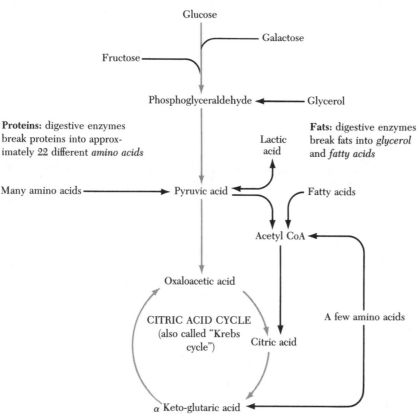

Carbohydrates: digestive enzymes break carbohydrates into the *monosaccharides glucose, galactose,* and *fructose*

Glucose

Galactose

Fructose

Phosphoglyceraldehyde ← Glycerol

Proteins: digestive enzymes break proteins into approximately 22 different *amino acids*

Fats: digestive enzymes break fats into *glycerol* and *fatty acids*

Lactic acid

Many amino acids → Pyruvic acid ← Fatty acids

Acetyl CoA ←

Oxaloacetic acid

CITRIC ACID CYCLE (also called "Krebs cycle")

A few amino acids

Citric acid

α Keto-glutaric acid ←

Figure 3–1. Metabolism of carbohydrates, proteins, and fats for energy. The first step involves breaking foods into simpler molecules: **monosaccharides** for carbohydrates, **glycerol** and **fatty acids** for fats, and **amino acids** for proteins. Note that carbohydrates, proteins, and fats, once they are broken down into simpler molecules, can join this basic metabolic pathway. A final step is the **citric acid cycle.** For the citric acid cycle to function, **oxygen** is required. In this cycle, acetyl CoA joins with oxaloacetic acid to form citric acid. Citric acid is then converted, in a series of reactions, back to oxaloacetic acid. Thus each revolution of the cycle results in the metabolism of one molecule of acetyl CoA. The citric acid cycle generates enormous amounts of ATP, a molecule that provides most of the energy used by the body. (A more detailed version of this diagram is presented in the appendix as Figure 3–1A.)

$$\text{Adenosine triphosphate} + \text{water} \rightarrow \text{adenosine diphosphate} + \text{inorganic phosphate} + 8000 \text{ cal usable energy}$$

$$\text{ATP} + H_2O \rightarrow \text{ADP} + Pi + 8000 \text{ cal}$$

third portion. They are also linked and, as illustrated, are attached to the ribose portion of the adenosine.

In giving off energy which is used by the body, the phosphate molecules split off from the ATP molecule. This reaction is shown at the top of the page.

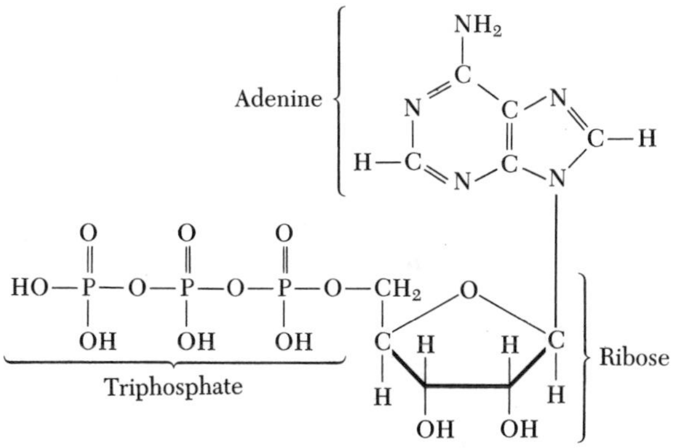

Figure 3–2. The chemical structure of adenosine triphosphate (ATP).

In similar reactions, adenosine diphosphate (ADP) loses a phosphate to become adenosine monophosphate (AMP), or ATP loses two phosphates to become AMP. Both of these reactions also produce energy that can be used.

As ATP becomes ADP or AMP, energy is released which is then used in some other physiological process. In order for this energy to be used, the ATP has to be "coupled" with other physiological systems. This coupling is accomplished in special and specific ways that depend upon the tissue amd function involved. That is, ATP is coupled one way to provide energy to transport certain molecules into or out of cells, another way to provide energy for forming the body's chemicals, and so forth.

In muscle, for example, the contractile process involves a coupling of ATP with muscle proteins. This coupling enables the proteins to slide past each other, thus causing muscle to shorten, or develop tension. Enormous amounts of ATP are used by the body in this process. (See Figure 9-1 in Chapter 9 which is devoted to skeletal muscles and movement and discusses this process in some detail.)

Thus, ATP is a fundamental source of usable energy for the body. Without ATP, virtually all of the functions in the body would stop. In using ATP, both AMP and ADP are formed, along with inorganic phosphates. In order to replenish ATP stores, AMP and ADP must be re-formed into ATP, a process that requires energy which is obtained from the breakdown of foods.

As foods are broken down into pyruvic acid and from there enter the citric-acid cycle, as illustrated in Figure 3-1, ATP is remade. This is the reverse of what we saw before—instead of releasing energy which is used by the body, the energy is taken from the foods to produce ATP. This chain of events can be summarized as shown at the bottom of the page. Although a small amount of ATP is formed as foods are transformed into pyruvic acid, by far the greatest production of ATP comes from the citric-acid cycle, where pyruvic acid and acetyl CoA are changed into carbon dioxide and water. This process is further discussed in the notes to Figure 3-1 and Figure 3-1A, which is in the appendix.

$$\text{8000 cal from the breakdown of foods} + \text{Inorganic phosphate} + \text{Adenosine diphosphate} \rightarrow \text{Adenosine triphosphate} + \text{water}$$

$$8000 \text{ cal} + Pi + \text{ADP} \rightarrow \text{ATP} + H_2O$$

Food for the Production of Chemicals

The body makes tens of thousands of chemicals, ranging from large proteins to simple sugars. As much as 3/4 of a cell's energy can be used for making chemicals. Just as there is a specific "coupling" of ATP to the contractile apparatus of muscle, there are specific couplings involved in the synthesis of chemicals. For example, in the formation of proteins, specific amino acids are first selected. To accomplish this selection, ATP activates or energizes an amino acid which then interacts with RNA (ribonucleic acid, which comes from genetic material within the cell) so that the amino acid is placed in the proper sequence required for the specific protein being produced. Later in the process another transfer of energy takes place that links the amino acids together to form the protein.

The proteins produced by the body have many different purposes. Some are used to form muscle, many are used to regulate chemical reactions (these are called **enzymes**), others become structural components needed for tissue repair and growth, and others are used as hormones or as antibodies for immunity. The chemicals used for these purposes are not broken down as are the chemicals used for energy. However, if the body requires more energy than it is able to receive through foods, it will break down these proteins and transform the amino acids by the process previously described.

Most of the amino acids can be formed within our cells; that is, we do not have to ingest them because the body itself can make them. However, some amino acids used within the body cannot be formed by our cells. These amino acids, called **essential amino acids**, must be furnished by the food we eat. (The essential amino acids are listed in Figure 3-1A in the appendix.) If the body is very undernourished or if it is deprived of proteins, the essential amino acids will not be available for protein synthesis (either because they are not being ingested or because they are being transformed to be used as a source of energy). The consequences to health in this case are serious.

Although carbohydrates are mainly used in the body as a source of energy, they are also used as components of many molecules, such as the hereditary material (DNA), mucus secreted by the stomach, intestines and other organs, heparin, which is secreted by many cells where it exerts an anticoagulating action on blood, and some of the molecules that make up cartilage and bone. In all cases these molecules can be made from other kinds of molecules besides carbohydrates; in other words, the body does not depend on carbohydrates to create its own chemicals.

Fats also serve different purposes. Body fat is produced in the body when the level of such nutrients as amino acids and glucose in the blood exceeds what the body can use at that time. This fat can be broken down again into fatty acids and glycerol (see Figure 3-1). Thus, body fat is a component that can be readily used for energy. The fats cholesterol and lecithin, essential constituents of cell membranes, are also formed in the body. Many hormones, called "steroids," are derived from cholesterol and are secreted by the adrenal glands and the reproductive organs. Although many fats are produced by the body and are therefore not "essential" (we don't have to ingest them as we do the essential amino acids), some fats, such as Vitamins A, D, E and K, must be ingested. This is also true of linoleic acid, which is required for normal growth and normal skin and connective tissue.

Thus, solid foods are used to form various molecules the body needs for its functioning. In some cases the chemicals required must be furnished by our diet, but in many more cases the body can and does make these chemicals itself.

Food and the Brain

In general, the brain uses food for the same purposes as do the other organs in the body: a) as a source of energy, and b) as a source for producing molecules needed for normal functioning.

The only nutrient used by the brain in appreciable quantities as a source of energy is glucose. In normal circumstances the body maintains very tight control of blood glucose levels; however, in certain circumstances, blood glucose levels fall to very low levels. When this occurs, as in hypoglycemic shock induced by excessive insulin secretion by the pancreas, or by the administration of excessive insulin to a diabetic (insulin and diabetes are discussed later in the chapter), the brain does not get enough energy-producing chemicals. Because energy metabolism in the brain is reduced, a state of fatigue, depression, irritability, and lethargy can ensue. In extreme cases, the lack of glucose can lead to convulsions and coma.

Although glucose is needed as a source of energy for the brain, amino acids and other chemicals are still required as a source for producing new chemicals. As with the other organs in the body, these chemicals maintain normal function. In the brain, however, special chemicals are needed for neural transmission and the modulation of neural activity.

Three important neural chemicals are **norepinephrine**, **serotonin**, and **acetylcholine**. When we eat such foods as meat and eggs, which contain a relatively large amount of the essential amino acid tryptophan, the amount of the neural transmitter, serotonin, increases in the brain. Similarly, when we eat foods rich in lecithin or sphingomyelin (like eggs, soybeans, liver and milk), blood choline levels rise rapidly. Choline is used by the brain to produce the neural transmitter, acetylcholine. Also, when we eat food containing large amounts of the essential amino acid, phenylalanine, or the amino acid, tyrosine, the amount of the neural transmitter, norepinephrine, increases in the brain.

Although it is tempting to offer a concise list specifying the behavioral functions with which each neural chemical has been connected, such a list would be misleading. Our knowledge of the functions of these chemicals is very limited. Briefly, they influence the activity of nerve cells and appear to affect our state of arousal (sometimes promoting drowsiness, sometimes excitability), eating behavior (sometimes increasing, sometimes decreasing appetite), sexual behavior, stress and reward responses, and many other functions. This topic receives more thorough discussion in Chapter 11.

II. PHYSIOLOGICAL/PSYCHOLOGICAL INTERACTIONS

The physiology/psychology of eating-hunger-satiety-digestion involves almost every part of the body. In its handling of solid foods, the body uses many systems in an elaborate network of physiological and behavioral processes. Figure 3-3 illustrates some of

Figure 3–3. Organs involved in the assimilation of solid foods. In addition to the organs listed, the blood (vascular system), abdominal and skeletal muscles, adrenal glands, kidneys, and adipose tissue are also important.

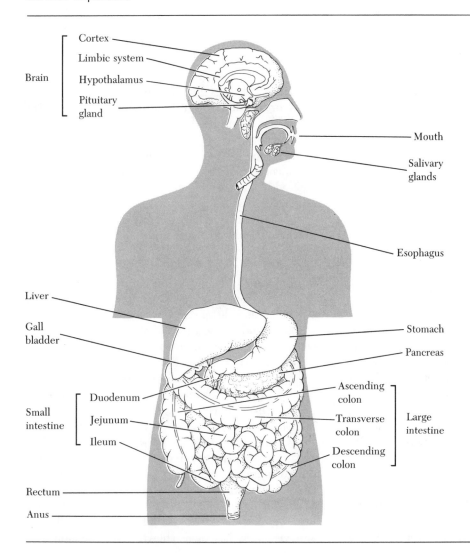

the main organs involved in our assimilation of solid foods. The use of these organs is discussed in the following pages as part of a discussion of the coexistence of physiology and behavior.

Coexistence and Inseparability of Physiology and Behavior

The question of which comes first, psychological and behavioral processes or physiological processes, is like the long-posed question regarding the chicken and the egg. Eating, hunger, and satiety can be associated with one another in the following general terms:

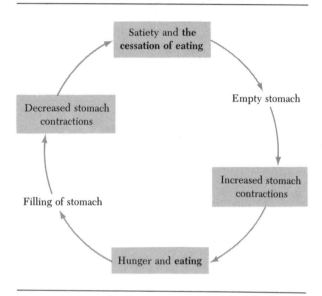

Figure 3—4. Continuity of physiology and behavior related to emptying and filling of the stomach. The boxed material represents processes subject to conscious experience. Behavioral activity is indicated by the use of boldface type.

Figure 3-4 has been drawn to show that behavioral and physiological functions are part of a continuous cycle. Furthermore, many of these processes are a part of our conscious experience, a fact which is emphasized by boxing these processes in this and in subsequent diagrams. Without hunger and eating there would be no filling of the stomach. Without food in the body there would be no satiety. The system diagrammed, once in motion, goes through its cycle in a few minutes.

Figure 3-5 illustrates a slower-acting cycle, again emphasizing the continuity and coexistence of physiology and behavior in the body's handling of solid food. In this illustration we see the involvement of the

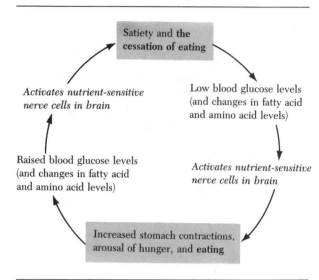

Figure 3—5. Continuity of physiology and behavior related to blood glucose levels. The boxed material represents processes subject to conscious experience. Behavioral activity is indicated by the use of boldface type, and the involvement of the brain by italic type.

blood (vascular system) and the brain in addition to those organs depicted in Figure 3-4. The role played by the brain will be discussed in some detail in the next section.

The following more complete illustration (Figure 3-6) incorporates the simpler diagrams just presented and adds the involvement of the intestines, abdominal and skeletal muscles, rectum, and sense organs. This diagram makes amply clear the elaborate network of physiological and behavioral processes that exists, and their dependency on one another. For example, the urge to eliminate waste products and the behavior of going to the bathroom to eliminate them is triggered by the sensations associated with the filling and distention of the rectum. These sensations would not occur if feces were not formed as a consequence of eating. Continuing to work backwards, we eat because we are hungry, and, when hungry, we find the smell and taste of food to be pleasant. After we have eaten and are sated, however, we often experience the taste and smell of food to be less pleasant than it was and sometimes even aversive (see Cabanac, 1971).

A further articulation of these workings is presented in Figure 3-7, where we see the involvement of the brain. Almost every aspect of our assimilation or elimination of solid foods relates in some way to the workings of the brain. Even in the case of smell, taste and vision, it has been shown experimentally that

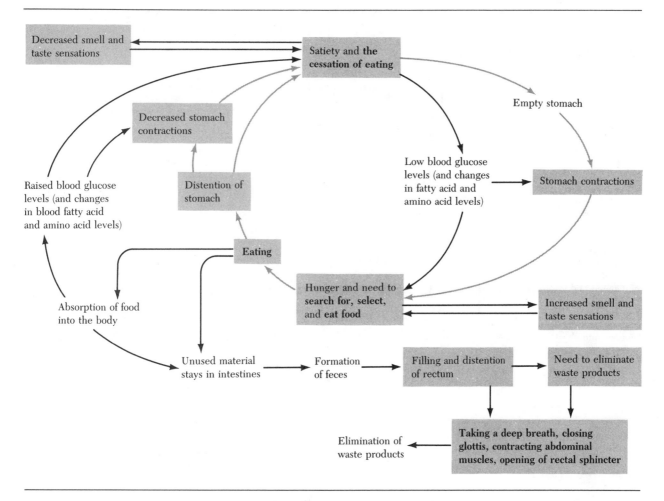

Figure 3–6. Continuity of physiology and behavior related to emptying and filling of the stomach, blood glucose levels, sensations of smell and taste, and the elimination of waste products. The boxed material represents processes subject to conscious experience. Behavioral activity is indicated by the use of boldface type.

some neurons respond to olfactory (smell), gustatory (taste), and visual stimuli only when the animal is hungry but not when it is sated (see, for example, Rolls and Rolls, 1977; Pager, Giachetti, Holley, and LeMagnen, 1972).

Figure 3-8 is a simplified diagram, summarizing the fact that physiological and behavioral processes act in a concerted, integrated manner—organized to provide food for energy and for the production of chemicals, and, in relation to these functions, to promote or to hinder its assimilation into the body. The ingestion of solid foods serves to form the molecules and the environment necessary for growth, maintenance, and actions of the body and, correspondingly, experiences of hunger and satiety are intimately correlated with levels of circulating glucose, fatty acids, and amino acids. The wisdom of this system is obvious: a state of

health is maintained when our need to eat is carefully correlated with the nutrients needed to produce ATP and other chemicals in the body. A working brain is necessary for these processes to occur, and we will discuss its involvement next.

The Brain

The **upper spinal cord**, the **hypothalamus**, and the **limbic system** are the areas of the brain that appear to be the most devoted to mechanisms of hunger, eating, satiety, and reward. Let's first discuss the involvement of the hypothalamus and the upper spinal cord.

The Lateral Hypothalamus and the Upper Spinal Cord. As illustrated in Figure 3-9, the **lateral hypothalamus** lies alongside the **medial hypothalamus**.

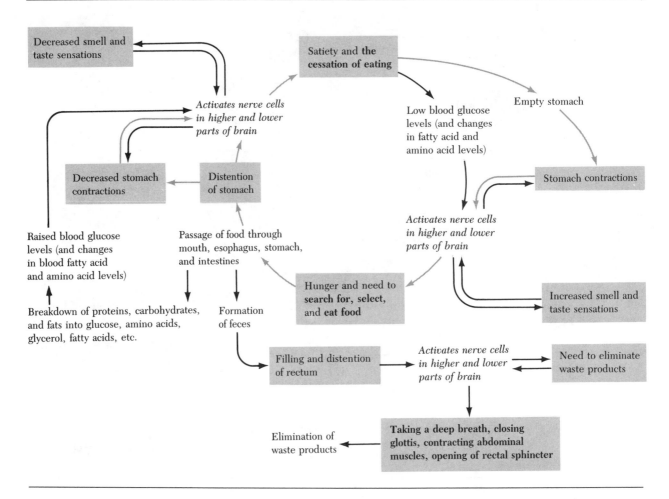

Figure 3–7. Continuity of physiology and behavior related to the assimilation of solid foods, emphasizing the key role played by the brain. The boxed material represents processes subject to conscious experience. Behavioral activity is indicated by the use of boldface type, and the involvement of the brain by italic type.

(Lateral areas are always farther from the middle of the brain; they are at the side of medial areas, which are closer to the middle). Eating and hunger responses are functions that are heavily represented within the lateral hypothalamic region; that is, various experimental techniques used to study how eating behaviors tie in with the workings of the brain consistently reveal the involvement of this brain area.

In these studies, for example, *electrical stimulation* of the lateral hypothalamic region has been found to cause an animal to eat, whereas *destruction* of this area abolishes or reduces eating behavior. In addition, a variety of *chemicals* affect this region in ways that indicate its sensitivity to the body's utilization of energy. These experiments have been most extensively conducted using glucose, fatty acids, and in-

sulin. Perhaps the most clear-cut results come from the responses of individual nerve cells. Specifically, when glucose is applied to neurons in this brain region, it has an inhibiting effect, as manifested in decreased neural activity. Conversely, free fatty acids stimulate lateral hypothalamic neurons (see Oomura, 1976). These findings correspond well with the fact that animals (or humans) that have not eaten for awhile show an increase in blood levels of free fatty acids and a decrease in blood glucose levels as fat and other chemicals in the body are utilized to produce energy. Both the increase in fatty acid levels and the decrease in glucose levels stimulate neurons in the lateral hypothalamic region, and this increased neural activity appears to be associated with hunger and eating responses.

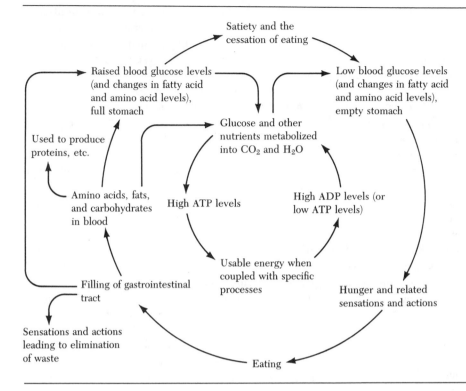

Figure 3–8. Basic processes involved in the body's assimilation of solid foods.

Figure 3–9. Involvement of the hypothalamus and upper spinal cord in the assimilation of solid foods. The double arrow signifies that hunger and satiety responses involve neural mechanisms within these connected regions of the brain.

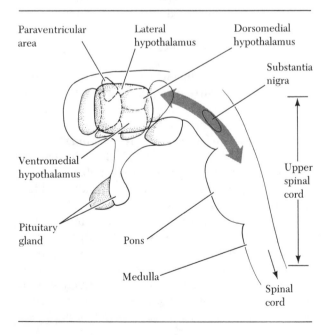

THE HYPOTHALAMUS

Hunger system: an important part of this "system" is contained in the lateral hypothalamic region. Electrical *stimulation* of this region of the hypothalamus induces eating behavior and destruction of this area reduces or abolishes eating behavior.

Satiety system: an important part of this "system" is contained in the medial hypothalamic region, closer to the middle of the brain than the lateral region. The ventromedial, dorsomedial, and paraventricular areas are all involved. Electrical *stimulation* of this region of the hypothalamus reduces or abolishes eating behavior and *destruction* of this area induces overeating.

THE UPPER SPINAL CORD

Hunger system: here, this "system" extends to the lateral hypothalamus and other areas from areas in the upper spinal cord that have not yet been precisely determined. *Destruction* of this system reduces or abolishes eating, producing symptoms similar to those observed after destruction of the lateral hypothalamic region.

Satiety system: here, this "system" extends to the medial hypothalamus from areas in the upper spinal cord that have not yet been precisely determined. Many reports indicate that when some areas of the upper spinal cord are *destroyed*, eating activity increases. These areas are widely dispersed in the upper spinal cord, however, and how they contribute to a satiety system remains unclear.

Thus three techniques—electrical stimulation, destruction, and application of appropriate nutrients—all indicate that the lateral hypothalamus is involved in eating and hunger responses. Although an interaction between blood levels of nutrients and eating behaviors appears to be definitely associated with the lateral hypothalamic region, this relation is not well understood. It is clear that many different mechanisms are involved (see, for example, Booth, 1968, 1972; Steffens, 1977), and the exact role played by one or another nutrient remains to be discovered. Furthermore, evidence implicating the involvement of the lateral hypothalamus in eating and hunger responses does not mean that other areas of the brain are not equally or even more involved in these behaviors. As discussed in Chapter 1, interpretation of experimental results always warrants caution. Let's briefly review some additional considerations that come into play when one attempts to evaluate experimental results.

When any region of the brain is carefully examined, it will be seen to consist of:

a) Neurons contained within that region—that is, the entire cell, consisting of the cell body, axon, and nerve ending, begins and ends within this region (see Figure 1-1);

b) Neurons whose cell bodies are contained within that region—that is, the cell body originates within this region but the axon goes to another region of the brain where it terminates;

c) Neurons whose nerve endings terminate within that region—that is, the cell body originates in another region of the brain but the axon goes to and terminates in this region;

d) Neurons whose axons pass through that region—that is, the cell body originates in other regions of the brain, the axon passes through this region, but the nerve ending, again, is in another region of the brain.

When any region of the brain is subjected to stimulation or destruction, neurons in all four of the above categories are affected. Because of this, as the foregoing review makes clear, it is possible that the neurons affected may be those transmitting information from one distant region in the brain to another distant region (category d), or the neurons may be those that send signals to other regions of the brain where eating responses are modified (category b), or they may be those regulated by other regions of the brain but terminating in the lateral hypothalamus as their "end-station" (category c).

In other words, one cannot state with certainty that the effects of electrical stimulation or selective destruction of the lateral hypothalamic region on eating and hunger prove that this region is a "center" for these responses. Indeed, as the neural mechanisms responsible for hunger and eating are slowly becoming understood, it is increasingly clear that we should *not* assume these activities to be regulated within a discrete, localized "center." Rather, we are looking at a neural "system" that courses through the brain, parts of this system being especially concentrated within the hypothalamus and upper spinal cord. Confirmation for this view comes from the finding that destruction of the **substantia nigra** in the upper spinal cord (see Figure 3-9) also reduces or abolishes eating (see Ungerstedt, 1971). In fact, similar effects are observed when surgical knife cuts are made at various points along a pathway connecting the upper spinal cord to the lateral hypothalamic region and other areas of the brain (see Grossman, Dacey, Halaris, Collier, and Routtenberg, 1978). However, even from these observations we should not assume that the lateral hypothalamic region affects eating behaviors merely because it contains axons of passage connecting the upper spinal cord to other regions of the brain. When investigators destroyed cell bodies in the lateral hypothalamus by using a chemical that destroys these bodies without damaging axons of passage, they found that eating was still reduced (Grossman, Dacey, Halaris, Collier, and Routtenberg, 1978).

From animal studies involving self-administered electrical stimulation of the brain, another aspect of lateral hypothalamic involvement in eating behaviors has been uncovered. (As you will recall, self-administered electrical stimulation is accomplished by inserting an electrode into the brain of the test animal—in this case, into the lateral hypothalamus—and then wiring it so that when the animal presses the lever, electrical current is passed through the electrode thus electrically stimulating its brain. If the animal repeatedly presses the lever, it is taken as an indication that the stimulation is rewarding because the animal seeks it. Conversely, if the animal avoids pressing the lever or presses a lever that has been wired to stop electrical stimulation, it is assumed that the stimulation is aversive.) Although the upper spinal cord, the hypothalamus, and the limbic system all contain structures whose stimulation appears to be rewarding—that is, the animal will repeatedly press the lever that sends electrical current through these structures—the lateral hypothalamic region appears to be one of the most responsive. Furthermore, studies have shown that *electrical stimulation of the lat-*

eral hypothalamus is more rewarding when the animal is hungry than when it is sated. This observation has led to the conclusion that electrical stimulation of the lateral hypothalamus not only induces eating but that reward and hunger mechanisms are, at least sometimes, organized together. We will now look at the medial hypothalamus.

The Medial Hypothalamus and the Upper Spinal Cord. As indicated in Figure 3-9, the functions of satiety and the cessation of eating are heavily represented in the **medial hypothalamus**. Again, this statement reflects the consistent and clear-cut findings that come from a variety of experiments designed to study how satiety and the cessation of eating tie in with the workings of the brain.

For example, in direct contrast to what occurs in the lateral hypothalamus, electrical stimulation of the medial hypothalamus reduces or abolishes eating behavior in test animals, whereas destruction of this area causes the animal to overeat, often to the point of extreme obesity (see Figure 3-10). Again in contrast to findings in the lateral hypothalamic region, glucose applied to the medial hypothalamus has a stimulatory effect on neurons whereas free fatty acids have an inhibiting effect (Oomura, 1976). Thus, when an animal (or human) eats, causing a rise in blood glucose levels and a fall in free fatty acid levels, these changes in blood nutrient levels appear to stimulate neurons in the medial hypothalamus and this presumably leads to satiety and the cessation of eating. This interpretation fits well with the finding that a preference for solutions containing high levels of glucose persists in rats with lesions of the ventromedial hypothalamus, which is a part of the medial hypothalamus, whereas in normal rats there is a shift, with continued drinking, to a bottle containing a less sweet solution. In other words, when some areas of the medial hypothalamus are destroyed, the animal does not, as does the normal animal, reduce its intake of glucose—an observation that suggests a disturbance in the mechanism responsible for shifting intake from high to low levels (Panksepp and Meeker, 1977).

Although there appear to be definite relationships connecting blood nutrient levels and reduced eating with the medial hypothalamic region, we must again point out that whatever these relationships, they are very complex and not well understood. For example, the ventromedial region of the medial hypothalamus does not appear to be indispensably involved in the reduction of food intake that normally occurs following blood infusions of glucose since a reduction still occurs after this area is destroyed (Novin, 1977). Furthermore, there is good evidence that the hypothalamus and other brain regions are influenced by

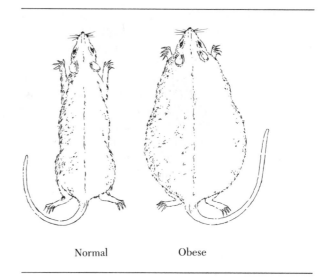

Normal   Obese

Figure 3-10. Comparison of a normal rat and a hypothalamic-obese rat. The obese rat (right), in which the ventromedial areas of the hypothalamus have been destroyed (see Figure 3-9), weighs over two times as much as the normal rat. (From Teitelbaum, P., and Campbell, B. Ingestion patterns in hyperphagic and normal rats. *Journal of Comparative and Physiological Psychology,* 51, 135–141, 1958.)

neural input from the intestines and other organs (which use as pathways nerves of the parasympathetic and sympathetic branches of the autonomic nervous system, discussed in Chapter 7), and that the brain's responses differ according to the nutrient involved, be it carbohydrate, fat or protein (see Novin, 1977; Powley and Opsahl, 1976). Finally, electrical stimulation of the hypothalamus leads to changes in carbohydrate metabolism in the liver and changes in acid secretion and motility of the stomach—in either case, of course, possibly altering the animal's desire for food (see Powley and Opsahl, 1976; Shimazu, 1977).

Studies in laboratory animals indicate that electrical stimulation of the medial hypothalamus is *not rewarding;* that is, electrical current passed through electrodes placed in this area does not, in general, lead to self-stimulation. In fact, it is sometimes aversive. These responses are fitting in as much as abolished or reduced eating, were they rewarding experiences, would mean that we would probably seek starvation.

As we have seen with the initiation of eating in relation to the lateral hypothalamic region, satiety and the reduction of eating are also not functions of a "center" within the hypothalamus. Rather, we are looking at a "system" that courses through the brain, parts of this system being especially concentrated within the hypothalamic region and upper spinal cord. For example, when parts of the upper spinal cord are damaged, this, too, increases eating behavior. There appears to be a system of neurons connecting the upper spinal cord to the medial hypothalamus. Within the medial hypothalamus, neurons belonging to this system are situated along the upper border of the ventromedial area and terminate in the paraventricular area (see Figure 3-9). Surgical knife cuts made at various points along this pathway result in increased eating behavior and obesity (see Gold, Jones, Sawchenko, and Kapatos, 1977; Grossman, 1979).

Support for the notion that the hypothalamus is part of a system that integrates physiological and behavioral responses related to eating behavior, satiety and reward comes from studies that strongly suggest interactions between the two regions of the hypothalamus. For example, as already mentioned, an animal will self-administer electrical stimulation in the lateral hypothalamic region more frequently when it is hungry than when it is sated. This observation is confirmed by the fact that ingesting food not only decreases lateral hypothalamic self-stimulation, but it also causes electrical stimulation in this region to become aversive (Hoebel, 1969). This latter effect appears to be mediated by the medial region of the hypothalamus because when the ventromedial area is destroyed, this shift from reward to aversion does not occur (Hernandez and Hoebel, 1978). Further evidence that the medial hypothalamic region exerts this inhibiting influence over the lateral hypothalamus, at least in this respect, comes from studies showing that destruction of the ventromedial region leads to an immediate increase in the rate of lateral hypothalamic self-stimulation (Hoebel, 1968). In other experiments it has been shown that distention of the stomach, intragastric feeding (directly into the stomach), and intravenous feeding all inhibit self-stimulation in the lateral hypothalamus—a response that occurs only when the ventromedial region is intact (Hoebel, 1968; Hernandez and Hoebel, 1978).

We therefore see that changes in blood nutrient levels in the lateral hypothalamus can modify hunger and eating responses, that electrical stimulation of this region induces hunger and eating behavior, that when this region is destroyed hunger and eating are abolished or reduced, and that it is an area which is usually rewarding when electrically stimulated. Conversely, we see that changes in blood nutrient levels and electrical stimulation of the medial hypothalamus induce satiety and abolish eating responses, and that this region is generally not rewarding when electrically stimulated. These interactions exemplify the co-existence of physiological and behavioral processes; that is, eating (or not eating), hunger (or satiety), reward (or lack of reward), and responses to appropriate nutrients are all organized together in these areas of the brain and, in their behavioral and physiological interplay, determine the actions involved in assimilating (or not assimilating) solid foods. The fact that this coexistent interaction of mechanisms occurs within the brain is not surprising, given the complexity of connections we see among brain regions and organs. What is especially noteworthy is how these mechanisms act in concert—in this case to promote or to hinder our assimilation of solid foods. Let's now look at the involvement of other regions of the brain.

The Limbic System. The limbic system, illustrated in Figure 3-11, comprises a much larger part of the brain than does the hypothalamus, and, phylogenetically, it is more "developed" (see Chapter 1). Although, with respect to eating behavior, the primary role of the limbic system appears to be its modification of hypothalamic and upper spinal cord activity, this system is very much involved in the assimilation of solid foods. Indeed, as indicated in Figure 3-11, every area of the limbic system appears to be involved in eating responses, but especially the **amygdala**. A variety of experiments have shown that destroying certain portions of the amygdala greatly reduces eating behavior (see, for example, Fonberg, 1976, 1977). When other parts of the amygdala are damaged, the opposite effect—an increase in eating responses—often occurs. As is the case in the lateral hypothalamic region, the amygdala also has reward systems that are active when the animal is hungry but inactive when the animal is sated (see Jurkowlaniec and Bialowas, 1981). The involvement of other portions of the limbic system in these behaviors has been shown often. For example, Robinson and Mishkin (1962) placed a stimulating electrode in a variety of brain structures in monkeys and demonstrated that electrical stimulation of these structures not only elicited the same responses (food intake in sated monkeys and food rejection in hungry monkeys) when the electrode was in the hypothalamus and amygdala, but also when it was in the **septum**, **cingulate gyrus**, **olfactory areas** and other areas illustrated in Figure 3-11.

The involvement of the limbic system in eating behaviors, among other responses, is dramatically illustrated by an unusual syndrome observed in early experiments with monkeys in which some outer cerebral cortex, the amygdala, and a large part of the hippocampus (a part of the limbic system—see Figure 3-11) was removed. (Damage restricted to the outer cerebral cortex did not produce these results.)

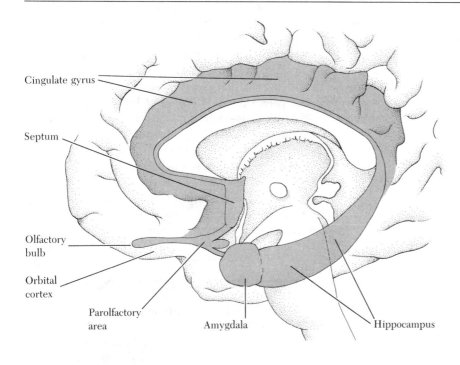

Cingulate gyrus

Septum

Olfactory
bulb

Orbital
cortex

Parolfactory
area

Amygdala

Hippocampus

Amygdala: depending on the precise area stimulated, electrical *stimulation* can increase or decrease gastrointestinal motility and secretion as well as eating behavior. Electrical *stimulation* has also been reported to elicit licking, chewing, and swallowing movements. Similarly, *lesion* (destruction) can increase or decrease eating behavior depending on the region of the amygdala that is destroyed. The amygdala is also believed to contribute to one's ability to select foods since monkeys (and humans) suffering from damage in the amygdala are sometimes indiscriminate in what they eat.

Other areas of the limbic system: there are a number of reports also implicating the hippocampus, cingulum, septum, olfactory, and orbitofrontal areas in the assimilation of solid foods. Responses to electrical stimulation and lesion include many of those listed for the amygdala, but they are often less dramatic and less consistent.

Figure 3–11. Involvement of the limbic system—composed of the amygdala, hippocampus, cingulate gyrus, septum, and olfactory areas—in the assimilation of solid foods.

These monkeys exhibited:

a) "psychic blindness," characterized by an impaired ability to recognize objects and sense their meaning;

b) strong oral tendencies, characterized by a marked increase in oral exploratory behavior;

c) a strong tendency to react to and attend to visual stimuli, seeming to be "distracted" by almost any object;

d) tame and docile behavior, characterized by the absence of aggression, rage responses, or fear;

e) increased and aberrant sexual activity.

This syndrome is called the **Kluver-Bucy syndrome** after the authors who described it (see Kluver and Bucy, 1937, 1938, 1939). In more recent years, there have been reports of the Kluver-Bucy syndrome in humans suffering from damage to the same areas of the brain as described above (see Marlowe, Mancell, and Thomas, 1975; Gascon and Gilles, 1973) and reports of some of the symptoms of this syndrome in

patients suffering from damage to the amygdala alone (see Sawa, Ueki, Arita, and Harada, 1954).

Among the disordered behaviors that comprise this syndrome is a marked increase in eating behavior, in some cases reflecting an increased desire for food and consequent overeating, but also characterized by an apparent inability to discriminate between appropriate and inappropriate food objects. In the extreme case, the animal (or human) will place virtually everything within sight into its mouth, including wrapping paper and other items that would otherwise not be ingested—such as feces. This points to the role of the limbic system in selecting *appropriate* behaviors, a topic also discussed in other chapters of this book because it applies to more than eating behaviors.

Important to our ability to search for, select, and prepare foods, for example, is the sensation of smell, or **olfaction**, which is also regulated by structures in the limbic system. In Chapter 6 we will see that olfaction appears to be fully served by the limbic system in contrast to most other sensory modalities which are well represented in—and often require normal functioning of—the outer cerebral cortex.

This is related to the fact that animals, generally, have a much more developed sense of smell than humans, yet they have much less outer cerebral cortex. The strong involvement of olfactory structures within the limbic system has been demonstrated by studies showing, for example, the increased activity of some neurons in these structures when a rat is presented with food odors, and that this activity is greatest when the animal is hungry (see Pager, Giachetti, Holley, and LeMagnen, 1972).

The Cerebral Cortex. Although the outer cerebral cortex is essential for normal muscular coordination and movement, vision, and other functions we use to assimilate foods, it does not appear to be a structure that is essential for the satiety, hunger, and reward functions that govern eating. This fact is especially evident with functions such as hunger, satiety and reward, but as we will see later, is true for many other experiences and functions as well. In other words, *some of our experienced functions are subcortical; that is, the outer, "newest," most developed part of our brain is apparently not the most essential structure for some of our experiences.*

Body and Self

The topics covered in this chapter might appear to be too physiological to be relevant, at least as they have thus far been treated. Now it is time to highlight the importance of the psychological and experiential factors integrally associated with almost all of these physiological processes. Many of the examples cited below to illuminate this side of the body/self profile may appear to be commonplace; yet they are important. Most of our lives are composed of such experiences. A primary first example is our day-in and day-out experiences of being hungry and wanting food, satisfying our hunger, then feeling sated and losing desire for food. The interplay of physiological and behavioral factors in this daily cycle has already been discussed.

In this same context, however, we have not touched on the many psychological factors that exert a powerful influence on the mechanisms involved in our body's assimilation of solid foods. For example, when we are *overly anxious* or *emotionally aroused*, the activity of the adrenal glands and the autonomic nervous system increases and this can decrease our appetite. The normal stomach contractions that signify hunger are inhibited by the sympathetic nerves which comprise part of the autonomic nervous system. In fact, during emotional stress there are sometimes stomach and intestinal contractions associated with experiences of nausea. Conversely, we can sim-

ply "dream up" a favorite dish and begin to actually salivate, particularly when we are already slightly hungry. As with the physiological responses described earlier, these *anticipatory responses* of the mind are, of course, connected to brain activity (for more information, see Woods, 1977). Any time we anticipate a meal—because of hunger, habit or any other stimulus—not only does salivation increase but gastric secretions and pancreatic secretions increase as well.

In functional terms, the secretions of the stomach serve to break down proteins and other large molecules, and the secretions of the pancreas allow fats, carbohydrates and proteins to become small enough to cross the walls of the intestines on their way to the blood. The pancreatic secretions mentioned above are released into the intestines. Another pancreatic secretion, **insulin**, is released into the blood. Insulin lowers blood nutrient levels because it increases glucose uptake by cells, promotes protein synthesis (a process that uses up amino acids), and accelerates fat deposition. The lowered blood nutrient levels can further increase a person's desire to eat. Thus, depending upon the strength of the anticipatory response and the physiological processes it sets in motion, we will experience varying degrees of hunger.

Another powerful influence on eating behavior is our *prior experience* with specific foods. Foods we disliked at an earlier age sometimes provoke a strong aversion—both physiologically (expressed as nausea and even vomiting) and psychologically—and we will not eat these foods.

We have talked about some conditions that influence our desire to eat. Let's now look at *fasting*. When we fast (or when a person actually is starving), many mechanisms are activated (see Figure 3-12). Levels of growth hormone, cortisol, epinephrine, and norepinephrine all increase to produce a stimulated state in our body. In addition, a host of digestive processes occur even though there is no actual filling of the gastrointestinal system. These factors are partly responsible for our feeling "light" and "energetic" during a fast. It is important to realize that although the body is often stimulated and therefore feels more energetic, no extra energy is produced by the act of fasting. In fact, some people become lethargic when they fast. Nevertheless, for many, fasting is a simple way to induce an aroused, alert state without evoking stressful stimuli such as anger or anxiety, or taking stimulants, or simply feeling rushed to accomplish something. Stress and arousal are discussed in some detail in Chapters 7 and 8. These (and other) chapters also discuss physiological and psychological mechanisms that influence our assimilation of solid foods.

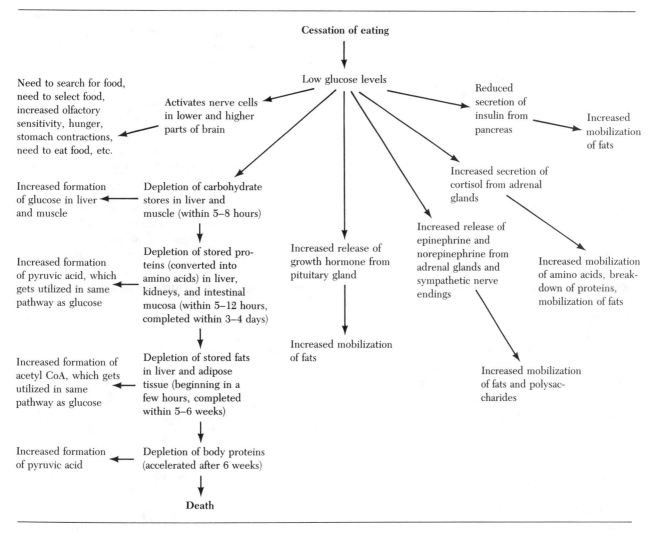

Figure 3–12. Mechanisms that are activated when a person goes on a fast. Note that the main effect is increased mobilization and formation of molecules that can be utilized for energy, a process involving an increased secretion of such chemicals as norepinephrine, epinephrine, growth hormone, and cortisol, all of which produce a stimulated state in the body.

It is important to recognize that the assimilation of food requires our *conscious, voluntary responses*. It is not sufficient that our bodies "work"—that the stomach muscles contract, that the pancreas release chemicals, and that blood nutrient levels rise and fall. These processes will occur, of course, whether or not we are conscious of them. However, the deliberate acts of seeking, selecting, preparing, eating, and eliminating solid foods requires voluntary actions.

Figures 3-4 through 3-7 illustrate, in boxes, those processes that are part of our conscious experience. Most of these have to do with eating and the elimination of waste products—processes that occur either *before* food enters the small intestine on its way into

the body or *after* it leaves the large intestines on its way out of the body. Distention of the rectum is an important signal of the need to eliminate. Other conscious experiences that are extremely important in the process of searching for and preparing foods are smell, vision, taste, salivation and stomach contractions.

Generally speaking, conscious experience is most necessary when we need information in order to make decisions or to exert voluntary actions. Hunger is experienced consciously, and we can act on it or not. Although we usually assess our state of hunger by stomach pangs caused by contractions of the muscles of the stomach, this need not be the case. For example, when a person is fed intravenously, sensations of hunger are reduced even though there is no filling of the stomach. In this case the conscious experiences of hunger or satiety are connected to circulating glucose and free fatty acid levels, as discussed previously.

Entirely different examples of our conscious experience come from those physiological processes that occur as nutrients are chemically changed to produce the molecules used for energy. *Muscle fatigue*, for example, is a state frequently experienced with heavy exercise. In this condition, the impulses from the brain to the muscles are operating normally but the muscles themselves are unable to perform work effectively. A major factor in muscle fatigue is the body's depletion of ATP. (As described earlier in the chapter, the process of muscle contraction involves a coupling of ATP with muscle proteins. In the process of contracting, muscle converts ATP into ADP and energy is released.) With intense exercise, our muscles are simply unable to produce enough ATP to maintain the degree of contraction required.

Another example, illustrating the connection between experience and processes that occur as foods are used for energy, involves *physical exercise and pain*. Because pain is a disagreeable sensation, most of us stop exercising at this point. Some of the processes involved are as follows:

a) With heavy exertion, the amount of ATP required by the muscle is greater than the amount that can be produced by the continuously active mechanisms in the cells, especially those requiring oxygen (which are those that produce the most ATP—see Figure 3-1A in the appendix);

b) Additional ATP is furnished by metabolic pathways that do not require oxygen. Because there is little additional oxygen present to carry pyruvic acid into the citric-acid cycle, this process results in a build-up of pyruvic acid;

c) The additional pyruvic acid is converted into lactic acid, which then builds up in muscle very quickly;

d) The excess lactic acid stimulates nerve endings, which elicit the sensation of pain. (This response might occur as a direct action of lactic acid or it might be a result of lactic acid interacting with other chemicals—we do not know.)

e) The experience of pain leads to the cessation of the strenuous activity;

f) Once the extreme exertion is reduced, the presence of oxygen allows most of the lactic acid to be reconverted into pyruvic acid, which is then reconverted into glucose or is used in the citric-acid cycle to generate more ATP.

The overall wisdom of muscles not working beyond the body's ability to furnish them with energy is obvious.

III. INVOLVEMENT OF MANY ORGANS AT ONCE

We have already indicated a number of times that many organs are involved in our assimilation of solid foods. We have mentioned hands and mouth, esophagus, stomach, small and large intestines, colon and rectum, vascular system, abdominal and skeletal muscles, and the sense organs. In addition, as noted in our discussion of fasting and emotional responses, the pituitary gland, the adrenal glands, the pancreas, the liver, adipose tissue (fat cells) and the autonomic nervous system are also involved.

Although the brain is extremely important and deserves considerable attention, it is only a part of a continuous process. Filling and emptying of the stomach, high or low glucose, fatty acid and amino acid levels, a distended or empty rectum, much or little stimulation of the organs of taste and smell—all of these processes determine to a large extent how the brain will respond at any given moment.

IV. RELATION TO HEALTH

In general, a good state of health is assured as long as the physiological and behavioral processes described above are working. We cannot overemphasize this simple fact. Often we focus on one or another aspect of our bodies that we consider to be unhealthy—like gaining too much weight or being underweight—yet we continue to eat when we need food, not eat when we don't, and eliminate waste products when necessary. Problems of obesity and undernourishment are, of course, real and important. Yet, they should not eclipse the general fact that our behavior and physiology coexist to keep us nourished day in and day out. This is especially apparent in young children. It is well known that young children will stop eating when they have received enough food and will eat when they need it. Similarly, when given a variety of foods to eat, young children will eat a balanced meal—sufficient amounts of vitamins, protein, carbohydrates, etc. However, as adults this sensitivity to the needs of the body is often dulled. A variety of factors cause this to happen. Most of these factors are related to education and learning:

1) We acquire habitual "tastes" and will eat some foods and reject others that are equally or sometimes more nutritious.

2) We often eat according to the time of day rather than in accordance with our body's needs.

3) Since a slim, trim physique is socially acceptable, what we do or do not eat is often based on how we will "look" rather than on our body's needs.

4) As a survival behavior, eating is powerfully purposeful. Although the purpose of eating is obvious, it is exactly this "purposiveness" that can lead a person to eat in order to satisfy a need to "do something meaningful" whenever the person feels "empty." This eating is not in response to the body's needs for food.

The experiences that lead us to be controlled by factors such as those listed above all share one property: they are *not* directly related to the healthy integrative processes outlined in this chapter. Let us now discuss some disorders.

The description of **anorexia nervosa** at the beginning of this chapter underscores the tremendous interaction between psychological and physiological states. That our society places a premium on thinness, particularly for women, has undoubtedly contributed to the increased incidence of this disease, which, as has been pointed out, can lead to death by starvation. Drugs seem to alleviate symptoms in some cases, as does psychotherapy. The effectiveness of drugs, even in some cases, indicates that altered brain functioning may be a major factor in the disease, although no specific area of the brain has been implicated in research to date. (Of course, the most obvious candidate would be the lateral hypothalamus. However, humans suffering from damage in this area do not have the symptoms of anorexia nervosa, although often there is reduced eating.) Drugs that alleviate depression appear to be more effective than others. The relationship of antidepressive and other drugs to our functioning is discussed in Chapter 11.

Obesity is a condition that is much more prevalent than anorexia nervosa. Approximately 30 percent of the American population is obese, which is defined as being at least 20 percent heavier than one's ideal body weight. A variety of factors, having to do with individual differences, contribute to this disorder.

Some evidence suggests that obesity is caused by how much fat one is able to carry. In lean people, fat cells develop during the first two years of life and proliferate again from age 10 to age 16. In obese people, proliferation of fat cells occurs during the first two years of life and during adolescence, just as in lean people, but the critical difference is that they also proliferate during the years in between. Thus, one theory holds that obese people deposit fat much more readily than lean people because they have more and larger fat cells.

Other reasons advanced to explain obesity are that obese individuals overeat because they are less responsive to signals of satiety than are lean individuals. There is some evidence that this lack of responsiveness involves satiety mechanisms within the brain. Various studies have shown that, in one way or another, the activity of the neural chemicals norepinephrine and serotonin within the brain differ between obese and normal animals. These neural chemicals have a definite effect on satiety mechanisms within the brain. In fact, most diet pills contain chemicals that affect the brain. Interestingly, brain mechanisms that suppress arousal are also involved in satiety. When we are sated, either after eating, drinking, or engaging in sexual activity, we usually experience a suppression of arousal, manifested in relaxation, drowsiness, and, sometimes, sleep. It appears likely that in some of us eating is a way to suppress arousal, thereby reducing excessive tension or other symptoms of an overstimulated state. This topic is discussed in Chapter 8 (see pages 177–178).

Stress can also influence eating behavior, causing some to overeat, others not to eat enough. What determines whether stress produces one or the other response (or neither) is complex. This topic is discussed in Chapter 7 in relation to the autonomic nervous system and the immune system. When a depression of appetite is the response to stress, it may be explained by an increase in neural activity that inhibits digestive processes in the stomach and intestines. Alternatively, but with the same effect, stress can cause an increase in the activity of the adrenal glands and the sympathetic nervous system, inducing a rise in blood glucose, fatty acid and amino acid levels. This increase in blood nutrient levels can also suppress the appetite.

The opposite effect—an increase in appetite—can occur when stress induces an increase in the release of insulin by the pancreas. As mentioned earlier, high levels of insulin cause blood glucose levels to fall because insulin promotes glucose uptake by cells.

Because insulin also promotes protein synthesis and fat deposition, it decreases amino acid and fatty acid levels in the blood. The low blood nutrient levels resulting from the release of insulin can, in some individuals, increase appetite.

Each of us is unique in our emotional responses, a topic also discussed more fully in Chapter 7. Briefly, stress can increase or decrease insulin secretion, depending on the individual's response to sympathetic and adrenal stimulation. In addition, stress not only affects the autonomic nervous system and the adrenal glands, but it also appears to increase the activity of various neural chemicals in the brain. For example, there is increased synthesis and release of norepinephrine within the brain during stress. This neural chemical has been reported to both increase or decrease eating behavior depending upon the area of the brain which is being affected (see pages 249–250, Chapter 11).

It is important to understand that the abnormal functions discussed in this section are not separate, isolated conditions; they result from the activity of the *same* mechanisms that operate to maintain health. In general, these mechanisms reflect an innate wisdom of the body. When we are overanxious and have no appetite, our stomach and intestines are probably in no shape to receive and digest food, and we shouldn't expect or demand it to do so. Similarly, when exposed to cold, our appetite usually increases. That is to say, if we gain some weight during the winter, the extra body fat will help to insulate us against the cold.

V. CONCLUSIONS

We have seen the variety of physiological factors that influence our experiences of hunger and satiety and, conversely, the psychological states that influence such physiological mechanisms as those involved in absorbing, utilizing, and eliminating solid foods. It should now be clear that these two aspects of our function are inseparable and have corresponding representations within the brain where the mechanisms regulating hunger, satiety, eating, and reward, as well as our responses to nutrients, all coexist.

It is especially noteworthy that these functions act in a concerted manner, resulting in an experienced *wisdom of the body* that serves to maintain health. This wisdom is expressed by the integration of many mechanisms serving our psychological state (e.g., hunger or satiety) and our physiological state (e.g., low or high nutrient levels) simultaneously. We will note this fact—that a portion of our experienced wisdom is frequently based on an integration of psychological and physiological factors—many times. Conversely, we will often note that when one or another psychological or physiological factor malfunctions, this malfunction frequently becomes the basis for our becoming unhealthy or sick.

There are many other statements we could make about our relation to solid foods. However, most of these assertions also apply to the other systems covered in subsequent chapters. Therefore, for the sake of simplicity we will add them one at a time. In the next chapter we will discuss another important food for our body: water. Although specific mechanisms are quite different, we will see that much of the organization described above for solid foods is similar to that involved in our assimilation of this liquid.

Recommended Reading

BALAGURA, S. *Hunger*. New York: Basic Books, 1973, 181 pages. *A nicely written book; it surveys eating behaviors, digestive mechanisms, and neural and chemical processes that are responsible for our assimilation of food.*

LEVENKRON, S. *Treating and Overcoming Anorexia Nervosa*. New York: Charles Scribner's Sons, 1982, 205 pages. *This book describes anorexia nervosa. The most prevalent conditions in which this disease occurs, case histories characterizing different symptoms, and various treatments are the main subjects covered. The author also attempts to encourage more psychologists to treat this disorder.*

NOVIN, D., WYRWICKA, W., and BRAY, G. (EDITORS). *Hunger: Basic Mechanisms and Clinical Implications*. New York: Raven Press, 1976, 494 pages. *This book is a comprehensive survey of mechanisms responsible for eating, hunger and satiety. Recommended for readers with advanced interest.*

STUNKARD, A. (EDITOR). *Obesity*. Philadelphia: W. B. Saunders, 1980, 470 pages. *This book covers the basic neural, genetic, morphologic and behavioral mechanisms responsible for eating and weight gain, and offers a detailed section on the treatment of obesity. Each chapter is written by experts in the field.*

Water: The Clinical Reality

Medical Disorder: Water Intoxication

Read this "overture" carefully before you read Chapter 4. The connections between the medical reality of water intoxication and the basic underlying physiological and psychological processes that regulate normal drinking behaviors are developed in this chapter. (For more information on water intoxication, see Dubovsky, Grabon, Berl, and Schrier, 1973; Wasterlain and Posner, 1968; Rymer and Fishman, 1973; Caron, Cappoen, Chopin, Lefebvre, and Warot, 1977; and Cherner, 1982.)

Water intoxication, caused by disease, neurologic damage, or severely abnormal behavior, is characterized by a low concentration of solutes in the blood, meaning that the osmotic activity of the blood and extracellular fluids is abnormally low. This condition, in turn, is caused by excessive loss of sodium from the body, by excessive water intake, or by a combination of both.

When the body's sodium levels fall or water levels rise, one becomes irritable and confused. Headache, giddiness, and feelings of unreality often develop, accompanied by a bad-tempered, querulous disposition. In serious cases, neural and muscular excitability increase, not only leading to irritability and confusion but also to fibrillation (fine, rapid contractions of muscle fibers) and spasticity of muscles, convulsions and seizures, delerium, lethargy, coma, and even death. The primary cause of these severe symptoms is the movement of water from the blood into the cells of the brain, causing them to swell and function abnormally.

Many types of neurologic damage—meningitis, brain tumors, head trauma—can cause water intoxi-

cation. In many of these cases, water intake may be normal but it is not excreted because of excessive levels of antidiuretic hormone which causes water retention. Antidiuretic hormone (ADH) is produced in the hypothalamic region of the brain and is then transported to the posterior pituitary gland. From there it is released into the blood, finally exerting its action on the kidneys. When ADH is present, water flows out of the collecting ducts of the kidneys into the blood and a concentrated urine is formed that contains very little water. (Under normal conditions this action of ADH is essential to the regulation of the body's water level. Water intoxication consequent to neurologic damage is likely to occur only when ADH is secreted in abnormally high amounts.) Disorders of other organs such as the lungs, pancreas, and kidneys can also lead to water intoxication. In these cases the cause does not appear to be the abnormal secretion of ADH but the secretion of ADH-like chemicals by these organs, or other abnormal functions.

Abnormal behavior and psychopathology can also cause water intoxication. On a simple level, a person might be working hard in very hot conditions and thus suffer excessive loss of salt (mainly sodium and chloride) in the sweat. If this person then drinks very large amounts of water, "heat cramps," characterized by fibrillary twitchings and painful spasms of the muscles, especially those of the abdominal wall, may develop. These symptoms can be alleviated by salt replacement. If water intoxication is untreated or severe, full-blown symptoms may appear and the person then requires prompt medical attention.

Various states of emotional and physical stress, because they influence the release of ADH, can cause water retention. In most cases water intoxication does not develop because the body's regulatory mechanisms compensate for minor imbalances. In psychiatric patients whose mental and/or emotional disturbance is severe, however, there have been reports of excessive secretion of ADH and water intoxication. Schizophrenia (characterized by a marked withdrawal from close relationships and a disturbed sense of reality) and manic-depressive psychosis (characterized by alternating periods of extreme excitement and severe depression) are among the conditions in which water intoxication has been reported (see Caron, Cappoen, Chopin, Lefebvre, and Warot, 1977). In some cases, the alleviation of psychotic symptoms has been observed to be associated with reduced levels of ADH and subsequent correction of a water overload (see Dubovsky, Grabon, Berl, and Schrier, 1973, for a report of a case involving schizophrenia).

Some persons suffering from water intoxication are classified as "compulsive drinkers" suffering from a condition called "psychogenic polydipsia." These persons have been known to consume five to eight liters of water a day for no apparent reason. One survey of 27 cases of psychogenic polydipsia reported that 67 percent involved patients who were either schizophrenic or otherwise mentally disturbed, 18 percent involved alcoholics, and the remaining 15 percent included persons suffering from a variety of other disorders (see Caron, Cappoen, Chopin, Lefebvre, and Warot, 1977).

In addition to the symptoms of water intoxication already described, the excessive ingestion of water frequently causes pain in the abdomen, nausea, vomiting, abdominal fullness, and tightness of the skin. Because the excess water dilutes body fluids and accelerates elimination of urine, there is a gradual "washing out" of solute in the kidneys, causing excessive elimination of sodium from the body. The only appropriate treatment for water intoxication caused by compulsive drinking is to restrict the patient's water intake. As the symptoms of psychological disturbance are alleviated, the compulsive need to drink water usually goes away.

4

Water

The only liquid that is essential to our body is water. Water makes up 60 to 70 percent of our body by weight, so it is by far the largest part of our selves. In addition, it is the major component of blood, all cells, and the spaces between cells. It also provides the medium in which all cellular activities take place.

In this chapter we will first discuss why water is so vital to our functioning, involving far more than satisfying our thirst, keeping our bodies clean, or cooking our food. We will explain the behavioral processes that are interwoven with physiological processes to produce an inseparable system which, despite its different mechanisms, is generally organized much like that discussed in the last chapter. Finally, we will discuss the relationships of the above workings to our health.

I. WATER AND ITS USE BY THE BODY

In our body, water exists only as a liquid. It consists of two atoms of hydrogen (H) and one atom of oxygen (O) to make up a molecule which is often referred to as H_2O.

Water is the only liquid that the body needs. All other liquids we might need contain chemicals, which we have classified as solid foods. Milk, for example, is approximately 87 percent water; the rest is protein, fat, carbohydrates, minerals, and vitamins. Because it is so common, we take it for granted, but water constitutes a unique food. It has special properties that the body takes good advantage of:

a) high melting and boiling points

b) high heat of vaporization

c) high specific heat capacity

d) high dielectric constant

e) low viscosity.

These special qualities as they are related to our functioning are discussed in turn below.

High Melting and Boiling Points

All chemicals that are similar to water, like hydrogen sulfide (H_2S), at body temperature are gases instead of liquids. It is obviously very important that water does not become a gas in our body.

High Heat of Vaporizaton

The heat of vaporization, which is a measurement of the heat required to vaporize a substance, is also much higher for water than for other chemicals that are similar to it. The body uses the evaporative property of water to regulate its temperature. When we sweat, the vaporization of water on our skin requires a great deal of heat, and this causes our skin to cool.

High Specific Heat Capacity

Heat capacity is a measurement of the amount of heat required to raise the temperature of a substance, in this case water, by a given amount. Water has a high specific heat capacity, meaning that it takes a considerable amount of heat to raise its temperature. Our body cannot function normally unless a relatively constant temperature is maintained inside it. The metabolic processes in the body are constantly generating heat, which raises our body's temperature; however, because of water's high heat capacity this effect is minimized.

High Dielectric Constant

The dielectric constant of water is a measurement of its ability to reduce the force between two charges placed in it. Water has a high dielectric constant, meaning that it serves as a good insulator for electrically charged chemicals. Because of this property, water is an excellent solvent for ionic substances such as sodium (Na^+), potassium (K^+), calcium (Ca^{++}), chloride (Cl^-), and bicarbonate (HCO_3^-). These ions and others are essential for all of our cellular processes. (Ions are atoms or groups of atoms carrying an electric charge.)

Low Viscosity

Water has a low viscosity and is therefore very mobile as a liquid. Not only does this mean that water adds extremely little resistance to the flow of body fluids (such as blood in our vessels), but it also means that water can easily and rapidly diffuse and equilibrate throughout our entire body. One way in which the body exploits this property is discussed below.

Osmosis. Whenever the concentration of solutes —any chemicals that are dissolved within the body— is greater in one compartment than another, water will immediately leave the more dilute compartment and enter the more concentrated one. This process is called "osmosis."

Most solutes are not as mobile as water. One reason for this is that solutes are contained within three compartments: within cells, within blood vessels and the heart, and within the spaces between cells— spaces that are outside of the vascular (blood) system. These compartments are separated from each other. For example, the walls of our blood vessels separate blood from other fluids, while the membranes that define the outer boundary of all of our cells separate these cells from the fluid surrounding them. Water travels freely through these boundaries, but most solutes do not. Therefore cell membranes, the walls of blood vessels (especially of the capillaries), and other borders separating the body's compartments act as "semipermeable membranes," allowing water to pass freely but not other chemicals that are "trapped" within them.

Osmotic forces lie behind many of the processes occurring in the body. For example, when we eat, we are loading ourselves with solutes. Most of these solutes will leave the stomach and intestines and enter the blood as amino acids, simple carbohydrates (like the monosaccharides, glucose and fructose), minerals, and, to a lesser extent, fats. These dissolved substances will quickly go to various cells in our body to be used for nourishment or stored for future use.

Each cell is quite selective about which solutes it will accept or how much of one or another solute it will absorb, so the concentration of dissolved nutrients will remain high in the blood and in the spaces between cells until they are used or eliminated in the urine. Certain nerve cells in the hypothalamus, called **osmoreceptors**, are very sensitive to these fluctu-

ations. When the concentration of solutes in the fluids that surround them goes up, water leaves these cells and they shrink slightly in size, thus increasing their neural activity. This increased neural activity appears to be related to our desire to drink—a common experience after eating a meal, for example. There is, in fact, a direct relation between brain functioning and the number of solutes dissolved in the body, a topic that will be further discussed later in the chapter.

Another example of the way in which osmosis works in and for our bodies involves the swelling of tissues. When we suffer allergic or immune reactions —like toxic reactions to poison oak or inflammatory reactions to cuts or splinters—or when we sustain injury to joints, such as spraining an ankle, there is a change in the semipermeable nature of the capillary membranes within the injured area. Some solutes (even some cells) leave the blood where they are normally contained and enter into the tissues to promote tissue repair and to participate in the defensive reactions that destroy foreign particles like bacteria (see Chapter 7). This process causes these tissues to swell because water from the blood will immediately follow in order to minimize any change in chemical concentrations that develops. As tissue repair progresses, the semipermeable nature of the capillary membrane is fully restored, the extra chemicals are removed, and swelling is quickly reduced.

The kidneys also make use of osmotic forces. One of the main functions of the kidneys is to filter the blood. This filtering function is accomplished by a variety of processes beyond the scope of this book to explain. What concerns us in terms of osmosis is that many of the chemicals that are destined to leave the body as waste products end up in the collecting ducts of the kidneys from where they enter the ureters on their way to the urinary bladder. Here the body is faced with a unique situation: as chemicals are filtered and excreted into the collecting ducts, water will follow, as explained earlier, to minimize concentration differences between the urine and the blood the kidneys are filtering. In so doing, the body could lose enormous amounts of water into the urine. (In fact, when faced with a water overload, the kidneys actually operate to remove the extra water in our body.) Usually we cannot afford to lose this water. The kidneys avoid this loss by having an environment whose concentration of chemicals is much higher than that found in other parts of the body. Then, as the filtrate—destined to become urine—passes through this environment, water flows out, into the concentrated fluid. The amount of water allowed to flow into this concentrated fluid is controlled by **antidiuretic hormone (ADH)**. As previously explained,

ADH is produced in the hypothalamic region of the brain and is then transported to the posterior pituitary gland from which it is released into the blood to finally exert its action on the kidneys. In the absence of ADH, water does not pass into the concentrated fluids of the kidneys, so a dilute urine is formed that contains a lot of water. When ADH is present, water flows out of the collecting ducts and a concentrated urine is formed that contains very little water.

II. PHYSIOLOGICAL/PSYCHOLOGICAL INTERACTIONS

The special properties of water just discussed are intrinsic to water itself; the body does not regulate them, it simply makes use of them. However, the *amount* of water the body contains must be regulated very carefully. There are a number of reasons for this:

1) There is a constant, *obligatory loss* of water by the body. This loss, which occurs through the skin, lungs, urine, and feces, adds up to about 2.4 liters per day. When we are dehydrated, this loss can decrease to less than one liter per day. Sweating alone can increase this loss to as much as 3-4 liters per hour.

2) There are many chemicals that are dissolved in the body's fluids. As the volume of water changes in the body, the amount of these chemicals and their concentrations also change. These changes in our chemicals can severely alter the body's functions and even cause death.

3) There is a need to maintain a relatively constant volume of blood. We mentioned earlier that the fluids in the body can be defined to exist in three general compartments: **intracellular fluid** (inside cells), **extracellular fluid** (outside cells), and **blood**. Of these three compartments, the volume of blood needs the tightest regulation. If the volume of blood falls below approximately 3.5 liters, death will occur, usually because of a condition of cardiovascular degeneration called "progressive shock." (The blood volume rarely exceeds normal levels—5-7 liters—because the extra fluid either leaves the blood vessels and enters the extracellular spaces or it is simply excreted into the urine.)

Under normal circumstances the body can easily handle a water overload. The converse situation, however—a water deficiency—cannot be corrected unless we take in water. Our body does synthesize a small amount of water as a result of metabolic processes, but this amount (about 0.2 liters per day) is much less than the amount required.

The organization of thirst-drinking-satiety-digestion involves almost every part of the body. Figure 4-1 illustrates some of the main organs involved in our assimilation of water. As we saw in relation to solid foods, here, too, our organs are involved in an elaborate network of systems that encompass physiological and behavioral processes. The use of these organs is explained below as part of our discussion of the coexistence of physiology and behavior.

Coexistence and Inseparability of Physiology and Behavior

Just as with solid foods, the physiology and behavior surrounding our use of water are part of one continuous, coexisting process. The cyclicity of this process is illustrated in general terms in Figure 4-2. Although receptors throughout our mouth and gastrointestinal tract signal us to stop drinking, those in the stomach and intestines seem to be the most important in this respect. By means of these receptors, satiety to water and the cessation of drinking often occur within a few minutes after we start to drink.

Figure 4-3 illustrates a slower-acting cycle, dependent on the level of water in the body's fluids rather than that in the stomach and intestines. When we drink water, it usually takes at least 30 minutes before it is fully absorbed into the tissue fluids. If it were not for the fast-acting system that involves the gastrointestinal tract, we would drink far too much water. What usually happens is the following: a) We drink water until our gastrointestinal receptors (including those in the mouth and throat) are activated. Their activation gives us a sensation of being sated, and we will stop drinking. b) If not enough water has been ingested to restore water levels in the tissues, parts of our brain will again be involved in giving us a sensation of thirst—usually 15 to 30 minutes later. c) If we are still thirsty, the same processes will be repeated until our brain no longer signals sensations of thirst, at which point we will stop drinking.

The following diagram (Figure 4-4) expands upon the simpler diagrams illustrated in Figures 4-2 and 4-3 to include the involvement of the kidneys, the bladder, and the muscles involved in urination. Here we see that when the body contains too little water, the pituitary gland increases its secretion of antidiuretic hormone (ADH). ADH allows more water to flow out of the collecting ducts of the kidneys back into the blood; therefore less water is lost in the urine and the body's supply of water is conserved. Conversely, when the body contains too much water, the pituitary gland decreases its secretion of ADH and more water is lost in the urine. Just as conscious processes are involved in thirst, drinking, and satiety,

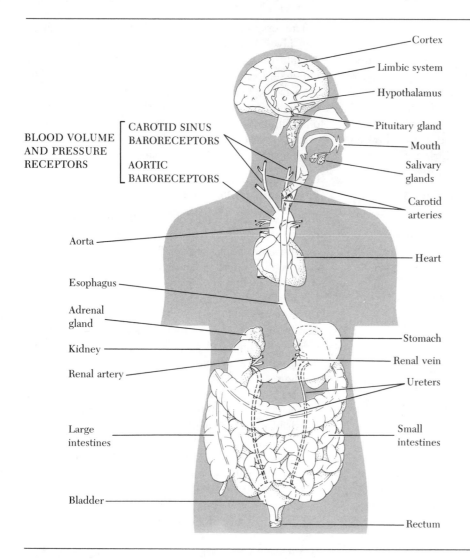

Figure 4–1. Organs involved in the assimilation of water. Special nerve endings in the walls of the carotid arteries and aorta, called **baroreceptors,** are sensitive to pressure. When the volume of blood increases even slightly, it exerts pressure on these receptors and activates them. Conversely, when the blood volume falls below normal, this pressure is reduced and the activity of these nerve cells decreases. As blood pressure changes, neural impulses from these neurons are transmitted into the brain where they influence ADH secretion and other processes.

Figure 4-4 illustrates the conscious experience of needing to eliminate urine as it fills and distends the bladder, and, in general, makes amply clear the elaborate network of physiological and behavioral processes involved in the body's assimilation of water.

Aside from altering ADH secretion, low fluid levels also affect the **renin-angiotensin system**. The workings of this system are diagrammed in Figure 4-5. When the blood volume begins to fall, as when we become dehydrated because we do not drink enough

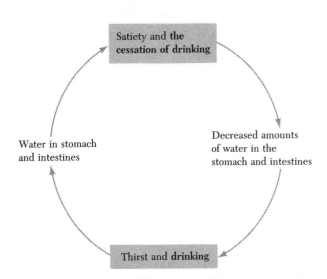

Figure 4–2. Continuity of physiology and behavior related to water in the stomach and intestines. The boxed material represents processes subject to conscious experience. Behavioral activity is indicated by the use of boldface type.

Figure 4–3. Continuity of physiology and behavior related to the amount of water in the body's fluids. The boxed material represents processes subject to conscious experience. Behavioral activity is indicated by the use of boldface type, and the involvement of the brain by italic type.

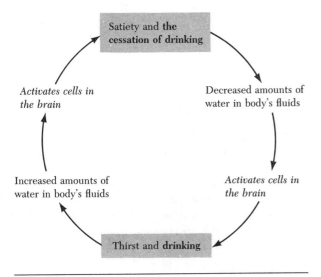

water, less blood flows through the kidneys. The kidneys respond by secreting **renin**, a substance released by special cells in the kidneys called "juxtaglomerular cells." Renin converts a substance in the blood and kidneys into **angiotensin**. (There are two forms of angiotensin, angiotensin I and angiotensin II, but to discuss their differences would take us beyond the scope of our discussion.) Angiotensin, a powerful vasoconstrictor, responds to the lowered blood volume by narrowing the blood vessels, which, in turn, causes blood pressure to increase. In addition, its vasoconstricting action causes the kidneys to pass less water into the urine; thus water is retained that would otherwise be lost. In other words, whenever blood volume is low the renin-angiotensin system causes both a compensatory rise in blood pressure and a compensatory retention of water.

Angiotensin also appears to act on some cells in the brain to initiate thirst—an additional compensatory response to lowered blood volume. Drinking water is extremely important in this case because, as indicated earlier, it is the only way that the amount of water in our body can actually increase.

That the brain is intimately involved in all of the processes mentioned above is emphasized in Figure 4-6, which shows that almost every aspect of our assimilation and elimination of water somehow relates to the workings of the brain. This apparently complex diagram simply combines what has already been illustrated in the previous diagrams and, again, calls attention to the elaborate interactions of physiological and behavioral processes associated with our body functions.

Figure 4-7 presents a simplified diagram summarizing those physiological and behavioral processes that involve the body's use of water. The wisdom of this system is obvious. Blood pressure, blood volume, the concentration of solutes in the fluids, the excretion of urine, a dry mouth and throat, thirst, and drinking are all regulated in a concerted manner, emphasizing the extent to which our health is served by the profound integration of processes that directly influence one another. A working brain is necessary for many of these processes, and we will discuss it next.

The Brain

In Chapter 3 we noted the well-integrated interactions that occur between nutrients like glucose and fatty acids and processes having to do with eating. In relation to drinking, something similar takes place. In this case, however, the predominant factors are closely related to the level of water in the body.

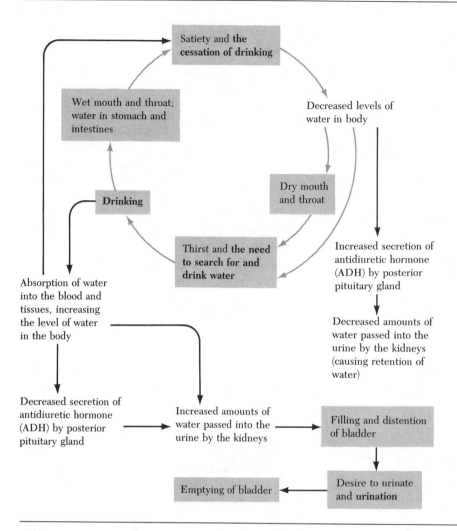

Figure 4–4. Continuity of physiology and behavior related to levels of water in the blood and tissues, stomach, intestines, mouth, and throat, as well as the secretion of antidiuretic hormone (ADH), and urination. The boxed material represents processes subject to conscious experience. Behavioral activity is indicated by the use of boldface type. Note that lowered levels of water in the body promote ADH secretion which causes water retention, whereas raised levels of water inhibit ADH secretion, causing water to pass into the urine.

Earlier we discussed that a change in the body's water levels has two important effects: it alters the concentration of solutes in the body (solutes are any chemicals that are soluble in water), and it alters the volume of the body's fluids. The brain is sensitive to these alterations, receiving its information through a variety of processes and specific receptors—**osmoreceptors**, **volume receptors**, and **baroreceptors**, which will be discussed in turn.

Osmoreceptors. A decrease in water levels will increase the concentration of solutes whereas an increase in water levels will decrease the concentration of solutes. We have already mentioned that there are osmoreceptors within the brain that respond to changes in the concentration of solutes. When the concentration of solutes rises in the environment surrounding these cells, either because of decreased water levels or because of an increase in dissolved

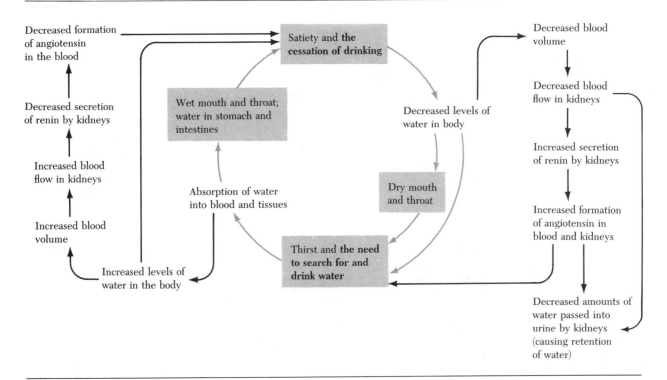

Figure 4–5. Continuity of physiology and behavior related to levels of water in the blood and tissues, stomach, intestines, mouth, and throat, as well as the secretion of renin and the formation of angiotensin. The boxed material represents processes subject to conscious experience. Behavioral activity is indicated by the use of boldface type. Note that lowered levels of water promote the formation of angiotensin which causes water retention and thirst, whereas raised levels of water inhibit the formation of angiotensin.

chemicals in the blood, as occurs after eating, these osmoreceptors are activated. This activation probably occurs because these cells shrink in size as water leaves them (you will recall that this movement of water is due to osmotic forces). Conversely, when the concentration of solutes falls, as occurs when water is ingested, these osmoreceptors become less active, presumably because they swell in size. Later we will see that these cells help to regulate thirst, drinking, and other processes having to do with water regulation.

Volume Receptors. Changed water levels also affect the volume of the body's fluids and can severely alter the body's functions, especially if there are changes in the volume of blood. We have pointed out that lowered blood volume leads to the release of renin into the blood by the kidneys, and that renin, in turn, converts a chemical in the blood and kidneys

into angiotensin. Angiotensin then exerts an action on some cells in the brain. Again, we will see that these cells help to regulate thirst, drinking, and other processes having to do with water regulation.

Baroreceptors. Also noted previously is that changes in blood volume change the pressure exerted by the blood against the walls of blood vessels. Special nerve endings lie in the walls of the aorta and carotid arteries—the major blood vessels that carry blood to the head and the rest of the body after it leaves the heart (see Figure 4-1). These special nerve endings are called baroreceptors because they respond to the pressure exerted by blood against them ("baro" is derived from the Greek word "baros" which means "weight").

When blood pressure decreases—in this case because of reduced blood volume, but there can be other causes—the baroreceptors trigger mechanisms

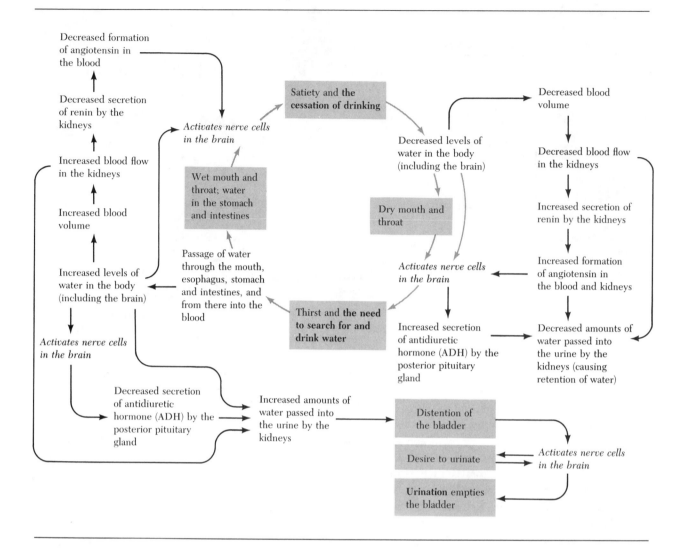

Figure 4–6. Continuity of physiology and behavior related to the assimilation of water, emphasizing the key role played by the brain. The boxed material represents processes subject to conscious experience. Behavioral activity is indicated by the use of boldface type, and the involvement of the brain by italic type.

in the brain that cause many of the small blood vessels in the body to constrict. Among other effects, this constriction decreases blood flow in the kidneys. The decreased blood flow in the kidneys increases the amount of angiotensin in the blood (you will recall that the decreased flow initiates the release of renin). In other words, angiotensin levels are increased via the baroreceptors as well as via the volume receptors in the kidneys.

Another response to decreased blood pressure is an increased secretion of antidiuretic hormone (ADH) by the posterior pituitary gland. In this case the baroreceptors trigger mechanisms in the brain that result in increased production and release of ADH. The increased levels of ADH in the body reduce the amount of water in the urine, as discussed previously, and, along with the effects of angiotensin, protect the blood volume in our body.

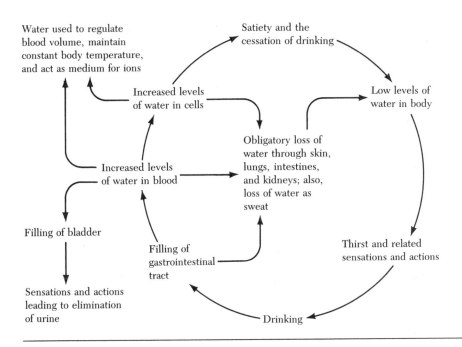

Figure 4–7. Basic processes involved in the body's assimilation of water.

When blood pressure is excessive, these processes are reversed. Acting on the brain, baroreceptor activity serves to increase blood flow, decrease the production of angiotensin, and decrease the secretion of ADH, all of which increases the flow of water into the urine and affects thirst and drinking behaviors as well as lowering blood pressure.

Neural Mechanisms. Although the specific processes within the brain that govern the use and regulation of water are quite different from those that operate for solid foods, many of the basic considerations are the same. For example, instead of blood glucose and fatty acid levels, we are now looking at blood volume, blood pressure, and the concentration of solutes in the body. Instead of hunger and eating, we are looking at thirst and drinking. Instead of satiety to solid foods and the cessation of eating, we are dealing with satiety to water and the cessation of drinking. Instead of the reward of eating, we are concerned with the reward of drinking. As with solid foods, the mechanisms governing thirst, drinking, satiety to water, and reward also appear to be most heavily represented within the **hypothalamus**, the **upper spinal cord**, and the **limbic system**.

The Preoptic, Anterior and Lateral Areas of the Hypothalamus. The hypothalamus is involved in almost every aspect of water regulation. Again, this

assertion is based on the fact that a variety of experimental techniques used to study drinking responses in relation to this brain region have produced clear-cut and consistent results over time. Specifically, four techniques—electrical stimulation of the brain region, its destruction, alteration of its osmotic environment (by changing the concentration of solutes), and the application of appropriate chemicals such as angiotensin—all indicate that the **preoptic**, **anterior**, and **lateral hypothalamic** regions are involved in drinking and thirst responses.

For example, as indicated in Figure 4-8, electrical stimulation of the preoptic or lateral areas of the hypothalamus causes an animal to drink, and destruction of these areas abolishes or reduces drinking. In addition, when the osmoreceptors existing within the preoptic and lateral areas of the hypothalamus of animals are stimulated by exposing them to a high concentration of solutes, drinking behavior is elicited. Conversely, when these receptors are destroyed, there is a cessation of drinking which is otherwise induced by a high concentration of solutes.

Osmoreceptors also exist in the **supraoptic area** (see Figure 4-8), but here they appear to regulate ADH secretion rather than thirst and/or drinking behaviors. When these receptors are exposed, in animals, to a high concentration of solutes, ADH is secreted. Electrical stimulation of the supra-optic

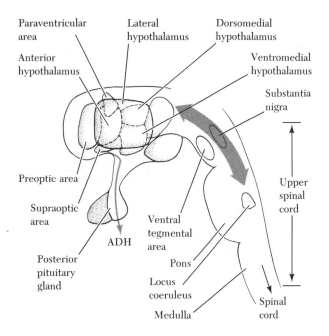

THE HYPOTHALAMUS

Drinking system: this "system" comprises neurons in the lateral hypothalamic region, the preoptic area, and the anterior hypothalamus. Electrical *stimulation* of this

region of the hypothalamus elicits drinking behavior; *destruction* of this region reduces or abolishes drinking behavior.

Satiety system: this "system" comprises neurons in the ventromedial hypothalamic region. *Destruction* of this region increases drinking behavior; however, it is unclear to what extent this effect is due to increased eating or decreased ADH release, both of which are known to increase drinking behavior.

THE UPPER SPINAL CORD

Drinking system: here, this "system" extends to the preoptic and anterior hypothalamic areas from areas in the upper spinal cord that have not yet been precisely determined. *Destruction* of this system reduces or abolishes drinking.

Satiety system: here, this "system" probably extends to the medial hypothalamic region from areas in the upper spinal cord that have not yet been precisely determined. There are a number of reports that *destroying* one or another area of the upper spinal cord leads to increased drinking. However, the roles any of these areas play in suppressing drinking remains unclear.

Figure 4–8. Involvement of the hypothalamus and upper spinal cord in the assimilation of water. The double arrow indicates that thirst and satiety responses involve neural mechanisms in these connected regions of the brain. The heavy arrows indicates that antidiuretic hormone (ADH) is produced by nerve cells in the supraoptic area, and is then transported within these cells to the posterior pituitary gland from which it is released into the blood.

area also causes the release of ADH and destruction of this area abolishes ADH secretion.

Receptors in the preoptic, anterior, and lateral regions of the hypothalamus also regulate thirst and drinking by responding to the angiotensin produced as the result of lowered blood flow, decreased blood volume, or decreased blood pressure. When these brain areas are destroyed, there is a cessation of drinking which is otherwise induced by angiotensin.

As with hunger and eating, experiments using self-administered electrical stimulation of the hypothalamic areas known to elicit drinking behavior indicate that thirst and drinking are associated with reward for the animal. In some cases, self-stimulation of the lateral hypothalamic region has been found to be more

intense when an animal drinks than when water is not available (see Mogenson and Morgan, 1967).

Often the brain's regulation of one function (such as drinking) can be shown experimentally to be intimately connected to its regulation of another function (such as reward or blood volume), yet this need not be the case. For example, given appropriate experimental conditions, self-stimulation, eating, and drinking are all behaviors that can be elicited by stimulating the lateral hypothalamus via a single implanted electrode. One might conclude from these findings that all of these functions are inseparably connected to each other. However, in other experiments electrodes have elicited eating but not drinking, drinking but not eating, eating and/or drinking but not self-stimulation, and self-stimulation without eating or drinking. The same can be stated about thirst associated with high solute levels or low fluid levels. Under appropriate experimental conditions, angiotensin in the hypothalamus will induce thirst and drinking but high levels of solutes will not, or high levels of solutes will induce thirst and drinking but angiotensin will not. This finding, *that the brain is very refined in its workings and that physiological and behavioral responses are organized in many distinct ways*, applies to many functions covered in this book, as will be discussed in more detail at the end of the chapter.

The Medial Hypothalamus. The cessation of drinking and satiety to water are functions that are still poorly understood. As indicated in Figure 4-8, there is some evidence that these functions involve the medial hypothalamic region because destruction of the **ventromedial area** of the hypothalamus and cuts behind this area have been reported to increase drinking (see, for example, King and Grossman, 1977). On the other hand, the response of increased drinking does not in itself prove that a satiety area has been destroyed. Many other interpretations are possible. For example, if ADH secretion is disrupted by the neural damage, the lack of circulating ADH will lead to an increased flow of water into the urine, and the subsequent loss of large amounts of water through urination will lead to increased drinking. Another possibility involves the association of drinking with eating. It is well known that if an animal eats more, it will also drink more water. At least 70 percent of the total intake of water by rats occurs just before, during, and immediately after meals (see Fitzsimons and LeMagnen, 1969). When the medial hypothalamic region is destroyed, eating behavior shows a marked increase (see Chapter 3). Since destruction of the medial hypothalamic region disrupts the satiety system for eating, the subsequent increased drinking could be merely a secondary result of the increased eating rather than an indication that a satiety system for water has been disrupted.

The issue is additionally complicated by studies showing that very small regions within and near the ventromedial area of the hypothalamus can be destroyed and result in (1) no change in drinking, (2) increased drinking, or (3) decreased drinking. In some experiments where increased drinking has resulted from this intervention, the response has been shown to be unrelated either to a decrease in ADH secretion or to an increase in eating (see King and Grossman, 1977). In these experiments, therefore, it appears that we are indeed looking at a satiety system for water intake within the hypothalamus. Moreover, when the animal is given an injection of hypertonic saline (a solution containing high amounts of sodium chloride), it will drink larger amounts of water than will control animals not suffering from damage to the ventromedial region of the hypothalamus (King and Grossman, 1977). From these experiments, one would conclude that this region of the brain exerts an inhibiting influence over drinking induced by high concentrations of solutes and, in this respect, acts as a satiety system. It is of interest to note that in a separate experiment (Kucharczyk and Mogenson, 1975),

the ventromedial region reportedly exerted an inhibiting influence over drinking induced by angiotensin. In this experiment, animals suffering damage to the ventromedial region of the hypothalamus drank more water than normal control animals when challenged with angiotensin, but not when given hypertonic saline. Confronted with this "discrepancy"—that in one experiment the ventromedial region appears to be involved only in satiety associated with adequate solute levels and in the other only with appropriate angiotensin levels—investigators have concluded that we are indeed looking at very refined workings of the brain. The specific areas of the ventromedial region that were damaged in these two separate experiments were quite different from each other, and suggest that different systems within the medial hypothalamus exert different inhibitory influences (see King and Grossman, 1977). Again, these points are discussed in more detail at the end of the chapter.

The Upper Spinal Cord. As we have seen in the previous chapter in connection with eating, drinking, too, is a function that is well represented within the upper spinal cord. As indicated in Figure 4-8, destruction of small regions of the upper spinal cord can lead to decreased drinking or increased drinking (for a review of these effects see Grossman, 1976; Swanson, Kucharczyck, and Mogenson, 1977; Mogenson, 1978). For example, when the **substantia nigra** or the **ventral tegmental area** is damaged, drinking behavior has been found to be reduced (Ungerstedt, 1971). Conversely, when the **locus coeruleus** and other regions of the upper spinal cord are damaged, drinking behavior has been found to increase slightly (Ahlskog and Hoebel, 1973). Although the role these regions play in the regulation of thirst and drinking still remains largely unknown, it is generally assumed that these parts of the upper spinal cord contain neurons that connect with the hypothalamus and other regions of the brain. For instance, when parts of the ventral tegmental area in the upper spinal cord are damaged, drinking behavior which would otherwise be elicited by injecting angiotensin in the preoptic area of the hypothalamus is disrupted (Kucharczyck and Mogenson, 1977).

The above findings concerning the involvement of the hypothalamus and the upper spinal cord are clearly another example of the coexistence of behavioral and physiological processes all organized together and concerted in their actions—an interplay of responses that are directed toward regulating water levels in the body. For example, both angiotensin and high levels of solutes within the hypothalamus induce thirst and drinking. In turn, the ingestion of water will increase blood volume and lower the concentration of solutes so that they return to normal levels. Combined with these responses are other responses that are not as closely tied in with behavior. When the concentration of solutes rises or the volume of blood falls, not only is there increased thirst and drinking, but the increased levels of angiotensin cause vasoconstriction (as do the baroreceptors acting via the brain) and the high concentration of solutes results in increased ADH levels (an increase that can also occur because of baroreceptor activity). The result is a decrease in the formation of urine, a response that helps to protect our fluid volume at a time when it needs to

increase. When the concentration of solutes falls or blood volume increases, just the opposite occurs: drinking is reduced and the flow of water into the urine is increased, lowering our fluid volume at a time when it needs to decrease.

The Limbic System. The limbic system is also involved in regulating drinking and thirst but, as with solid foods, its primary action appears to be in modifying the activity of lower structures of the brain rather than in eliciting direct initiatory behavior. As indicated in Figure 4-9, the structure most heavily involved appears to be the **septum**, where destruction increases drinking behavior and electrical stimulation

Figure 4–9. Involvement of the limbic system—composed of the amygdala, hippocampus, cingulate gyrus, septum, and olfactory areas—in the assimilation of water. The septum and the amygdala appear to be especially involved.

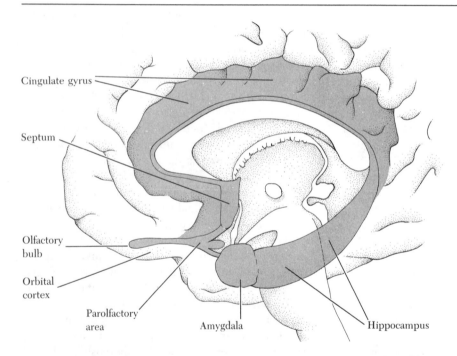

Septum: electrical *stimulation* of this area decreases drinking (even though observations of rat behavior suggest that self-stimulation in this area is rewarding). *Damage* to this area causes excessive drinking, and appears to disrupt mechanisms that match water intake to food intake and match water intake to appropriate smell or taste stimuli.

Amygdala: electrical *stimulation* of the amygdala both increases and decreases drinking depending on the precise area that is stimulated. *Damage* to this area both

increases and decreases drinking. The results of damage are generally opposite to those of electrical stimulation—i.e., drinking decreases in areas that elicit drinking when electrically stimulated and drinking increases in areas that suppress drinking when stimulated.

Other areas of the limbic system: a number of reports indicate that other areas of the limbic system are involved, but none so clearly as the septum and amygdala.

suppresses it. The **amygdala** also exerts a modifying action on drinking and thirst mechanisms, sometimes increasing, sometimes decreasing these responses depending upon where the electrode is placed (see Grossman and Grossman, 1963).

There is some evidence that the septum is involved in altering an animal's response to the *taste* and *smell* of water. For example, rats suffering damage to the septum not only drink more water, but also, when compared to normal rats, they will drink twice as much water containing salt (Lubar, Boyce, and Schaefer, 1968). In addition, rats with septal damage will drink more water containing sweet-tasting saccharin and less water containing unpleasant-tasting quinine (see Carey, 1971). Thus, some parts of the limbic system appear to be involved in determining the animal's ability to select appropriate amounts of water, perhaps according to taste and smell. Also, because portions of the septum and amygdala are involved in suppressing drinking, these regions appear to be a part of a satiety system.

When those portions of the septum that *inhibit* drinking when electrically stimulated are tested in self-stimulation experiments, they are often found to be *rewarding* (Wishart and Mogenson, 1970). This is in sharp contrast to observations of eating behavior. (With eating behavior, you will recall, reward is associated with eating, not with reduced eating.) These disparate responses correspond with the finding that food deprivation increases self-stimulation of the lateral hypothalamus whereas water deprivation does not change the rate of self-stimulation of this region (Mogenson, 1969). In fact, when solute levels are increased (by injecting an animal with hypertonic saline) self-stimulation of the lateral hypothalamus *decreases* (Hoebel, 1968).

At first glance, this result—that injection of hypertonic saline will cause rats to drink but will reduce lateral hypothalamic self-stimulation—might seem to contradict the finding that drinking and reward are associated with each other; however, we must remember that another signal for reduced self-stimulation of the lateral hypothalamus is satiety to food. As food is ingested, the amount of solutes in the blood increases. Thus there is competition between high levels of solutes decreasing reward associated with eating and high levels of solutes increasing reward associated with drinking. Apparently, reduced reward associated with ingesting food is dominant. For example, in one study, after it had been established that both eating and drinking could be elicited by electrical stimulation of the lateral hypothalamus with a single implanted electrode, the experimental rats were tested for self-stimulation. There was no change in

the rate of self-stimulation of the lateral hypothalamus (it remained high) when animals were tested after drinking, but after they ingested food, the rate of self-stimulation was markedly reduced (Mogenson, 1969). The septum may play a role in these differing responses. As noted earlier, a rat that is food-deprived usually drinks less water; however, food-deprived rats suffering damage to the septum sometimes drink much more water than normal (Wishart and Mogenson, 1970). It therefore appears that damage to the septum disrupts neural mechanisms that match water intake to food intake. In this context, it is also interesting to note that, although the hypothalamus and upper spinal cord appear to be the main regions of the brain that regulate drinking in response to the angiotensin released by low blood volume or lowered blood flow, the septum appears to be involved as well. For example, rats suffering damage to the septum drink more water in response to angiotensin than do normal rats, but not in response to high concentrations of solutes (see Blass and Nussbaum, 1974). Thus the ability of the septum to regulate drinking does not appear to be strongly related to solute levels, an important finding if the septum is to successfully integrate those processes matching water intake to food intake. The interpretation of the findings listed above is speculative. We have discussed this in some detail only to give the reader an idea of how complex these interactions can become. More research needs to be done before we will understand the exact mechanisms that are involved.

The Cerebral Cortex. The outer cerebral cortex does not appear to be essential for the satiety, thirst, and reward functions that regulate drinking. As we have seen with eating, these functions are largely regulated *subcortically*. Although the outer, most developed part of our brain is neccessary for vision, muscular coordination, and movement—all functions that we use when seeking and drinking water—vision and muscular coordination are not directly regulated by neural processes having to do with water levels in the body.

Temperature Regulation. Before we leave the discussion of the brain's involvement in regulating the body's use of water, we must mention an additional function, *the regulation of body temperature*, that is also under neural control. Although many aspects of temperature regulation involve other processes, such as muscular activity (shivering to produce heat) or the secretion of thyroid hormone (that directly alters the rate of chemical reactions and thus affects body heat), many temperature-related mechanisms do make use of water. For example, when it is cold the blood vessels in the skin constrict. This response tends to increase the temperature of the body's water because less of it is circulating in the skin and, therefore, less is exposed to the cold. Conversely, when it is hot the blood vessels in the skin dilate. This response tends to cool the temperature of the body's water because more of it is exposed to the external (and presumably cooler) environment. Also, when it is hot we sweat; the water that covers the surface of the skin then evaporates and cools the skin. Because sweat is a fluid that comes from the body, sweating decreases the body's fluids. The amount of fluid that is lost through sweating must be replenished through drinking. In many animals, cooling occurs through panting. As the air passes over the fluid in the mouth, it facilitates evaporation and therefore cooling. These temperature-regulating mechanisms are all effective because blood is very mobile and therefore its temperature immediately influences the temperature of other organs as it flows through them.

Many of these processes appear to be initiated by temperature-sensitive nerve cells in the **hypothalamus**. When the temperature surrounding nerve cells in the anterior and preoptic areas of the hypothalamus goes up, the activity of these neurons increases. Among other effects, this increased activity causes sweating, dilation of the blood vessels of the skin, and panting. Other temperature-sensitive neurons in the posterior region of the hypothalamus become more active when the temperature goes down. In this case, the activity of the neurons causes shivering and constriction of the blood vessels of the skin.

When we are hot, we usually experience a loss of appetite and lethargy, and there is an attendant decrease in levels of thyroid hormone. When we are cold, appetite often increases and we become more active, and there is an attendant increase in thyroid hormone. The digestion of solid foods, muscular activity, and thyroid hormones all increase the chemical reactions that produce heat. Conversely, when these processes are slowed there is reduced heat production. The hypothalamus also participates in regulating these responses since appetite (Chapter 3), one's level of arousal (Chapter 8), and thyroid secretion (Chapter 10) all involve this region of the brain.

The **spinal cord** also appears to be involved in temperature regulation. When the spinal cord is directly heated or cooled, temperature-sensitive neurons initiate similar changes in the blood vessels of the skin (dilation or constriction), as well as sweating, shivering, and other appropriate responses (see Cabanac, 1975).

Hot and cold receptors in the skin also send neural impulses into the brain to produce the sensations of warmth and cold we consciously experience (see Chapter 6). This conscious involvement is necessary, of course, to trigger our voluntary behavior in regulating body temperature, a topic that is discussed below.

Body and Self

In general, our experiences with water are so commonplace that we do not recognize the complexity of the physiological and behavioral interactions involved in our body's handling of this substance. When we are thirsty, we drink and, unless we are sick, we take for granted the process of emptying the bladder. (In fact, when we are suffering from urinary tract infection, we sometimes become acutely aware of the apparent refusal of the body to regulate its water needs—though dehydrated, we don't actively want to drink and must "force" fluid even though its elimination may be painful.) The constant interplay of physiological and behavioral factors involved in the recurrent cycle of being thirsty and desiring water, satisfying our thirst, then feeling sated and losing desire for water has already been discussed.

Entirely different experiences and behaviors are associated with the body's use of water to regulate its temperature. We have mentioned several times that our body must maintain a constant temperature in order to function properly. When the body overheats, for example, it employs processes to cool it down—but there are severe limitations to these mechanisms.

When the body is excessively hot, it makes use of two basic mechanisms to lose heat: **radiation** and **evaporation**. Radiation is the loss of heat that occurs when the temperature surrounding our body is lower than body temperature. Heat is lost in the form of infrared radiation, which is an invisible radiation of heated bodies. Under normal circumstances well over half of our heat loss occurs through radiation. Evaporation, on the other hand, causes a loss of heat when water from the body evaporates. Evaporation is responsible for about one quarter of our heat loss. Evaporative cooling is greatly increased by the secretion of sweat onto the surface of our skin.

There are limitations, however, in the body's ability to use radiation and evaporation to regulate its temperature. Radiation will cool the body only when the outside temperature is *cooler* than the body's. If the outside temperature is warmer, the body will actually *gain* heat. With evaporation, under extreme conditions, the amount of sweat produced can be as much as three to four liters per hour. As an additional limitation, unless we replenish the water lost through sweating by drinking, the body will compensate for the decrease in fluid volume by reducing the amount of sweat produced. Ultimately, the resulting decrease in heat loss can lead to heat stroke. In any case, the amount of heat that can be lost through sweating is, in itself, limited, and when heat production by our body exceeds a certain limit (which varies considerably among individuals), heat stroke can occur.

Behavior plays a significant part in offsetting these limitations. For example, outdoors when we are hot, we generally seek out a shady area or a cool room, environments that facilitate cooling by radiation. Of course, when we drink we replenish the water lost through sweating, and when we take off clothing we increase the surface area of our skin exposed for cooling. When we turn on a fan, we are facilitating evaporative cooling of our skin, especially when we are sweating.

Much the same can be said of excessive cold. When body temperature falls below approximately 34.4°C (94°F), the ability of the hypothalamus and spinal cord to control body temperature through shivering and through increasing the rate of chemical reactions is greatly impaired. One reason is that the low temperature in itself reduces the rate of all chemical reactions. In fact, a vicious cycle can be created where the decreased rate of chemical reactions reduces our heat production which, in turn, further lowers body temperature and leads to an even greater reduction in the rate of chemical reactions, and so forth. Again, behaviors—like going into a warm room, putting on well-insulated clothes, or, in some instances, engaging in exercise—help greatly to compensate for the body's limitations.

Although the neural mechanisms responsible for the behavior involved in temperature regulation are poorly understood, they appear to involve pathways that course through the hypothalamus. For example, when the lateral hypothalamus of a rat is destroyed, such behaviors as pressing a lever to turn heating lamps or cooling fans on or off can be abolished, in contrast to responses like shivering and constriction of the skin's blood vessels, which remain undisturbed. Conversely, when the preoptic area is damaged, responses like dilation of blood vessels are impaired, but the behaviors noted above remain normal—the animal will press the lever to regulate its temperature (see Roberts and Mooney, 1974; Van Zoern and Stricker, 1977; Satinoff, 1978).

Another example connecting our experience to processes that occur as water is used involves the relation between **venous return** and the functioning of the heart. Venous return is the rate of blood flow into the heart from the veins. The heart is capable of pumping all the blood that enters into it, whether the

4 to 6 liters per minute typical of normal resting conditions or the 15 or more liters per minute during exercise. Thus, the amount of blood that the heart pumps is generally controlled by the amount of blood that enters into it from the veins. There are many factors that influence venous return but it is beyond the scope of this book to discuss them. One particular process, however, is of interest here; it is called the **venous pump**.

The veins of our body have one-way valves inside them. Because of these valves, any time the veins are compressed, the blood squeezed out flows toward the heart (see Figure 4-10). That is, venous pressure in the area being compressed is reduced and venous pressure in the area closer to the heart is increased. Every time we move a limb or tense a muscle, some blood is moved toward our heart and venous pressure in the compressed area is reduced.

When we stand absolutely still, or sit still in a chair, this venous pump does not work. Under these conditions the venous pressure, especially in the lower parts of our legs, can increase three to four times because of hydrostatic pressure, which increases in the feet from 25 mm mercury (Hg) to about 90 mm Hg when we are standing still, and from 25 mm Hg to

Figure 4–10. One-way valves in the veins. Whenever the vein is compressed, these valves assure that blood is pumped toward the heart.

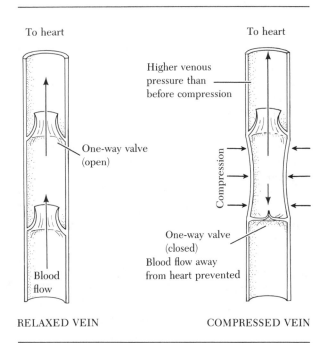

RELAXED VEIN   COMPRESSED VEIN

about 65 mm Hg when we are sitting still in a chair. This increased pressure causes water to leave the blood vessels in the lower extremities. As discussed earlier, water is extremely mobile and can easily enter the extracellular fluid compartment, which, as noted earlier, is composed of the spaces between cells—spaces that are outside of the vascular (blood) system. As much as one liter of fluid can leave the blood in the lower legs in as short a time as 15 minutes. In some cases, this exit of fluid will lead to an inadequate return of blood to the heart and a person will *faint* because not enough blood is pumped to the brain. Of course, when we faint we usually fall to the ground, and lying flat then reduces the venous pressure in the lower limbs and increases venous return to the heart. If, on the other hand, we do not stand absolutely still but, instead, engage in even such minor activities as wiggling our toes or moving our feet, the venous pump would begin to function.

When venous pressure increases in the lower extremities of a person sitting or standing very still, blood flow decreases because of a "back pressure" that impedes the flow of blood. The decreased blood flow reduces oxygen stores because oxygen is used up in the inactive area, and this reduced level of oxygen can eventually lead to a *painful* sensation (an experience of discomfort). Because the rise in venous pressure is very fast (occurring within 30 seconds of inactivity), most of us will not stand still or sit still in a chair for a very long time. On the other hand, when we sit close to the ground, as when sitting cross-legged, there is no increase in hydrostatic pressure in the feet; it remains at about 25 mm Hg. One can be still in this posture for very long periods.

These two examples involving temperature regulation and our posture demonstrate how the actions of water in our body relate to behaviors and experiences other than the basic act of drinking. Of course, the converse statement is just as correct—these are also examples of how our behavior modifies the actions of water.

Another example involves emotional states. Although the precise mechanisms are not well understood, there is a well-documented relationship between our emotional states and the excretion of urine. Experiments have shown that excitement, anxiety, anger, and other emotional reactions can inhibit the excretion of urine and cause us to retain water (see, for example, Verney, 1947) or, conversely, they can increase the excretion of urine and cause us to lose water (see Schottstaedt, Grace, and Wolff, 1956). This variability of outcomes is undoubtedly due to the tremendous number of factors that are involved. (Variability in physiological responses is a common finding in studies of emotional influences on body functions. We have seen this variability in Chapter 3 when we noted that some people respond to stress by eating, some by fasting, and we will see it again in subsequent chapters.) In general, we know that emotional states modify the activity of the sympathetic and parasympathetic branches of the autonomic nervous system (see Chapter 7) and that this altered activity can modify the release of ADH, the release of chemicals by the adrenal glands, and the flow of blood through the kidneys—all of which alters the kidneys' ability to concentrate the urine. In addition, our dietary habits and our pattern of water consumption, the state of health of the kidneys, the levels of minerals in our body (especially sodium), and the distribution of water in the body are also factors that modify our excretion of urine.

As urinary excretion becomes abnormally high or low, the concentration of solutes in our body can also change. Again, many factors are involved. There is some fairly convincing evidence that a change in the concentration of solutes in the blood will lead to corresponding changes in the brain (see Covey and Arieff, 1978). Not only is there a change in the concentration of sodium in the brain under these circumstances, but there is also a change in the brain's production of amino acids and other chemicals (see Covey and Arieff, 1978; Baxter and Baldwin, 1978; Chan and Fishman, 1979). Because some of these chemicals act as regulators of neural activity, it is reasonable to suspect that changes in one's mental and/or emotional state can, in part, be related to changes in kidney function and subsequent changes in the level of solutes in the blood. Therefore, not only do emotional states affect kidney function, but kidney function can affect emotional states. This point is further discussed in Section IV of this chapter.

Conscious experiences having to do with our assimilation of water are organized in a manner similar to that described in the last chapter in relation to food. One obvious reason is that the organs of drinking (hands and mouth) and the organs that allow water to enter the blood (stomach and intestines) are the same as those we use for solid foods. In addition, both drinking and eating demand our conscious activity and voluntary behavior. In the case of water, we consciously assess our state of thirst by how dry our mouth and throat are. However, water placed directly in the stomach or intestines, or infused into the blood will activate satiety mechanisms without involving our conscious, voluntary behavior. These experiences of satiety are not caused by wet sensations in the mouth; they are connected to the activation of osmoreceptors and receptors which are sensitive to blood volume, as discussed earlier.

Figures 4-2 through 4-6 indicate the interplay between processes subject to conscious experience (boxed material) and processes usually not experienced (unboxed material) in our assimilation of water. As with solid foods, our conscious experiences mainly involve functions that *precede* the entry of water into the small intestines or come *after* it enters the bladder and is on its way out as urine. Conscious experiences are very important in enabling us to search for, select, and drink water; they also provide a signal for us to eliminate it as urine.

III. INVOLVEMENT OF MANY ORGANS AT ONCE

Just as with solid foods, water-related processes in our body also involve many organs, all participating in an elaborate network of physiological and behavioral processes. We have seen that the organs of drinking (hands and mouth) as well as the cardiovascular system, esophagus, stomach, small and large intestines, pituitary gland (which secretes ADH), kidneys, bladder, and brain are all involved. Although the involvement of the brain is important, it is clear that the regulation of water is critically dependent on the kidneys. In addition, the volume of the blood, the concentration of solutes in the extracellular fluids, a distended or empty bladder, much or little stimulation of the organs of taste and smell—all of these processes interact with the brain and determine to a large extent how it will respond at any given moment. It is therefore apparent that our body is well equipped to protect the volume of fluid that it contains. As discussed earlier, this protection is especially important for the vascular system where a drop in blood volume or a severe drop in blood pressure can lead to death.

IV. RELATION TO HEALTH

The properties of water discussed in the beginning of this chapter clearly indicate its vital contribution to our functioning. In addition, it is obvious that the physiological and behavioral mechanisms we have covered in this chapter are well designed to keep the amount and distribution of water in our bodies at an optimum level. Taken as a whole, these behavioral and physiological processes are extremely successful in regulating our assimilation of this food. Problems are rare for a variety of reasons:

a) Because the body eliminates excess water very easily, drinking too much water is not a problem under normal circumstances;

b) Excess water is not transformed into something else which is then stored, such as fats and proteins—it is simply redistributed in the body until it can be eliminated;

c) Because water is used by the body as one specific form of food, and because water is usually readily available for us to drink, very little is required of us to assure that water is properly selected. Problems of "undernourishment" exist only when water is not available to drink.

Of course, abnormal and unhealthy conditions can occur in relation to the body's assimilation of water. Perhaps the most common situation where drinking is *not* directly related to the integrative processes outlined in this chapter occurs when we are satisfying a need to give ourselves something "meaningful" to do. As with eating, drinking is a strongly purposeful behavior, and, as such, is often substituted for more appropriate responses to feelings of emptiness and restlessness. From this motivation, we sometimes drink much more water than our body needs although, as mentioned above, this excess is readily eliminated. In this context, we should note that drinking to satisfy problems of "meaning" is certainly one of the reasons why some people drink too much alcohol. A connection between the consumption of water and the consumption of alcohol is suggested in some studies. In laboratory rats, for example, there are areas of the lateral hypothalamus whose stimulation not only elicits the drinking of water but also causes animals to drink intoxicating amounts of alcohol (see Amit, Stern, and Wise, 1970; Wayner, Greenberg, Carey, and Nolley, 1971). Results of these separate studies suggest that the drinking of water and the drinking of alcohol may involve similar neural mechanisms since, in some cases at least, these behaviors can be elicited by stimulating the same regions of the brain.

Another situation that conflicts with the integrated processes described in this chapter is when we are forced to sit or stand very still for prolonged periods. Young children notoriously do not sit still. It is the result of education and custom that we gradually learn that it is impolite to fidget, or that it is an expression of nervousness or impatience best not expressed. As discussed earlier in the chapter, however, even slight movement decreases the unhealthy effects of hydrostatic pressure in the veins. It is interesting to note that very young children are not expected to conform to this behavior, and their physical movements are usually not considered to be abnormal or mischievous.

The description of **water intoxication** at the beginning of the chapter emphasizes that problems of overdrinking do occur, although severe physiologic impairment is not a common result and, when it does occur, rarely persists. One interesting survey has shown that almost one-fifth of psychiatric patients reported to be suffering from water intoxication were alcoholics (see Caron, Cappoen, Chopin, Lefebvre, and Warot, 1977). Again, this finding points to a relation between the consumption of water and the consumption of alcohol. (It should be noted, however, that alcoholism involves much more than simply abnormal drinking behavior; it is an enormously complex psychological and physiological disorder.)

Conditions of abnormal thirst and drinking of water usually reflect a serious medical disorder that is causing too much fluid to be eliminated from the body. These abnormalities are not of the thirst-drinking-satiety-reward systems that regulate our assimilation of water, however. Rather, they are due to disorders of metabolism, diseased kidneys, and/or damage to those areas of the brain that normally regulate the secretion of antidiuretic hormone from the posterior pituitary gland (see pages 43–44).

Diabetes mellitus (commonly referred to as "diabetes") is a condition in which, among many other abnormalities, the pancreas fails to produce sufficient quantities of insulin. Because of this failure, the cells in the body take up less glucose and glucose levels in the blood consequently become very high. (Low levels of insulin are not the only cause of high blood glucose levels, but we will not discuss this fact.) These high levels of glucose are more than the kidneys can handle, so the excess "spills over" into the urine. Because of osmosis, the extra glucose in the urine pulls water along with it, and the result is excessive urination of fluid containing glucose, other solutes, and water. The excessive concentration of solutes in the body (mainly glucose, but sometimes also fatty acids) and the loss of fluid make the diabetic thirsty, and the patient will drink abnormally large amounts of water. This increase in water does a great deal to offset the abnormally high concentration of solutes in the body, so the excessive drinking is an important compensatory behavior, but not a cure. Treatment involves dietary changes, the administration of insulin, or other measures that deal with the pancreatic or other organic deficiencies.

Diabetes insipidus usually is caused by inadequate secretion of antidiuretic hormone (ADH) into the blood from the posterior pituitary gland. This type of diabetes results from head injury, brain tumors, or other trauma that either damage the cells in the supraoptic area of the hypothalamus (the cells that produce ADH, see Figure 4-8) or injure the transport mechanism that allows ADH to flow to the posterior pituitary gland. In either case, the result is greatly increased excretion of dilute urine. (You will recall that when ADH levels are too low, the kidneys do not reabsorb enough water. Thus too little water flows out of the collecting ducts into the concentrated fluids around them, and a great deal of water is lost in the urine.) As in diabetes mellitus, the elimination of large quantities of water stimulates thirst receptors and causes the diabetic to drink excessively large amounts of water. Again, the increased water intake is a compensatory behavior that seeks to make up for the loss of water through the kidneys. Proper treatment usually involves the administration of ADH (vasopressin, lysine vasopressin), ADH analogs (desmopressin), or other medications.

Earlier, we noted that conditions of anxiety and other emotional states can influence drinking and the excretion of urine by the kidneys. Furthermore, we noted that the concentration of solutes in the body influences the activity of neural chemicals in the brain and therefore could influence the brain's activities. There is some very interesting evidence suggesting that by increasing the concentration of solutes in the blood manic symptoms can be improved in patients suffering from **mania** (see Baxter, Tachiki, Blaser, Baldwin, and Gosenfeld, 1980). (Mania is a disorder characterized by excessive excitability, high levels of psychomotor activity—muscular movement of purely mental origin—rapidly changing thoughts, inability to focus attention, often extreme euphoria and, sometimes, episodes of destructive violence.) Baxter and his colleagues have shown that manics have a low concentration of solutes in their blood and that as their symptoms of mania go up and down, so does the concentration of solutes (which are higher when the patient is improved). They further suggest that the drug, lithium, commonly prescribed for this disorder, alleviates symptoms because it increases the concentration of solutes in the blood (exerting its effects via the kidneys). They also point out that small alterations in the concentration of solutes has an effect on neurochemicals in the brain, and suggest that this effect might be responsible for the characteristic mood swings of the manic patient.

Again, we must emphasize that abnormalities in our assimilation and regulation of water are not separate conditions existing in isolation, but stem from the same mechanisms operating to maintain our health. When a person is suffering from diabetes insipidus or diabetes mellitus, the abnormally high levels of thirst and drinking that develop are adaptive responses that the body uses to maintain its constant volume of water and a constant concentration of solutes. Diabetics can become severely dehydrated if they stop drinking excessive amounts of water before the disorder is treated. Similarly, when overanxiety results in water retention, it is the wisdom of the body preparing itself for meeting what it perceives as an emergency. As with other defensive physiological reactions, the "emergency" may not be real, but the body does not distinguish between a "real" and a mistaken sense of danger. Operating on a "better safe than sorry" principle, the body prepares to protect blood volume in case of a hemorrhage due to a wound, or a physical accident that prevents our finding water to drink.

In the next chapter, which covers breathing and air, we will see similar mechanisms in action. (Defensive reactions are discussed at some length in Chapter 7.)

V. THE WORKINGS OF REFINED SYSTEMS: DIFFERENT TYPES OF "THIRST" AND "HUNGER"

Before ending the chapter we must comment on the refinement of systems that contribute to our assimilation of foods. A detailed description of physiological and behavioral processes related to hunger and eating was the topic of Chapter 3. In this chapter we have mentioned, however, that electrical stimulation of the hypothalamus with a single electrode will sometimes elicit eating, hunger, drinking, thirst, and reward. Under different experimental conditions, an electrode might elicit eating but not drinking, drinking but not eating, eating and/or drinking but not self-stimulation (no reward), or self-stimulation without eating and/or drinking (see Mogenson, 1971; Olds, Allen, and Briese, 1971). Researchers have interpreted these findings to mean that the brain operates in an extremely refined manner, and that these systems—even though they appear to operate all at once to regulate the level of water in the body or our ingestion of solid foods—are separate. We will discuss this interpretation first as it relates to thirst, then to hunger.

Different Types of "Thirst"

Neural systems that regulate ADH secretion, those that regulate thirst because of altered concentrations of solutes, and those that regulate thirst because of changes in blood volume sometimes appear to be almost indistinguishable from each other in the hypothalamus or spinal cord. Nevertheless, they are not the same. Destruction of small areas in the hypothalamus and upper spinal cord produce a variety of responses, including drinking induced by low blood volume but no response to high concentrations of solutes, and drinking induced by high concentrations of solutes but no response to decreased blood volume (see Blass and Epstein, 1971; Buggy and Johnson, 1977; Kucharczyck and Mogenson, 1975, 1977; Brody and Johnson, 1980). In other words, drinking is a behavior related to a variety of stimuli that have one or another physiological effect, and these stimuli and their effects may actually define different types of thirst. For example, the thirst associated with dehydration is clearly different from the "thirst" associated with a dry mouth that is induced by an emergency or a threatening situation (see Chapter 7, Table 7-2). The first type of thirst will be satisfied only by replenishing the body's fluids, whereas the second is often satisfied merely by wetting the mouth. (Sometimes a person will chew gum or roll a marble in the mouth to increase salivation, and alleviate the "thirst" induced by a stressful situation.)

Different Types of "Hunger"

Equivalent statements can be made about "hunger." Preferences for carbohydrates as opposed to proteins, responses to blood glucose and insulin levels, and reward processes can all be shown to involve separate mechanisms within the hypothalamus. For example, there are some sites in the hypothalamus where stimulation does not elicit eating, drinking, or other behaviors (like sex), yet these sites are nevertheless rewarding. These "pure" self-stimulation sites are intermingled among other sites whose stimulation is not only rewarding, but evoke eating, drinking, and sexual behavior. These behaviors may occur alone or in combination (see Olds, Allen, and Briese, 1971). Furthermore, there are neural mechanisms in the hypothalamus that, when activated, cause an animal to select carbohydrates over other dietary constituents (see Fahrbach, Tretter, Aravich, McCabe, and Leibowitz, 1980; Tretter and Leibowitz, 1980). In addition, it appears that activating still a *different* neural system will lead to a preference of proteins over carbohydrates, and this system, once again, is different from systems assuring that an animal will ingest a sufficient quantity of calories (see Wurtman and Wurtman, 1977). The obvious conclusion is that eating is a behavior related to a variety of stimuli, and that these stimuli and their effects may actually define different types of hunger. We know in our own experience that the hunger pangs of an empty stomach are clearly different from the empty feelings we experience when we are not "really" hungry, but, at the same time, not sated.

If an obese person could really understand and accept that his/her hunger might not be an experience based on a need for nutrients but, instead, on a need for experiencing satiety and the relaxation and reduced arousal associated with being sated, he or she would be better able to find ways of coping with overeating. In dealing with this kind of situation, it is extremely useful for the person to realize that *both* conditions (a need for nutrients and a need to reduce tension) can create hunger, and that one type of hunger is no more legitimate than the other. In other words, they both reflect the activity of physiological and behavioral mechanisms within our bodies. These hungers are different from one another, however, and need to be handled differently.

These findings confirm that processes such as "hunger" and "thirst," which are generally discussed as "singular" behaviors, are varied in their nature and expression rather than unique phenomenological entities. This multiplicity, which can be confirmed both experientially and physiologically, is a fact that we will come across many times in this book. It is fundamental to understanding the relation between Body and Self, a relation which is often obscured by our insistence that something is singular when in fact it is not.

VI. CONCLUSIONS

The material presented in this chapter makes it amply clear that we are superbly organized, both behaviorally and physiologically, to make use of and regulate water. Most of the physiological and behavioral processes outlined above are directed to the same goal: maintaining a constant level of water in our body.

We have seen that physiological conditions strongly influence our experiences of thirst and drinking and, conversely, that behavior and psychological states clearly affect the physiological mechanisms involved

in absorbing, utilizing, and eliminating water. These functions are inseparably connected to each other—one cannot function fully without the other. This integration of behavior and physiology has a corresponding representation within the brain. Mechanisms of thirst, satiety to water, drinking, and reward coexist with mechanisms that respond to the level of solutes in the body, blood volume, and body temperature, and this integration is especially evident from research involving the upper spinal cord, the hypothalamus, and the limbic system. As we mentioned in the last chapter, the presence of coexistent interactions among diverse brain functions is not surprising; what is important to note is that these interactions are organized so that the mechanisms being regulated act in a concerted manner—in this case, to maintain an optimal level of water in the body.

The next chapter deals with air and breathing. Breathing allows us not only to assimilate the oxygen we need, but to quickly get rid of excessive carbon dioxide. As we have seen with solid foods and water, we will see that the behavior and physiology of breathing, and our use of air, are organized in a concerted, well-integrated manner. In addition to its involvement in basic physiological processes vital to life, breathing is also involved in other functions—laughing, crying, speech, and arousal. With some of these functions, breathing is not as intimately connected to basic regulatory processes.

Recommended Reading

ANDERSSON, B. "Thirst—and brain control of water balance." *American Scientist*, 59, 408-415, 1971. *This article discusses the effects of hydration and dehydration on physiological mechanisms, especially those related to the brain and thirst.*

CHERNER, R. "Abnormal thirst: when a patient can't get enough to drink." *Consultant*, 22, 3, 341-346, 1982. *A clear, concise article describing the causes of thirst, ways of evaluating the thirsty patient, and a few disorders that cause abnormal drinking.*

EPSTEIN, A., KISSILEFF, H., and STELLAR, E. (editors). *The Neuropsychology of Thirst: New Findings and Advances in Concepts.* Washington: V.H. Winston, 1973, 357 pages. *This book offers a variety of papers by experts in the field, and covers neural, chemical, osmotic, and volume-related mechanisms that regulate thirst. Some discussion of thirst abnormalities is included.*

Air: The Clinical Reality

Medical Disorder: Hyperventilation Syndrome

Read this "overture" carefully before you read Chapter 5. The connections between the medical reality of hyperventilation syndrome and the basic underlying physiological and psychological processes that regulate normal breathing are developed in this chapter. (For more information on hyperventilation syndrome, see Heyman, 1979; Compernolle, Hoogduin, and Joele, 1979; and Lum, 1976.)

Hyperventilation syndrome is a condition characterized by feelings of giddiness and dizziness, numbness of the limbs, and, often, feelings of unreality and a host of other symptoms, such as blurred vision, pounding heart, muscular spasms, epigastric discomfort (discomfort in the pit of the stomach), and fainting. Although these symptoms usually last for a few minutes only, they can last as long as a half hour or more and can recur several times a day.

Hyperventilation syndrome is caused by overbreathing triggered by emotional upset or attacks of anxiety. The person often feels tightness in the chest as though the lungs cannot be adequately filled and, because of the sense of suffocation, frequently sighs and takes deep breaths. This overbreathing alters the pH of the blood, causing the body to become too alkaline. The alkaline condition originates from too much carbon dioxide being eliminated from the body and results in nerve cells becoming overexcitable. (The symbol "pH" denotes the body's concentration of hydrogen ions. When the concentration of hydrogen ions in any part of the body goes down, the pH goes up, signifying a more alkaline environment in that part of the body. The relationship of pH to carbon dioxide levels is discussed more fully in subsequent pages of this chapter.) In prolonged attacks of hyperventilation, tremors and spastic contractions of the muscles may occur and result in tetany (continuous muscular contractions) with carpopedal spasm (tetany in the hands).

Often the person does not understand that he or she is overbreathing, especially in a first occurrence, and these symptoms can induce a state of panic that makes the anxiety worse. The resulting chain reaction —anxiety producing hyperventilation and the symptoms of hyperventilation producing more anxiety— sometimes leads the now disoriented, perhaps faint person to the emergency room of the local hospital where the simple remedy of breathing into a paper bag quickly reduces these symptoms. The magical relief comes because one breathes in air that contains a higher-than-normal level of carbon dioxide, which lowers the body pH and restores it to normal. Holding one's breath for longer-than-normal periods is also effective in retaining carbon dioxide and thus lowering body pH.

In many cases, once the person realizes that these symptoms are easy to treat and relatively easy to control, the incidence of hyperventilation syndrome decreases significantly. Nevertheless, any prolonged or recurring anxiety deserves to be looked at by a psychotherapist, for here, as with other physical conditions, the symptoms the body expresses are signals that the self may not be well, or needs attention.

Air

If someone were to ask how your breathing relates to your emotions, you might have to pause to think. While you know, in general terms, that breathing serves the vital function of bringing oxygen into your body and removing carbon dioxide from it, you probably don't give much thought to how you use air. You simply breathe in and out, day after day. Yet, breathing is involved in a broad range of experiences, including emotional states of being anxious and nervous to being calm and relaxed, to outward expressions such as laughing, crying, or weeping, to mundane behaviors such as sneezing, coughing, sniffing, or yawning, and to speech. Although we cannot take time here to discuss all of the above processes in detail, we will consider: a) the basic properties of air; b) the mechanisms responsible for rhythmic breathing; c) the major factors that influence our breathing rate; d) some aspects of breathing and health; and e) the relation between emotional states and breathing.

I. AIR AND ITS USE BY THE BODY

The atmosphere is a mixture of gases. The percentages by volume of each of the major gases in the lower atmosphere are:

Constituent	Volume Percent
Nitrogen	78.08
Oxygen	20.95
Argon	0.93
Carbon Dioxide	0.03
All others (including neon, helium, krypton, xenon, hydrogen, and methane)	0.01
	100.00

Although we will discuss each in turn, for the body the most important gases are oxygen and carbon dioxide.

Nitrogen

Gaseous nitrogen is very prevalent in our atmosphere but, in general, the body does not make use of this gas. The nitrogen we breathe in is not metabolized by the body, nor does it have any known effect on bodily function under normal circumstances.

(Nitrogen is an essential element—all amino acids, and therefore all proteins, contain it, as do the B vitamins—but the body's source of nitrogen is in the food we eat rather than in the air we receive through breathing. A few species of bacteria and algae can synthesize nitrogen compounds from atmospheric nitrogen. These nitrogen compounds are then used by plants to form plant proteins. We make use of this nitrogen by ingesting these plants, or by ingesting meat or other products that come from plant-eating animals.)

Oxygen

The importance of atmospheric oxygen has already been discussed. The amount of oxygen our body receives is controlled to a great extent by the amount of oxygen in the atmosphere. Our bodies require oxygen for "oxidative phosphorylation," a process that generates enormous amounts of ATP (see Chapter 3). In this respect, oxygen is as necessary for the production of usable energy as are solid foods.

Argon

As with gaseous nitrogen, the argon we breathe in is not metabolized by the body, nor does it have any known effect on bodily function under normal circumstances.

Carbon Dioxide

Under normal conditions, the amount of carbon dioxide in our body is not related to the amount in the atmosphere. Rather, it is controlled by our body's metabolic activities. Tremendous amounts of carbon dioxide are formed in the process of converting the energy contained in carbohydrates, fats, and proteins into the energy contained in ATP (see Chapter 3). In effect, then, carbon dioxide is a waste product that must be eliminated.

Carbon dioxide is also important in the regulation of acid-base balance, which is expressed as "pH." By definition, the symbol pH signifies the concentration of hydrogen ions in the following manner:

$$pH = \frac{1}{\log [H^+]}$$

where $[H^+]$ is the hydrogen ion concentration. This equation shows that when the concentration of H^+ increases in any environment (including any part of the body), pH goes down, signifying a more acid environment. When the concentration of H^+ decreases, the pH goes up, signifying a more alkaline environment.

In the overture to this chapter we mentioned a relation between the amount of carbon dioxide in the body and the amount of hydrogen ions. There exists an enzyme in most cells of our body, but especially in red blood cells, that greatly accelerates the reaction between carbon dioxide and water to produce **carbonic acid**. (You will recall that an enzyme is a protein that speeds up the rate of chemical reactions.) The carbonic acid immediately dissociates into **hydrogen** and **bicarbonate ions**. The chemical reactions for these processes, which are reversible as indicated by arrows, are shown at the bottom of the page. Thus, without entering a detailed explanation of the relationship between CO_2 and pH, there are more hydrogen ions—that is, pH goes down—when the concentration of CO_2 (and therefore carbonic acid) increases. Similarly, there are fewer hydrogen ions—that is, pH goes up—when the concentration of CO_2 (and therefore carbonic acid) decreases.

When we exhale under normal resting conditions, the amount of CO_2 in the expired air is about one hundred times greater than the amount in an equivalent volume of the atmosphere. This elimination serves two functions: a) as already mentioned, it removes CO_2 from the body as a waste product of me-

tabolism, and b) it serves to maintain a constant pH of 7.4 in the body. If we were to breathe at one half our normal rate, with no change in our metabolism, the build-up of CO_2 in our body would lower pH to approximately 7.1. Conversely, if we were to double our breathing rate, the loss of CO_2 would raise pH to about 7.6. It is because of this relationship that breathing has such an important effect on the body's pH. In extreme acidosis, the pH can drop to 7.0; in extreme alkalosis it can rise to 7.7. If the blood pH extends even a little beyond these limits, death will result within a few hours.

II. PHYSIOLOGICAL/PSYCHOLOGICAL INTERACTIONS

As with other processes discussed so far in this book, the physiology and behavior of breathing also involves almost every part of the body. As a food, air enters our body through the mouth, trachea, and bronchi, is transferred into the blood, and then exerts its actions by acting on cells and organs throughout the body. Figure 5-1 illustrates some of the main organs involved in our assimilation of air. The body's use of these organs is covered in the following pages as part of our discussion of the coexistence of physiology and behavior.

Nitrogen Narcosis

Although this chapter will focus on the physiological and psychological mechanisms of breathing and how they relate to oxygen, carbon dioxide, and body pH, we will first describe an interesting condition called "nitrogen narcosis," which clearly demonstrates how atmospheric gases can influence psychological states and the activities of the brain.

When a person goes deep-sea diving or is placed in some other high-pressure environment, the amount of nitrogen gas dissolved in the body's fluids and tissues can rise dramatically. Under these conditions a person sometimes experiences **nitrogen narcosis**, which is characterized by: a) a state of euphoria and exhilaration (usually beginning once the amount of nitrogen dissolved in the blood has exceeded four times normal, which occurs when the body is more than one hundred feet below sea level); b) a state of drowsiness (once the amounts of nitrogen exceed five to six times normal); c) weakness and lack of coordination (when nitrogen levels exceed seven times

$$CO_2 \; + \; H_2O \; \rightleftarrows \; H_2CO_3 \; \rightleftarrows \; H^+ \; + \; HCO_3^-$$

carbon dioxide + water ⇄ carbonic acid ⇄ hydrogen ion + bicarbonate ion

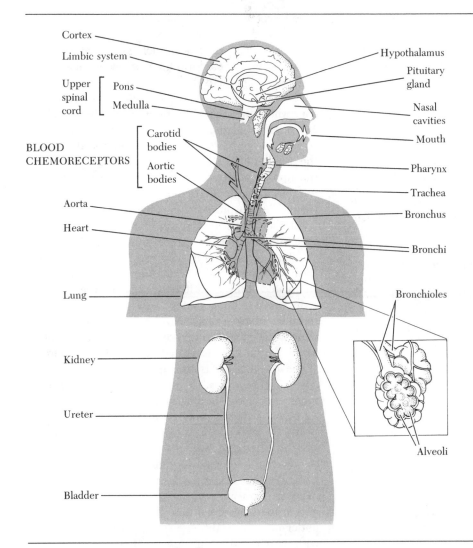

Figure 5–1. Organs involved in the assimilation of air. In addition to the organs listed above, the abdominal and skeletal muscles are also important for breathing. The carotid and aortic bodies, located in association with the aorta and carotid arteries, contain special nerve cells called **chemoreceptors.** These chemoreceptors, which are sensitive to oxygen and carbon dioxide levels in the blood, send neural impulses into the brain to help regulate our rate of breathing.

normal); and d) almost complete stupor (when blood levels exceed ten times normal, which occurs at depths of more than three hundred feet below sea level).

It is currently believed that nitrogen narcosis occurs under these conditions because nitrogen dissolves very easily in the fats of the body. All cells have an outer boundary, called the "cell membrane," that envelops the rest of the cell. Because the membrane surrounding cells, including nerve cells, is mostly lipid (fat), it is supposed that the excess nitrogen in some way depresses neural activity through a physical effect on the membranes of neurons. Notice that the symptoms of nitrogen narcosis are similar to what occurs with alcohol intoxication. (In spite of early excitatory effects, alcohol is a depressant.) In fact, these symptoms are observed with many anesthetics. Very large amounts of the inert gases **helium, xenon,** and **argon** in the body produce effects similar to those observed in nitrogen narcosis. These anesthetic effects are believed to be due to the same mechanism discussed above for nitrogen.

Let us now proceed to discuss those physiological and psychological processes at work in our day-to-day assimilation of air.

Coexistence and Inseparability of Physiology and Behavior

The activity of breathing, involving inspiration and expiration, differs from eating and drinking in that respiration usually occurs *without* voluntary effort or conscious experience. In discussing the ways in which the physiology and behavior of breathing interrelate and coexist, it is necessary first to understand the basic mechanisms that control respiration.

Figure 5-2 illustrates the basic mechanisms involved in rhythmic breathing, which relies on stretch receptors in our lungs, inspiratory and expiratory neurons in the upper spinal cord (in an area called the medulla—see Figure 5-6), and the muscles of inspiration and expiration. When we inhale, the lungs become stretched, activating special nerve cells called **stretch receptors** that are located mainly in the bronchi and bronchioles. (The trachea splits into two branches, each called a bronchus—plural, bronchi. In turn, the bronchi form finer branches called bronchioles.) When activated by stretching, these nerve cells transmit neural impulses into the upper spinal cord where they inhibit inspiration and thereby check any further inflation of the lungs. As we exhale, the stretch receptors in the lungs compress, decreasing the number of neural impulses being transmitted into the upper spinal cord and releasing the inspiratory neurons from the inhibition that has been acting upon them. Thus inspiration begins again.

Another basic mechanism involved in rhythmic breathing relies on **reciprocal inhibition** between inspiratory and expiratory neurons in the upper spinal cord (see Figure 5-3). When inspiratory neurons are stimulated, they inhibit expiratory neurons. After a short while (approximately three seconds), the inspiratory neurons stop firing, possibly because of fatigue which is thought to occur as a result of depletion of the neural chemicals that activate these neurons. When these neurons stop firing, the inhibition imposed on the expiratory neurons is released, causing them to become stimulated and, in turn, causing inhibition of the inspiratory neurons. After a short while, the expiratory neurons stop firing, again possibly from fatigue, thereby releasing the inhibition imposed on the inspiratory neurons. This alternation between the firing of inspiratory and expiratory neurons is presumed to be the mechanism that permits us to breathe rhythmically, without interruption, under normal conditions. (This process is illustrated with dashed arrows in Figure 5-3.)

Although reciprocal inhibition is a well-established mechanism whereby nerve cells influence one another, it has not been proved absolutely that this mechanism is, in fact, responsible for rhythmic breathing. Nevertheless, it is a useful and generally accepted model for looking at how the upper spinal cord might be functioning to regulate our breathing. (For more details on neural mechanisms that can explain the rhythmicity of breathing, see Cohen, 1981.)

To function, both systems—one involving stretch receptors, the other involving reciprocal inhibition within the upper spinal cord—rely on the lungs, the muscles of breathing, and an intact spinal cord.

The mechanisms responsible for rhythmic breathing are essential because each inhalation requires a prior exhalation, each exhalation requires a prior inhalation, and so on. Any additional mechanisms can alter the *rate* or *pattern* of our breathing, but its rhythmicity must continue if we are to survive. Let's

Figure 5–2. Rhythmic breathing involving lung stretch receptors. Shrinkage of the lungs excites inspiratory neurons in the upper spinal cord whereas stretching of the lungs inhibits them. Note the continuity of physiology and behavior. The boxed material represents processes subject to conscious experience. Behavioral activity is indicated by the use of boldface type, and the involvement of the brain by italic type.

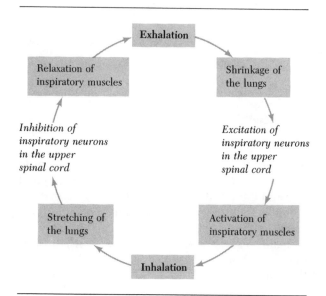

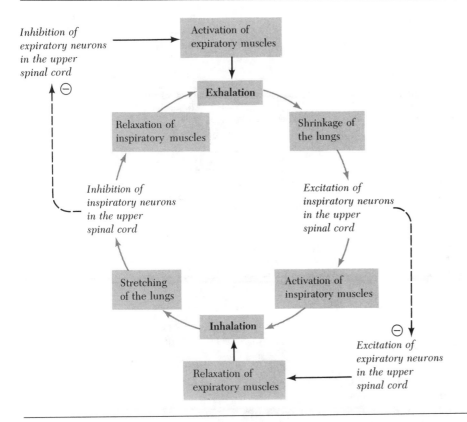

Figure 5-3. Rhythmic breathing involving reciprocal inhibition. The dashed arrows with a minus ($\ominus$) sign indicate reciprocal inhibition. As inspiratory neurons become excited, expiratory neurons are inhibited (indicated by the $\ominus$ to the right in the diagram) and cause the expiratory muscles to relax. As inspiratory neurons in the upper spinal cord stop firing, expiratory neurons are "disinhibited"; i.e., inhibition is removed by inhibiting an inhibition, and this process results in the excitation of expiratory neurons which, in turn, activates expiratory muscles and promotes exhalation.

now look at those physiological processes that alter the rate of breathing.

Our rate of breathing is closely tied to the levels of oxygen and carbon dioxide in our blood, as well as body pH. As illustrated in Figure 5-4, when blood oxygen levels fall, or blood CO_2 levels rise, or body pH decreases (increased H^+), neurons in the upper spinal cord are activated and our rate of breathing increases. The increased rate of breathing then raises oxygen levels in the blood and lowers CO_2 levels because more CO_2 is expired. In turn, the lower CO_2 levels will raise body pH because of the reduced concentration of hydrogen ions. Thus, the increased rate of breathing serves to adjust oxygen, carbon di-

oxide, and pH levels so that they will return to normal. Conversely, when blood CO_2 levels fall or body pH rises (reduced H^+), the activity of respiratory neurons in the upper spinal cord is suppressed and oxygen, carbon dioxide, and pH levels are thereby restored to normal.

Respiratory neurons in the upper spinal cord are directly responsive to changes in the level of carbon dioxide and hydrogen ions in the body. For example, as CO_2 and H^+ levels rise in the brain, respiratory neurons—both expiratory and inspiratory—increase their activity. The brain, however, is not directly responsive to oxygen levels, but responds to the activity of special **chemoreceptors** in the carotid and

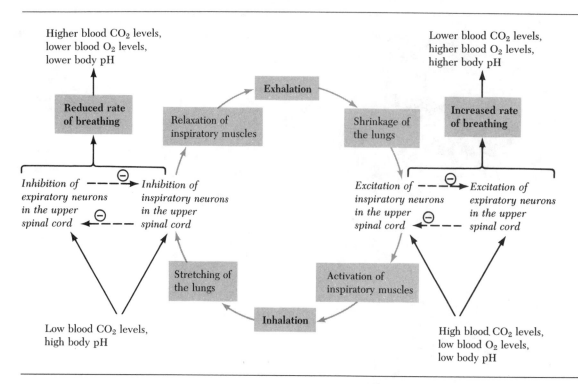

Figure 5—4. Effects of carbon dioxide, oxygen, and pH on breathing rate. (For clarity, responses of the kidneys have been left out; see Figure 5—4A in the appendix.) The boxed material represents processes subject to conscious experience. Behavioral activity is indicated by the use of boldface type, and the involvement of the brain by italic type.

aortic bodies (see Figure 5-1). When blood O_2 levels fall below normal, the activity of these chemoreceptors increases, resulting in an increased transmission of neural impulses into the upper spinal cord. These neural impulses then act to increase the activity of respiratory neurons. The chemoreceptors are also responsive to changes in blood CO_2 and H^+ levels, but this effect is less powerful than the direct effect of CO_2 and H^+ in the brain.

The regulation of oxygen, carbon dioxide, and body pH levels not only involves breathing, but also the **kidneys**. Although regulation by the kidneys is a much slower process than regulation through breathing, this regulation is nevertheless essential to normal body functioning. (The kidney's involvement has been added in Diagram 5-4A, which is in the appendix.)

The mechanisms outlined above describe a highly organized set of processes, all functioning to maintain proper oxygen, carbon dioxide, and pH levels in our body. None rely on voluntary behavior or are associated with conscious experience, although they can be critically affected by conscious behaviors. A host of

other processes related to behavior and conscious experience influence the *rate* and *pattern* of breathing. The influence of behavior and emotions on breathing are summarized in Figure 5-5 where those aspects most subject to our conscious experience are boxed.

Some behaviors and emotions alter respiration mostly as a result of changes in the rate of metabolism. For example, when a person rests or relaxes, the rate of chemical reactions necessary to provide energy for muscular tension and/or movement decreases. This decrease lowers the amount of oxygen the body needs (remember that muscular contraction requires ATP and that oxygen is associated with the production of this molecule) and the amount of carbon dioxide produced (because fewer nutrients are being used to form ATP). These actions, in turn, lead to a decrease in the rate of breathing. Conversely, exercise increases the rate of chemical reactions and increases blood CO_2 levels, decreases blood O_2 levels, and decreases body pH, all of which increase our breathing rate. This increase in breathing rate is, of course, a healthy response to exercise and restores O_2, CO_2, and pH to normal levels.

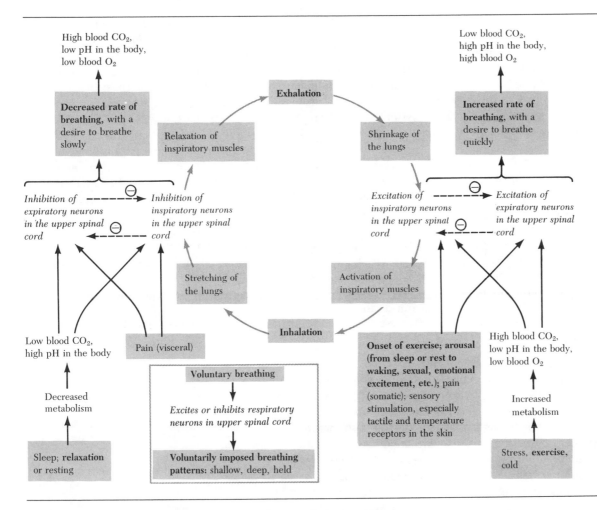

Figure 5–5. Influence of behavior and emotions on breathing. Note the continuity of physiology and behavior. Boxed material represents processes subject to conscious experience. Behavioral activity is indicated by the use of boldface type, and the involvement of the brain by italic type.

Stress can also increase the rate of chemical reactions and increase the rate of breathing, and pain, while often associated with an increase in the rate of breathing, can also decrease it, as when it originates from organs within the abdominal cavity, such as the stomach, intestines, and kidneys.

In addition, many different types of arousal are capable of increasing the rate of breathing. In one's arousal from sleep to a waking condition, or from quiet rest to attentiveness, the increase in respiration is due largely to stimulation of the **reticular system**, a portion of the brain associated with arousal that is discussed briefly in the next section and in some detail in Chapter 8. When we are emotionally excited or sexually aroused, the increase in the rate of breathing is a combined result of accelerated metabolism and a direct effect of activities occurring in the brain, especially within the reticular system.

Although the behavioral and emotional aspects of breathing are different from those for eating or drinking, the fundamental interactions occurring between behavioral and physiological mechanisms are similar. One can easily appreciate from examining Figure 5-5, for example, that once behavior has modified the rate of respiration, respiration becomes part of a continuous process, altering the levels of oxygen and carbon dioxide and the body's pH, which, in turn, further affect the rate of breathing—usually in the opposite direction. These interactions are discussed later in the chapter.

The Brain

Figures 5-2 through 5-5 make it amply clear that the brain plays a key role in determining many of the physiological/psychological interactions that occur with our breathing. The involvement of the **upper spinal cord**, the **hypothalamus**, **limbic system**, and the **cerebral cortex** are discussed below.

The Upper Spinal Cord. Even the most basic aspects of breathing involve the brain. We already mentioned that the upper spinal cord is necessary for the rhythmicity of inspiration (inhalation) and expiration (exhalation). In the upper spinal cord, the **medulla** appears to contain the neurons most essential for rhythmic breathing. The smooth rhythm of normal breathing also depends on neuronal activity in the **pons**, whose location in the upper spinal cord, along with the location of the medulla, is shown in Figure 5-6.

Figure 5-6 also indicates that when a cut is made through the upper spinal cord severing the pons and medulla from the rest of the brain, an animal will continue to breathe normally although it will be completely comatose. This finding is consistent with the fact that rhythmic breathing does not require the participation of conscious or voluntary behavior.

The upper spinal cord contains three regions that are especially important for normal rhythmic breathing: the **medullary rhythmicity area**, the **apneustic area**, and the **pneumotaxic area**. The medullary rhythmicity area is comprised of the inspiratory and expiratory neurons responsible for the basic rhythmicity of breathing, as explained earlier. These cells are directly sensitive to carbon dioxide and hydrogen ions. When the level of these goes up (a lower pH), this increases the activity of both inspiratory and expiratory neurons and the breathing rate increases. Conversely, when the level of CO_2 or H^+ goes down (a higher pH), the breathing rate decreases.

Figure 5–6. Areas of the hypothalamus and upper spinal cord involved with respiration. Note that a line represents a cut through the upper spinal cord that isolates the pons and medulla from the rest of the brain above. When the brain is so cut, the animal is in a state of coma yet rhythmic breathing is maintained. Note also that the respiratory areas of the upper spinal cord are embedded within the reticular system. The triple arrow indicates that respiratory responses involve neural mechanisms in these connected regions of the brain that include areas other than the hypothalamus and upper spinal cord.

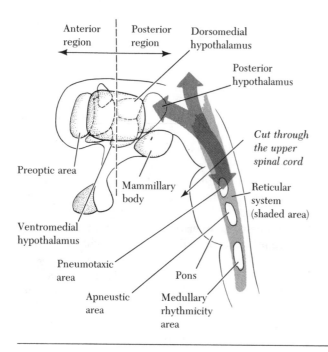

UPPER SPINAL CORD

Medulla: contains the medullary rhythmicity area; contains the inspiratory and expiratory neurons responsible for the basic rhythmicity of respiration.

Pons: contains the apneustic area and the pneumotaxic area; provides an inspiratory drive to respiration (when stimulated, inspiration is stronger and more prolonged), whereas the pneumotaxic area accelerates breathing and provides an expiratory drive.

HYPOTHALAMUS

Preoptic area: involved in temperature regulation. When body temperature rises, cells in this area increase the rate of respiration (panting).

Posterior region: includes the posterior hypothalamus, mammillary body, dorsomedial hypothalamus, and ventromedial hypothalamus; when stimulated, increases the rate of breathing. The posterior region is involved in many arousal mechanisms.

The apneustic area and pneumotaxic area within the pons also contain respiratory neurons that are sensitive to carbon dioxide and hydrogen ions. In addition, the apneustic area provides an inspiratory drive to respiration, and the pneumotaxic area provides an expiratory drive. When stimulated, neurons in the pneumotaxic area can accelerate the rate of breathing. Normal, smooth breathing is accomplished through the concerted actions of all of these areas in the upper spinal cord. In other words, even though rhythmic breathing can be maintained by the medullary rhythmicity area alone, this breathing is weak and gasping in nature.

The involvement of the medulla in receiving neural impulses from chemoreceptors located in the carotid arteries and the aorta has already been explained. (You will recall that the chemoreceptors are especially sensitive to blood oxygen levels.)

The Hypothalamus. The hypothalamus is generally believed to exert a stimulatory effect on breathing. This action appears to be related to two functions: *temperature regulation* and *arousal*. In animals, when body temperature rises, neurons in the **preoptic** and **anterior** hypothalamic regions are activated (see page 48, Chapter 4) and panting ensues. This action is believed to be exerted via the pneumotaxic area in the pons because some neurons in the pons are known to be controlled by temperature-sensitive cells in the preoptic and anterior areas of the hypothalamus.

Earlier, we mentioned that many different types of arousal increase the rate of breathing. Arousal mechanisms, in part, are regulated by neurons within the posterior region of the hypothalamus. Electrical stimulation of this region, which includes the **dorsomedial**, **ventromedial**, **mammillary**, and **posterior** areas (refer to Figure 5-6), usually accelerates breathing. In addition, electrical stimulation of the posterior region of the hypothalamus is often associated with increased blood pressure, increased heart rate, increased secretions of the adrenal glands, alerting responses, rage reactions, attack or flight behaviors, sexual behavior, and other responses to be discussed in Chapters 7, 8, and 10. In one way or another, all of these physiological and behavioral responses are associated with arousal.

The posterior region of the hypothalamus is intimately connected to the **reticular system**, a system of neurons that extends from the upper spinal cord to many regions of the brain. The reticular system is described in some detail in Chapter 8. Here, we will note only that, among other effects, the reticular system is responsible for and integrates many aspects of

arousal. Again, as illustrated in Figure 5-6, the primary regions of the upper spinal cord that are responsible for breathing are embedded within the reticular system. Therefore, it is no surprise that increased arousal and increased breathing often appear to be associated.

In summary, then, when we are emotionally excited or sexually aroused, the increase in the rate of breathing is a combined result of accelerated metabolism, stimulation of the autonomic nervous system (the system of neurons that influences blood pressure, heart rate, and other functions, as described in Chapter 7), and the activation of the posterior hypothalamic region and reticular system. Although these areas of the brain seem to play the most significant role in arousal mechanisms and breathing, the limbic system and outer cerebral cortex are also influential.

The Limbic System. Electrical stimulation of the limbic system has been reported to both increase and decrease the rate of respiration. As indicated in Figure 5-7, electrical stimulation of portions of the **cingulate gyrus** and **amygdala** have been reported to accelerate breathing. However, the most common effect of electrically stimulating these and other portions of the limbic system—i.e., the **olfactory area**, **piriform area**, **orbital cortex**, and **hippocampus**, see Figure 5-7—is to inhibit breathing (see Kaada, 1960; Plum, 1970). In addition, sneezing, sniffing, coughing, and vocalization are also evoked by stimulating various portions of the limbic system. In other words, the limbic system appears to be very much involved in regulating breathing and in associated functions that make use of the respiratory apparatus. For example, sniffing, which serves olfaction (smell), appears to involve mainly the olfactory areas and the amygdala.

Of particular interest to researchers is the finding that when portions of the limbic system are electrically stimulated, respiration can become so depressed that blood CO_2 levels become very high and blood O_2 levels become very low. While this is happening, the animal (in this case a monkey) *offers no resistance to its physiological state* and simply lies quietly. In contrast, when equally abnormal CO_2 and O_2 levels result from restricting air flow through the trachea, the monkey will visibly increase its respiratory effort and struggle to escape (Reis and McHugh, 1968). It is tempting to conclude from this study that, under appropriate circumstances, higher regions of the brain can override the basic drives that regulate body pH, blood CO_2, and O_2 levels. This possibility will be discussed under Body and Self later in this chapter.

The Cerebral Cortex. Although it is clear that the cerebral cortex regulates respiratory patterns,

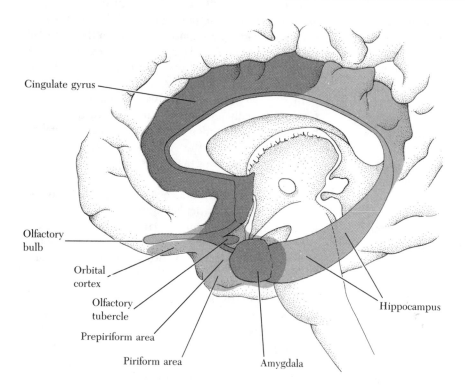

Cingulate gyrus

Olfactory bulb

Orbital cortex

Olfactory tubercle

Prepiriform area

Piriform area

Amygdala

Hippocampus

Amygdala area: includes amygdala, piriform area, prepiriform area, and orbital cortex. *Stimulation* primarily inhibits respiration but can also accelerate it; also elicits sneezing, coughing, and sniffing.

Hippocampus: anterior end of hippocampal gyrus (see area D, Figure 5-8). *Stimulation* inhibits respiration; *stimulation* evokes vocalization (monkeys).

Cingulate gyrus: *stimulation* of anterior area inhibits respiration; *stimulation* of medial area accelerates respiration.

Olfactory area: includes olfactory bulb and olfactory tubercle. *Stimulation* elicits sneezing; sniffing; slow, deep, regular breathing; and inhibition of breathing.

Figure 5–7. Areas of the limbic system involved in respiration. The orbital area of the frontal cortex and the piriform area of the temporal cortex are included in the drawing because they are so closely tied in with the limbic system. (These areas are also shown in Figures 5–8 and 5–9 illustrating the involvement of the cerebral cortex in respiration.)

exact mechanisms are not understood. Perhaps the most sophisticated use of the respiratory system occurs in the behavior of speaking. As indicated in Figure 5-8, a well-localized portion of the frontal cortex serves functions related to speech (see area B). When this area is damaged, the fine coordination of movements necessary for speech—including use of the larynx, which contains the vocal cords, and use of the respiratory system—is impaired. Electrical stimulation of this area elicits vocalization, characterized by a sustained vowel sound.

Figures 5-8 and 5-9 indicate other areas of the ce-

rebral cortex that affect respiration. Electrical stimulation of these areas has produced both an increase and a decrease in the rate of breathing, depending upon the precise location of the stimulus (see Kaada, 1960; Plum, 1970). In addition, it appears that the frontal cortex is responsible for the ability to voluntarily hold one's breath. Although the exact location of these cortical areas is not known, they appear to be part of a pathway that goes from the frontal cortex through the brain to the pons in the upper spinal cord. When parts of this pathway are damaged, voluntary breathing is disrupted (see Plum, 1970).

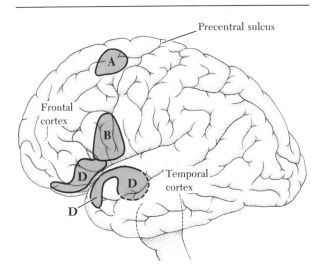

Precentral sulcus

Frontal
cortex

Temporal
cortex

FRONTAL AND TEMPORAL CORTEX

Area A: area in front of the precentral sulcus. *Stimulation* accelerates breathing in monkeys; *stimulation* elicits vocalization in humans (a sustained vowel sound which cannot be stopped with voluntary effort).

Area B: speech area, surrounding inferior precentral sulcus; includes Broca's area but extends upward along both sides of precentral sulcus. *Destruction* impairs coordination of movements necessary for speech, usually much more dominant in the left hemisphere than in the right. *Stimulation* elicits vocalization in humans (a sustained vowel sound).

Area D: orbital-insular-temporal area and a region of the anterior hippocampal gyrus. *Stimulation* inhibits respiration in monkeys.

Figure 5–8. Areas of the cerebral cortex involved in respiration. Lateral view of the cerebral cortex, as seen from the side.

Laughing and crying appear to primarily involve neural pathways that interconnect the limbic system and the cerebral cortex; these pathways then go to the upper spinal cord (see Black, 1982; Cantu and Drew, 1966). Functions such as voluntarily holding one's breath, laughing, crying, and talking are not concerned with such vital processes as the regulation of body pH or blood oxygen levels, nor are they organized to respond to abnormal levels of blood gases in any concerted, integrated manner. In fact, there is

some evidence that these functions involve neural mechanisms quite separate from those that regulate pH and oxygen, even in the upper spinal cord (for a review, see Plum, 1970).

The involvement of the cerebral cortex in regulating respiratory patterns is further suggested by the following: through *prior training*, it is possible to modify the increase in breathing which usually occurs *before* the levels of metabolites (such as CO_2) are changed by exercise. For example, when faced with a particular exercise, the breathing rate of a trained athlete increases in anticipation of the intended exercise much more appropriately than the breathing rate of an inexperienced person. These anticipatory reactions are believed to originate in the cerebral cortex of the brain.

Self-Stimulation. Because breathing is fundamental to life, it is not surprising to find that areas of the brain important for respiration are also rewarding or aversive in response to self-administered electrical stimulation. In the upper spinal cord many sites are "positive"—i.e., an animal will repeatedly press the lever that delivers a stimulating current through an electrode implanted in this area. There are also "negative" sites in the upper spinal cord—i.e., an animal will avoid pressing the lever. Positive and negative sites appear to be interdispersed throughout the upper spinal cord, although there appear to be more rewarding sites in some areas than in others. In the amygdala, cingulate gyrus, olfactory areas, and orbital cortex, the positive sites outnumber the aversive sites.

Although it is apparent that many of the areas of the brain that affect breathing contain cells that are rewarding when stimulated, it is not obvious how to translate these findings to conscious pleasure/pain or reward/aversion experiences in humans. (See Mora, Avrith, Philips, and Rolls, 1979, for evidence concerning reward and the orbital cortex; see Olds and Fobes, 1981, for a general review.) For example, a brief reflection on our own experience will indicate that the "reward" or "pleasure" of breathing is quite different from the reward of eating or the reward of drinking, so the fact that different areas of the brain are rewarding when they are electrically stimulated does not necessarily mean that they are all served by the same mechanisms. (This point will be discussed further in Chapter 11.) Nevertheless, with respect to processes that govern our assimilation of air, we can conclude that an intricate connection appears to exist between reward and the need to breathe, just as there is an intimate connection between reward and the need to eat, or drink.

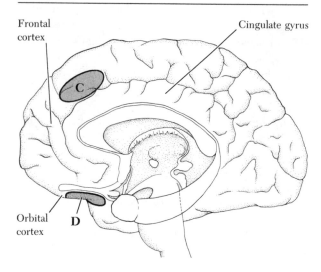

Frontal cortex

Cingulate gyrus

C

Orbital cortex

D

FRONTAL AND TEMPORAL CORTEX

Area C: supplementary motor area above cingulate gyrus. *Stimulation* evokes vocalization in monkeys (a sustained vowel sound).

Area D: orbital-insular-temporal area and a region of the anterior hippocampal gyrus. *Stimulation* inhibits respiration in monkeys.

Figure 5–9. Areas of the cerebral cortex involved in respiration. Medial view of the cerebral cortex, as seen when the brain is opened from the middle.

Body and Self

Again, *experiences are associated with almost all of these physiological processes.* When we prepare to swim under water, sprint a short distance, or lift a heavy object, we are usually instructed to take a number of rapid, deep breaths and then a final deep inhalation, holding our breath with our lungs inflated. Trained swimmers, weight lifters, and even household movers are more skilled and efficient than most of us in performing this respiratory pattern. This behavior produces the following effects:

a) By taking a number of rapid, deep breaths, we quickly lower the level of CO_2 in the blood. Because of this reduction we are able to hold our breath for a longer period since high levels of CO_2 are a strong stimulus for breathing.

b) By holding our breath with the lungs inflated, stretch receptors in the lungs are activated. When

activated, these stretch receptors also inhibit breathing and permit us to hold our breath longer.

c) The reduced levels of CO_2 increase the blood pH. The higher blood pH increases the excitability of the nervous system, placing us in a stimulated state of readiness. The increase in blood pH also helps temporarily to offset the effect of exercise to reduce our body pH because of the accumulation of metabolites. (This offsetting effect probably helps to delay the onset of muscle fatigue.)

The respiratory pattern of taking a number of rapid, deep breaths and then holding our breath pertains only to strenuous activity that is carried out over a very short period of time. In our daily life, there are many conditions, such as being aroused from sleep or from rest to activity, various emotional reactions, (fear, rage, excitement, etc.), and physical exercise, where our breathing rate is increased for prolonged periods of time. *The increased breathing will quickly raise blood pH unless there is a simultaneous elevation of blood CO_2 levels brought about by increased metabolism.* As illustrated in Figure 5-10, the body does respond to many conditions—physical and emotional—by increasing its metabolism; higher levels of CO_2 and increased breathing then occur because glucose and other chemicals are utilized to produce more ATP to meet potential energy requirements. Once the situation has passed (for example, the roller-coaster ride is over), both the excitement and the increase in metabolism are reduced with a corresponding reduction in the breathing rate.

In some emotional states—anxiety, for example—little or no increase may occur in metabolism, and, as just mentioned, the body is then quickly placed in an unbalanced state. As illustrated in Figure 5-11, because this emotional state does not trigger the physiological "alarm" reaction in our body, whatever the fear or danger perceived (or imagined), it is *not* capable of mobilizing our body's stores of usable energy, and thus there is little or no elevation of the CO_2 levels that have been depressed by increased respiration. If this state of imbalance persists over several hours, the kidneys partially compensate for the elevated pH by eliminating bicarbonate, thereby lowering blood pH to near-normal values (see Figure 5-4A in the appendix). Because a considerable amount of sodium and water are eliminated at the same time, urine production is increased.

Figure 5-11 also shows that when we increase our rate of breathing as a direct *voluntary* act, there is a rapid elevation of body pH. We will usually do this for less than a minute, however, before the discomfort forces us to stop. (Rapid breathing can be maintained

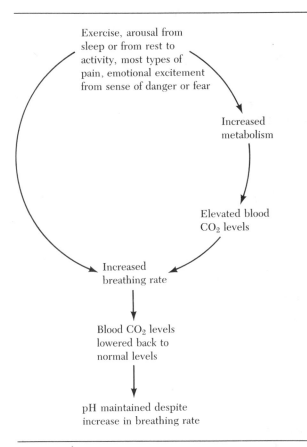

Exercise, arousal from
sleep or from rest to
activity, most types of
pain, emotional excitement
from sense of danger or fear

Increased
metabolism

Elevated blood
CO_2 levels

Increased
breathing rate

Blood CO_2 levels
lowered back to
normal levels

pH maintained despite
increase in breathing rate

Figure 5–10. Changes in breathing triggered by emotional and physical conditions that increase respiration without changing body pH. When the body increases its activity, there is an increased demand for molecules to be metabolized for energy, a process that produces more CO_2. The increased rate of breathing simply maintains CO_2 levels and body pH at normal levels.

in special circumstances—first stages of labor, for one—as long as the person deliberately takes very shallow breaths; in this case, no additional CO_2 is being expired—one is merely moving the air occupying "dead space" in the bronchi and trachea.)

One of the effects of a raised blood pH is a reduction in the amount of *free ionized calcium* (Ca^{++}) in the blood. This reduction occurs because the lowered concentration of hydrogen ions increases the binding of free calcium to proteins. Both nerve and muscle are extremely sensitive to blood levels of free ionized calcium. When calcium levels fall, the permeability to sodium in nerve and muscle cell membranes progressively increases and makes nerve and muscle much more excitable; that is, they are activated (depolarized) much more readily than is normal. This

excitability is manifested in the twitchings of facial muscles one may observe in a very nervous or anxious person who is breathing rapidly. In extreme cases, the increase in blood pH can lead to convulsions and tetany.

Conversely, with depressed respiration there is a decrease in blood pH, which raises free Ca^{++} levels in the blood. This increase in Ca^{++} levels decreases the permeability of nerve and muscle cell membranes to sodium and makes nerve and muscle less excitable than normal. These physiological events can be expressed in a depressed person by his or her sluggishness and flaccid facial muscles. In extreme cases, the decrease in blood pH leads to disorientation and coma. Increased respiration is a more common correlate of emotional upset than decreased respiration. A low pH can occur, however, when respiration is depressed by too much sedation, by narcotics, or when a person is suffering from severe asthma, or emphysema.

The long-standing advice to "take a deep breath" when we are anxious or under acute stress and need to calm down, has its physiological validity: In so doing, we are interrupting the vicious cycle illustrated in Figure 5-12. If we anticipate entering a situation that will make us anxious, taking a few deep breaths *before* facing it will often relieve some of the nervousness. Furthermore, in many cases, the "first minute is the worst" and so, by temporarily overriding our inclination to breath rapidly, we avoid the vicious cycle illustrated in the figure. Such remedies are effective, of course, only if the stress is not too severe or is short-lived.

Sleep is another behavior that involves reduced respiration for long periods. When we go to sleep, we usually do not experience any of the excitement or drive to increase our breathing, as otherwise occurs when the rate of our breathing is reduced. This reduced drive is partly because our rate of metabolism is reduced—we are relaxed and there is little muscular activity. Under these conditions, less oxygen is needed and less carbon dioxide is being produced in our body. On the other hand, there is, in addition, a slight shift in the respiratory response to carbon dioxide when we are sleeping, for we are now functioning with a greater concentration of CO_2 in the body as well as a reduced body pH. In deep sleep, the CO_2 in the body can rise to levels 15 percent or more above normal waking levels without any struggle or effort to increase the rate of respiration. Although exact mechanisms are not known, there is some evidence that the mechanisms involved may originate in the brain (see earlier comments on the limbic system and the findings of Reis and McHugh, 1968).

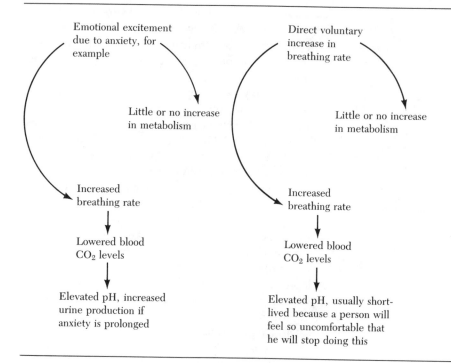

Figure 5–11. Changes in breathing and body pH triggered by emotional and physical conditions that increase respiration and body pH. When the body does not perceive a need for action, there is little or no increased demand for molecules to be metabolized for energy. In this case, the increased rate of breathing quickly lowers blood CO_2 levels and elevates body pH.

There are other behaviors that reduce or stop normal breathing for very short periods—chewing, straining (as in muscular exertion), laughing or crying, and speaking. Here, too, the varying shifts in blood gases and body pH are tolerated without effort or struggle to increase breathing, in contrast to other circumstances, such as when air passages are obstructed. Again, it appears that the limbic system and other regions of the brain override basic regulatory mechanisms so that these "appropriate" behaviors can take place (Reis and McHugh, 1968).

For thousands of years man has acknowledged the importance of breathing in spiritual development. Although the use of breathing in yoga and meditation are best known, altered breathing is a part of just about every spiritual discipline. In various ways breathing has been connected to "pure life," the "general life of all things existing," "life energy," and the "heart," to name a few. Whatever the case may be, it is clear that in addition to the ordinary emotions

accompanying respiration—those that involve the need to alter breathing patterns because of blood CO_2 levels, pH, nervousness, etc.—there is also a widely acknowledged experience of the "extra ordinary." As discussed previously, altered breathing can modify the excitability of the nervous system, and so it is not so surprising that it could help place a person in an inner state conducive to experiencing the unusual.

In attempting to make use of breathing for personal growth, many people now do "breathing exercises." Most breathing exercises require conscious direction, and so there is always the possibility of interfering with the automatic regulation of body pH under the control of the upper spinal cord. As mentioned in the previous section, in experiments with monkeys whose respiration was reduced by electrical stimulation of the limbic system to such an extent that blood CO_2 and O_2 levels were very abnormal, the animals made no effort to escape or to increase breathing. These studies suggest the possibility that a person, through

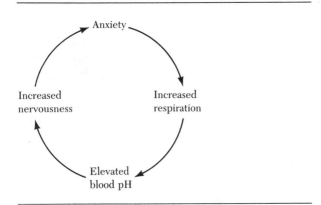

Figure 5—12. Anxiety and respiration: the vicious cycle of overbreathing and increased nervousness. When anxiety or other forms of emotional excitement increase respiration, the elevation of body pH that *may* occur (it may not, as indicated in Figure 5—10) can increase neural excitability. This can become a vicious cycle—anxiety elevating body pH whose elevation, in turn, increases anxiety, and so on.

breathing, could induce an imbalanced state rather than the desired state of open-mindedness. Of course, when we are anxious, stressed, or otherwise in an activated state, it is not possible to sit and immediately breathe slowly and deeply—the slow breathing would be opposed by our state of arousal. However, if we are first able to relax and "let go" of thoughts and emotions that stimulate our metabolism and increase respiration, deep breathing can be effectively practiced. Used in this manner, the attempt to breathe slowly and deeply can make it easier to achieve a state of quiet. In other words, breathing can be used as a sort of biofeedback which, by helping us to recognize and respond more quickly to states of arousal, allows us to become more serene and open.

Although conscious experience and voluntary effort are not necessary for breathing, conscious experiences of breathing are often very powerful. Generally, we are conscious of our breathing only when we are breathing too slowly or too quickly; in the extreme situation involving suffocation, we will do everything possible to get more air and will be conscious of little else. Sometimes we place ourselves in situations that threaten to overload our respiratory system. Those who live or work temporarily at high altitude, for example, are usually quite conscious of the effects of behavior on the respiratory system. Even a hiker, seeking the pleasure of mountain climbing, will

quickly learn to wait a few days before becoming engaged in strenuous exercise at altitudes of 10,000 to 15,000 feet. During this time, the body becomes "acclimatized" to the increase in pH resulting from accelerated breathing, and, eventually, the climber is able to breathe much more rapidly than before, without discomfort. At altitudes above 17,000 to 20,000 feet, an experienced climber will usually wait several weeks before engaging in strenuous activity. During this period, blood hemoglobin levels rise dramatically, enabling the body to utilize more oxygen. (Hemoglobin, present in all red blood cells, is a chemical that carries oxygen—and, to a lesser extent, carbon dioxide—throughout the bloodstream.)

III. INVOLVEMENT OF MANY ORGANS AT ONCE

From the above discussion, it is apparent that our breathing involves many organs. In addition to the obvious—mouth, nose, trachea, bronchi, and lungs —are the kidneys, the chemoreceptors, the vascular system (containing hemoglobin, which carries oxygen and carbon dioxide), various glands activated by stress (see Chapter 7), all cellular metabolic mechanisms, and the brain. Although the brain is extremely important for respiration, it is important to realize the extent to which it functions in conjunction with other organs and systems in the body.

IV. RELATION TO HEALTH

As long as breathing is regulated by the basic, involuntary, subconscious mechanisms outlined earlier —those involving the upper spinal cord, metabolites such as CO_2, and the kidneys—our body is maintained at an optimal level of functioning in relation to carbon dioxide, oxygen, and body pH.

Abnormalities in breathing usually reflect a medical problem. There is a broad range of possibilities— anything from lung disorders (emphysema and pneumonia) to heart failure, severe diarrhea, increased acidity of the blood, as in the build-up of metabolites in diabetics, excessive vomiting, asthma, bronchitis, and kidney failure. These disorders can severely alter the rate of breathing, either increasing or decreasing it. In these medical conditions, alterations in breathing represent a compensatory mechanism that seeks to restore body pH or blood oxygen levels to normal. Again, these abnormalities in breathing are not isolated conditions; they involve the same mechanisms that operate to maintain our health. For example, when the lack of insulin in a diabetic causes an abnormal build-up of metabolites leading to acid overload, the resulting decrease in body pH stimulates respiratory neurons in the upper spinal cord. The consequent increase in respiration causes more carbon dioxide to be eliminated, and usually raises body pH to values normal enough to prevent coma or other serious effects. Of course, treatment of the metabolic abnormalities is the only regimen that will alleviate the symptoms.

Abnormal respiratory patterns that do not signal severe physiological disorders also exist. As is evident in Figure 5-5, *behavior and emotions usually increase the rate of respiration.* This increase has only a small effect on blood oxygen levels, which are usually already maximal in the body. Also, unless suffering from a lung disorder, such as emphysema, (or at altitudes above ten to twelve thousand feet, or undergoing intense exercise) a person usually obtains enough oxygen from the atmosphere.

Although a change in the rate of our breathing has little effect on blood oxygen levels, it has a very pronounced effect on carbon dioxide levels. The pH changes in our body as a result of altered CO_2 levels are rapid and the effects immediately alter every chemical reaction in the body. This state of imbalance must be corrected quickly and exactly to restore and maintain a pH of 7.4.

The **hyperventilation syndrome**, a condition described at the beginning of the chapter, is a symptom of emotional disturbance and anxiety, and a fairly common cause of overbreathing. Less dramatic causes of increased respiration were discussed earlier. The fact that anxiety increases respiration is not in itself a harmful process. As discussed in the previous chapter in relation to water retention (see page 53), whether the anxiety is based on "real" or "imagined" dangers is a major factor in the physiological events that occur in association with the emotional state. In a truly threatening situation requiring prompt and intense physical exertion, the increase in respiration is designed, so to speak, to help us maintain a high level of physical effort for a short period of time. (This point was discussed earlier in the chapter when we gave the example of a person taking quick, deep breaths before engaging in intense physical exercise.) For anxiety related to emotional states of "free-floating" fear or apprehension, however, where the perceived threat is not immediate, the body may not "agree" that the increased breathing be matched by a corresponding increase in metabolism. In general, some form of short- or long-term psychotherapy or counseling is effective for cases of chronic anxiety.

V. CONCLUSIONS

You should now be able to better appreciate the wisdom involved in the psychology and physiology surrounding our use of air. To recapitulate, breathing is largely controlled by neurons within the upper spinal cord—cells which respond to levels of carbon dioxide in the blood, body pH, and signals from the chemoreceptors in the carotid arteries and aorta that are sensitive to blood oxygen levels. Unlike eating and drinking, breathing usually takes place without our conscious participation. Because abnormally high or low rates of breathing have a rapidly deleterious effect on the body, it is indeed fortunate that the regulation of our breathing is basically free from our consciousness.

Although breathing is tightly regulated by the mechanisms mentioned above, it also serves other less vital purposes—such as talking, laughing, and crying. For these behaviors, many areas of the limbic system and frontal cerebral cortex participate, apparently moreso than they do in eating or drinking. If, however, we compare the vital functions of regulating blood oxygen, carbon dioxide, and pH levels to the vital functions of regulating blood nutrient levels and water levels, we see that respiration is organized in a manner similar to that for eating and drinking: The interplay of physiological and behavioral responses are most heavily integrated within the upper spinal cord and hypothalamus to assure that the behavior of breathing corrresponds with the physiological requirements of taking in air and eliminating enough (but not too much) carbon dioxide so that body pH remains constant and we receive enough oxygen. The respiratory control of blood gases is also regulated by limbic and cortical structures, but their involvement is less marked and not essential to life.

The emotional processes that most affect breathing are those involved with mechanisms of arousal, whether increased (as with emotional excitement) or decreased (as with relaxation). In most cases, the altered level of arousal has a corresponding metabolic rate, assuring that changes in respiration conform with the body's needs to regulate pH, blood carbon dioxide, and blood oxygen levels. In some cases, we can safely alter our level of arousal and our emotional state by changing our breathing but, in other cases, consciously controlling our breathing will upset the delicate balance between body pH and blood carbon dioxide levels. For this reason, those of us who wish to alter our breathing pattern must be sensitive to our level of arousal.

For the most part, the behavioral and physiological events outlined in this chapter illustrate a profound integration. As they coexist, metabolic, emotional, and behavioral processes all interact with respiratory processes to assure a state of optimal functioning. In regulating oxygen, carbon dioxide, and body pH levels so that they remain optimal, not only do physiological processes and psychological states strongly influence our rate of breathing, but, conversely, our rate of breathing strongly influences our physiological and psychological states. Of course, abnormal and unhealthy conditions can occur in relation to our assimilation of air, but the strength and immediacy of our physiological responses to any alteration in breathing usually assures that too much or too little air will not be tolerated. In comparison, our "excesses" and "deficiences" in eating and drinking, which also produce imbalances, are tolerated to a much greater extent.

The next chapter deals with sensory stimuli and the senses. Sensory stimuli are the "foods" required for our sense organs. Once functioning, these organs provide us with most of the information we receive from the external as well as internal worlds. Many functions are served by the senses—functions ranging from the perception of pain, body temperature, taste, and smell to experiences of reading and listening to speech. As with respiration, some of these functions are vital to life and are well-integrated with basic physiological and behavioral processes, and some are not.

Recommended Reading

COMPERNOLLE, T., HOOGDUIN, K., and JOELE, L. "Diagnosis and treatment of the hyperventilation syndrome." *Psychosomatics*, 20,9, 612-625, 1979. *This article discusses the symptoms, diagnosis, and treatment of the hyperventilation syndrome, including its more subtle symptoms.*

GOLDENSOHN, E. "Role of respiratory mechanism." *Psychosomatic Medicine*, 17, 377-382, 1955. *This article identifies the areas of the brain that contribute to the regulation of our breathing, and briefly discusses their involvement in emotional behaviors and other reactions. This article is recommended for the reader who is already familiar with some neuroanatomy.*

LUM, L. "The syndrome of habitual chronic hyperventilation." In: *Modern Trends in Psychosomatic Medicine, Volume 3*, edited by Hill, O. Boston: Butterworths, 1976, pp 196-230. *This is an excellent article discussing the causes of hyperventilation, the effects of hyperventilation on bodily and psychological processes, and the treatment of the hyperventilation syndrome.*

STEVENSON, I. and RIPLEY, H. "Variations in respiration and in respiratory symptoms during changes in emotion." *Psychosomatic Medicine*, 14, 476-490, 1952. *This article discusses evidence that emotional states such as anxiety, resentment, sadness, and dejection affect a person's rate of breathing and breathing patterns.*

Sensory Stimuli: The Clinical Reality

Medical Disorder: Conversion Reactions

Read this "overture" carefully before you read Chapter 6. The connections between the medical reality of conversion reactions and the basic underlying physiological and psychological processes that regulate normal sensory functions are developed in this chapter. (For more information on conversion reactions, see McHugh, 1982; Lazare, 1981; Jones, 1980; Merskey, 1979; Weintraub, 1978; Theodor and Mandelcorn, 1973.)

The person described as suffering a conversion reaction is one who subconsciously imitates the signs of a physical illness, often as the result of suggestion. The symptom must not have a physical basis, nor even be an organic problem triggered by emotional disturbances (see Chapter 7).

Conversion reactions can appear as specific sensory disorders (blindness, deafness, a lost sense of smell, a lost sense of touch, abnormal painful sensations), paralysis, impaired powers of voluntary movements, or as generalized symptoms (weakness, dizziness and indigestion). These symptoms are generally associated with some sort of "payoff" for the individual; that is, they are often used, subconsciously, as a way to gain some end—whether it is attention and sympathy, the avoidance of an intensely distressing situation, or monetary compensation. The symptoms often have some symbolic meaning for the person, who—it is important to recognize—does not experience the disorder as psychological but as a "true" illness with an organic cause.

Diagnosis of conversion reactions is often quite difficult. Close examination will usually reveal that the symptoms are not in conformity with what is known of the anatomy, physiology, and psychophysics of an illness. This close examination of physical symptoms is very important because it is essential to establish positive evidence of conversion rather than basing the diagnosis on exclusion (where the diagnosis is based solely on the fact that all other possibilities have been rejected). The personality of the patient may give some indication, although many investigators believe that there is no stereotyped personality associated with conversion reactions. Those who do see a "type" have suggested that the typical patient is likely to be vain, self-indulgent, exhibitionistic, dramatic, emotionally labile, and attention-seeking. Others believe that such patients express a "hysterical" personality, characterized by a dramatic expression and appearance, an ability to play the role of others, suggestibility, a previous history of conversion symptoms, sexual problems, and psychiatric symptoms such as phobias, depression, and chemical dependence. ("Hysteria" is a term also used to describe the kinds of psychological and "physical" disorders typically involved in conversion reactions.)

Sensory disturbances are among the most dramatic symptoms associated with conversion reactions. Such symptoms can involve a loss of sensation over one area of the body, and even blindness or deafness. As just mentioned, the loss of sensation over one area of the body often does not conform with known patterns that would be evident were there a true neurological disorder. In addition, the pattern of the defect will often change from one examination to another, and be subject to suggestion. In some cases, it is possible to demonstrate sensation in the affected area when the patient is asleep.

Visual difficulties vary from blurred vision to total blindness. Some patients report tunnel vision, others report blindness in one eye. Although all of these symptoms can be due to organic illness, careful testing will usually show whether or not the visual impairment is based on optical, physiological, or psychophysical principles. In many cases of conversion, the patient reports seeing something that would not be visible if the defect were organic. (For a concise example, see Theodor and Mandelcorn, 1973).

Deafness is a less frequent symptom of conversion reactions than blindness. Because hysterical deafness disappears during sleep, one means of verifying the diagnosis is to startle the sleeping patient with a loud noise.

If possible, diagnosis and treatment should occur promptly because symptoms can solidify when hospitalization and testing continue over time. Furthermore, the longer the symptoms persist, the more difficult they are to remove. Treatment consists of careful exploration of the physical symptoms to eliminate organic causes; once it has been established that the symptoms represent a conversion reaction, it is of utmost importance to deal with the psychological conflicts or the distressing situation, and to ascertain the nature of the "payoff." To succeed, the physician and/or therapist must have an empathetic attitude and a strongly held belief that the patient can be cured. It is not useful for the therapist (nor the family or friends) to express attitudes of disdain—insisting that the person is "faking it," or that it is "just in the mind." Rather, the emotional state and the life of the individual should be examined carefully to determine what stressful situations—whether short- or long-lived—may have precipitated the symptoms. Once the nature of the psychological problems are understood, the client and therapist should strive together to help the client work through these problems; at the same time, the therapist needs to persistently persuade the patient to perform the functions which he or she claims are disabled.

In over half such cases, spontaneous symptomatic recovery occurs when the precipitating event was transient and the emotional intensity attached to it simply dissipates with time.

Sensory Stimuli

As discussed in Chapter 2, in addition to solid food, liquids, and air, sensory stimuli also qualify as food. Sensory stimuli consist of any and all agents capable of exciting the sense organs. Examples of sensory stimuli are light and sound waves, gravitational and accelerational forces, objects at temperatures either above or below that of the skin, and chemicals dissolved in the saliva of the mouth.

When activated, the sense organs send signals into the brain, giving rise to "sensations," "perceptions," or simply "information." These effects are complexly interrelated, and sharp distinctions among them cannot be made. For example, the baroreceptors and chemoreceptors of the carotid arteries and aorta are organs specifically sensitive to changes in blood pressure and oxygen content of the blood. When activated, these sense organs send signals to the brain and, as a result, changes occur in urine output, blood pressure, and the rate of breathing (see Chapters 4 and 5). These signals are not consciously "perceived," although the "information" is nevertheless received by the brain and dealt with "perceptively"—that is, the areas of the upper spinal cord receiving this information are able to discriminate among the different types of input.

On a more experiential level, the complexity of the relations among "sensations," "perceptions," and "information" can be demonstrated with an example of a visual experience. If you are sitting in a train that is stopped alongside another train, and the second train slowly starts to go forward, you will receive the *visual* "sensation" of movement. However, depending upon whether you assume that your train or the other train is standing still, you may "perceive" the second train to be moving forward or your own train to be moving backwards. One way of looking at this situation is to see "information about" and "sensation of" movement as independent of the "perception" of movement. Another way is to say that our "perception" of who is moving is what gives us the "sensation" of either sitting still or being the one in motion.

It is not the purpose of this book to explain such phenomena, which have challenged psychologists and philosophers for years and is best explained by them. The questions to be answered here are: What stimuli comprise this type of food? As foods, how are sensory stimuli "digested?" What is the effect of not receiving sensory stimulation? What are the senses and which are the sense organs? In what ways do psychology and physiology coexist to produce our sensory experiences? Answers to these questions will provide the body of knowledge that is necessary for any subsequent formulations of how we perceive and sense ourselves and the external world.

I. SENSORY STIMULI AND THEIR USE BY THE BODY

The Sense Organs

In addition to the classical five senses—sight, hearing, smell, taste, and touch—are many more: equilibrium and balance, temperature, pain, stretch, pressure, and our sense of limb position and movement. Each of our senses is served by one or more specialized receptors, called **sense organs**. The sense organs are exquisitely adapted to respond to specific sensory stimuli. For example, the rods in the retina of our eyes are so sensitive that they respond to just one quantum of light—the least possible amount of energy that can be delivered by light. If the cochlea of the inner ear were any more sensitive, we would hear the sounds of molecules randomly hitting the eardrum. The active ingredient in garlic can be smelled in concentrations of less than one billionth of a gram per liter of air. The hair on our skin sets off touch receptors at the slightest pressures. Some pressure receptors are so sensitive that they respond to deformations of less than one five thousandths of a millimeter (less than eight millionths of an inch).

Receptors will respond to stimuli other than those to which they are most sensitive, but the thresholds for these responses are much higher. For example, pressure on the eyeball will excite visual receptors, but the energy required is much greater than what is needed when visual receptors are excited by light or when touch receptors are excited by pressure. Even though free nerve endings (see below) are the sense organs for three different senses—cold, warmth, and pain—these receptors also appear to be adapted to specific stimuli. Cold, for example, will stimulate one nerve ending, warmth will stimulate another, and extreme warmth or cold will stimulate a third nerve ending that elicits pain. The fact that any given receptor system will respond to one stimulus over another is the basis for the term **adequate stimulus**. The adequate stimulus for visual receptors is light and for auditory receptors, sound.

Figures 6-1 through 6-7 illustrate the many parts of each sense organ, collectively referred to as an "apparatus." The visual apparatus, Figure 6-1, consists of transparent tissues and fluids that allow light to pass through until it strikes the retina. The iris controls the amount of light that enters the eye. The muscles of the iris change its size to make the opening, called the pupil, either larger or smaller. The lens focuses the image on the retina. The retina contains specialized photoreceptors, called "rods" and "cones," that respond to light and convert its energy into neural activity. This activity eventually leads to neural impulses that are propagated into the brain via the optic nerve. The central part of the retina, called the fovea, is the area that gives us the clearest vision when light hits it. (The conversion of energy contained in the sensory

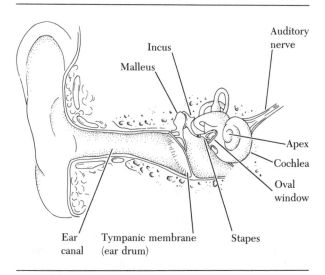

Figure 6–2. The auditory apparatus: the ear, ear canal, middle ear, and cochlea.

stimulus—in this case, light—into neural impulses is discussed in the next section.)

The auditory apparatus, illustrated in Figure 6-2, consists of the ear, ear canal, middle ear, and cochlea. The middle ear contains three tiny bones, called the malleus, incus, and stapes. When sound waves strike the tympanic membrane (the ear drum), this membrane moves with each vibration of the sound wave, and this movement is transferred to the oval window of the cochlea by way of these bones. As the oval window moves, special cells within the cochlea become activated; this activity triggers neural impulses that are propagated into the brain via the auditory nerve.

The vestibular apparatus illustrated in Figure 6-3 is responsible for much of the neural activity that controls our perception of motion, balance, equilibrium, and our position in space—collectively referred to as the vestibular senses. Gravitational forces and forces induced by movement of the head cause specialized cells within this apparatus to become active. Within the inner ear, the semicircular canals, the ampullae (plural of ampulla), the utricle, and the saccule contain these special cells. The activity of these cells triggers neural impulses that are propagated into the brain via the vestibular nerve. (The conversion of the energy of motion and the energy of gravitational forces into neural impulses is covered in the next section.)

The olfactory (smell) apparatus is illustrated in Figure 6-4. This apparatus consists of the nose, nasal cavity, and the olfactory epithelium. The olfactory

Figure 6–1. The visual apparatus: the cornea, iris, lens, and retina.

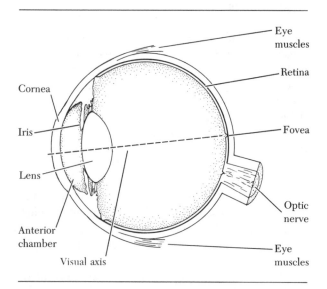

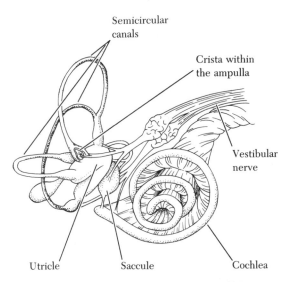

Figure 6–3. The vestibular apparatus: the semicircular canals, utricle, and saccule of the inner ear.

Figure 6–4. The olfactory apparatus: the nose, nasal cavity, olfactory epithelium (a mucous membrane), and olfactory cells.

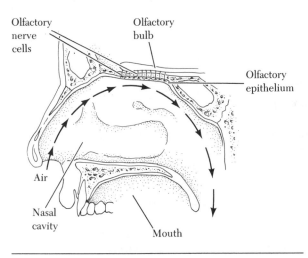

epithelium is a mucous membrane containing special cells that respond to chemicals that come into contact with it. In turn, the activity of these cells triggers neural impulses that are propagated into the brain via the olfactory nerves. As shown in this figure, the olfactory nerves travel only a short distance before they enter the olfactory bulb, a structure that is part of the limbic system.

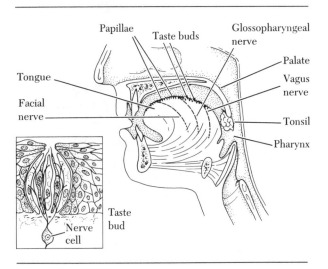

Figure 6–5. The taste apparatus: the surface of the tongue, the palate (roof of the mouth), tonsils, and pharynx. These tissues contain taste buds—special cells that respond to chemicals.

Taste is served by special cells, called taste buds, that are on the surface of the tongue and in the palate (roof of the mouth), tonsils, and pharynx. Collectively these make up the taste apparatus illustrated in Figure 6-5. Activation of the taste buds triggers neural activity that is propagated into the brain via several nerves, as indicated in this figure.

Sensations of pressure, temperature, and pain are served by organs dispersed throughout the body. It is the skin, however, that contains the greatest number of these organs and the most diverse types. For this reason, Figure 6-6, which illustrates the touch-pressure apparatus, also identifies the sense organs found in the skin. The touch-pressure apparatus is made up of many types of specialized receptors. (Touch is actually the result of very light pressure applied to the skin and is therefore a sensation of light pressure.) When pressure is applied, one or another of these receptors is activated, which then triggers neural impulses that are propagated into the brain. Hairless skin, like the skin of the fingertips, palms and lips, contains all of these receptors (except those around hair); it is therefore extremely sensitive to touch and pressure. Hairy skin is not as sensitive as hairless skin, although it contains many free nerve endings that respond to pressure, as well as hair end-organs that respond to pressure exerted against hair. As can be seen in Figure 6-6, free nerve endings are fine, branched endings of nerve cells that are not associated with hair follicles or any other specialized

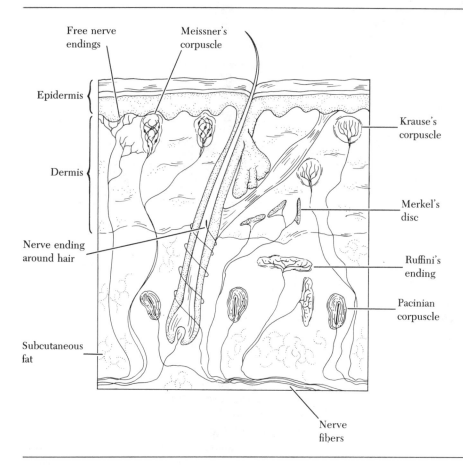

Figure 6–6. Sensory receptors in the skin: the touch-pressure, temperature, and pain apparatuses.

The touch-pressure apparatus: Meissner's corpuscles, free nerve endings, Pacinian corpuscles, Merkel's discs, Ruffini corpuscles, and Krause's corpuscles.

The temperature apparatus: temperature-sensitive receptors in the skin, probably free nerve endings.

The pain apparatus: free nerve endings distributed in the skin and, to a greater or lesser extent, in all of the deep tissues of the body.

receptor; it is for this reason they are called "free." Other nerve endings are contained in specialized organs—in the case of skin, Pacinian corpuscles, Meissner's corpuscles, Krause's corpuscles, Ruffini's endings, and Merkel's discs.

All free nerve endings do not respond to the same sensory stimuli. Those mentioned above respond to pressure in hairless and hairy skin, but others respond to temperature and/or pain. The temperature apparatus consists of temperature-sensitive receptors —probably free nerve endings—that respond to

warmth or cold. When the temperature surrounding these receptors goes up (warmth receptors) or down (cold receptors), it activates nerve cells and thus triggers the neural impulses that are then propagated into the brain. The pain apparatus consists of free nerve endings that respond to excessive compression or deformation of tissue, extreme warmth or cold, tissue damage, and other stimuli. These free nerve endings are distributed in the skin and, to a greater or lesser extent, in all of the deep tissues of the body.

The vestibular apparatus is not the only apparatus

that gives us a sense of our body in space. Other sense organs in the muscles, tendons, and joints respond to movement and pressure and give us a sense of movement and position of our body and its limbs (see Figure 6-7). When we move our limbs, when muscle contracts or relaxes, or when there is pressure exerted on muscles or joints, sense organs, especially in the joints, are activated and convey information to the brain about limb position. In addition, free nerve endings in the joints and muscles also act as pain receptors and sometimes as temperature receptors. Muscle spindles, also illustrated in the figure, are specialized sense organs that participate in regulating the neural activity that controls muscle contraction. Muscle contraction is discussed in Chapter 9, which covers muscles and movement.

The many sense organs we have just described are extremely diverse in their structure, adapted to be especially sensitive to one or another stimulus. The energy of the sensory stimulus is always used to pro-

Figure 6–7. Sensory receptors in the muscles and joints: pressure, pain, and temperature apparatuses

Joint receptors: Ruffini endings, free nerve endings, and Pacinian corpuscles. The free nerve endings are pain and temperature receptors, and the Ruffini and Pacinian corpuscles are pressure receptors.

Muscle receptors: Golgi tendon organs, muscle spindles, and free nerve endings. The free nerve endings are pain receptors. The Golgi tendon organs and muscle spindles help regulate the contraction of muscle. (Muscle contraction is discussed in Chapter 9.)

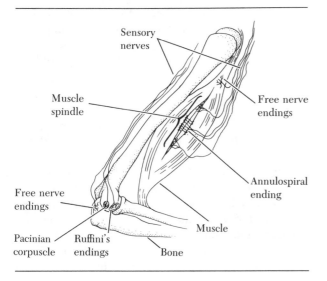

duce neural impulses that are propagated into the brain. This process is discussed below.

Use of Stimulus Energy to Produce Neural Impulses

Our sensory receptors are constantly excited by sensory stimuli. There are many sensory stimuli, all different from each other. For example, the sensory stimulus for vision is light. For hearing it is sound waves. For the vestibular apparatus it is gravity and accelerational or decelerational forces, usually induced by motion of the head. For smell and taste it is chemicals, either vaporized in air (smell) or dissolved in the fluids of the mouth (taste). For temperature it is the amount of heat in the environment surrounding the body, and for touch and pressure it is anything that mechanically displaces the skin or the internal organs. There are many stimuli that elicit pain, most associated with damage to tissue. Burns, ischemia (lack of oxygen), distention of internal organs, stretching of the arteries, inflammation, lacerations, fractures, pinching of tisssue, prolonged muscle tension are all stimuli that elicit pain.

Each sensory stimulus contains *energy* that is used by the sense organs to produce **electrochemical activity**. In turn, the electrochemical activity triggers the neural impulses that are propagated into the brain. (The electrical activity of all nerve cells is actually the result of chemical processes; hence the term "electrochemical" applies to neural activity within the brain as well as within the sense organs.) In other words, the energy contained in the sensory stimulus is eventually linked with chemical processes, processes that are then associated with, and responsible for, the neural impulses that are then propagated into the brain. The sense organs are therefore digestive organs because, as discussed in Chapter 2, "digestion" is defined as the *entire* process through which foods—in this case, sensory stimuli—are treated so that the body can use them. As digestive organs, the sense organs are specifically adapted to receive the energy contained in one or another sensory stimulus and to produce electrochemical activity that can then be used by the brain.

The energy of light is contained in electromagnetic radiation with a frequency ranging from 380 to 760 millimicrons (the visible spectrum). As light strikes the retina, its energy changes the shape of a portion of a special molecule found in the photoreceptors of the retina. This changed shape then initiates a series of chemical reactions that produces the electrochemical activity responsible for neural impulses that are propagated into the brain from the eyes.

The energy of sound waves is contained in mechanical vibrations, usually of air molecules (but also of fluids and solids). These vibrations range from 16 to 20,000 cycles per second (the auditory spectrum). When the vibrating air molecules strike the eardrum, they cause it to vibrate at the same frequency as the air molecules. This vibration is then transferred to the oval window of the cochlea. In turn, vibration of the oval window causes the fluid inside the cochlea to compress, and this displaces a membrane within the cochlea. As this membrane is displaced, special hair cells within the cochlea are deformed. This deformation produces electrochemical activity responsible for initiating neural impulses that are propagated into the brain from the ears.

Gravity causes otoconia (calcium carbonate crystals) to exert pressure on special hair cells in the utricle and saccule of the inner ear. This phenomenon occurs at all times, whether the body is still or moving, and the resulting deformation of the hair cells produces electrochemical reactions. In addition, whenever the head moves, the energy contained in the accelerational or decelerational forces induced by this movement causes fluid to move in the semicircular canals, and this movement exerts pressure on the cristae within the ampullae (see Figure 6-3). In turn, hair cells embedded within the cristae begin to move, again producing electrochemical activity.

For the olfactory apparatus and the taste apparatus, the precise form of energy used to produce electrochemical activity in the taste buds (taste) or in the olfactory epithelium (smell), is not known. It is surmised that the molecules responsible for sensations of taste and smell come into contact with the appropriate receptors and then, perhaps according to their shape, their ability to form some kind of weak bond with the receptors, or their vibration, the molecules above are used by these receptors to produce electrochemical activity.

The energy of pressure is contained in the mechanical force required to deform the sense organ. The energy of temperature is thermal. The energy of pain is chemical, mechanical or thermal, depending upon the circumstance. In each case, this energy is used by one or another sense organ to produce electrochemical activity, sometimes because of mechanical deformation (pressure and touch receptors), sometimes because of heat (temperature receptors), and sometimes because of chemicals that act on these receptors (pain receptors—although these

receptors are also sensitive to excessive deformation and heat).

All of these electrochemical activities produce **graded electrical activity**; that is, the electrical activity of the sensory receptors slowly increases or decreases, depending upon the strength and quality of the sensory stimulus. For example, in the ear there are voltage changes produced by receptors in the cochlea, changes that are near-perfect electrical representations of the vibrations that caused it. In fact, if these voltage changes are fed into an audio amplifier, the original sounds of the stimulus are reproduced. In the eye, the intensity of the voltage changes produced by the rods and cones of the retina are proportional to the energy contained in the light the eye receives.

Neural Impulses into the Brain

For each sensory system, the graded electrical activity described above initiates neural impulses that are propagated along neurons to enter the lower spinal areas, the cerebral cortex, or any other areas of the brain. In contrast to the graded activities of the sensory receptors, *the neural impulse is not graded*—it is "all-or-none"; that is, a neuron produces either a full-sized impulse or no impulse at all. This all-or-none property means that all neurons transmitting signals from the sense organs must convey sensory information by *how often* neural impulses are propagated. A nerve cell's "rate of firing"—the number of neural impulses transmitted per unit time—is called its **firing frequency**.

Because the range of stimulus intensities and qualities to which the receptors respond is much greater than the neuron's range of firing frequencies, neural impulses generated from nerve cells must transmit sensory information in some codified manner. The manner whereby neural impulses are codified to reflect qualities of the sensory stimulus is called **coding**. There are two main ways in which this coding takes place:

1) TEMPORAL CODING. In most systems, the more intense the stimulus, the more rapid the neuron's *rate of firing*. This represents one type of temporal coding. Another has to do with the *pattern of firing*. For example, some visual neurons change their pattern of firing according to the position of the visual image on the retina. A neuron might show a burst of activity when it is excited by light applied to a spot on the retina. If the light is now moved to an adjacent area, this same neuron

will show a burst of "inactivity;" that is, it will stop firing. Other neurons will do the opposite—they will show a burst of activity when the light is moved away. These different patterns in the rate of firing, which represent temporal coding because they are based on the ability of a neuron to alter how often it propagates impulses, convey information about the location of the image on the retinal field.

2) SPATIAL CODING. Sensory pathways in the brain are *neural pathways* that are composed of thousands, even millions of neurons. The composite pattern of the activity of these neurons represents spatially-organized information because this type of coding relies on the anatomical distribution of neurons, usually organized to transmit neural activity from one region of the brain to another.

In general, neural pathways can be looked at as roads or highways, organized to accept traffic from various other roads that feed into it, or to allow traffic to leave and head for other locations. If we modernize the pathway to the status of a freeway, then each neuron can be looked at as a lane of the freeway (when it is long) or as a piece of the lane when it is short. (Some neural pathways are composed of long neurons, others are composed of many short neurons.) In this comparison, each car in a lane can be looked at as a neural impulse. When there is a great deal of traffic, all lanes are full. When there is little traffic, each lane may have only a few cars in it. If there are stop lights, there may be gaps in the traffic as it moves along; if dashed lines separate each lane, cars can move from one lane to another, and so forth. The result is a particular pattern of "traffic" flow that depends on the design of the highway and how the highway is being used by the cars travelling on it. In like manner, although each neuron may be able to fire only at a limited rate (just as each lane can accept only a limited number of cars), the composite rate can be much higher, or the composite pattern of these impulses can be much more diverse than is possible for a single neuron.

For example, in auditory pathways the composite rate can closely approximate the frequency of lower tones applied to the ear, even though each individual neuron in this pathway is firing at a much slower frequency. Similarly, as a pain stimulus becomes progressively more intense, more and more neurons are activated. As a result, there is an increase not only in the composite firing frequency of the nerves transmitting these pain signals, but also in the overall strength of the signal.

3) TOPOGRAPHIC CODING. This type of coding is really a special case of spatial coding. It is so important, however, that it is listed separately. Topographic coding refers to the fact that *only certain regions of the sense organs and the brain respond to a stimulus*. For example, in the cochlea, low tones stimulate the apical end (the tip), while high tones stimulate the basal end (closest to the oval window—see Figure 6-2). In other words, tones of different frequencies excite receptors and neurons located in different regions of the cochlea. Similarly, in the eye, the location of each part of the environment that makes up the image has a corresponding location on the retina. If one is looking at a checker board, for example, each dark square and each light square is cast on a different region of the retina, each exciting different visual receptors and neurons at an intensity that is proportional to the intensity of light coming from that square. Again, different regions of the tongue respond to different tastes. The sensation of sweetness is most intense when the sweet stimulus is placed on the tip of the tongue; bitterness is most intense when the stimulus is placed on the back of the tongue. Sourness receptors are along the edges, saltiness generally on the top of the tongue towards the front. Signals from touch, pressure, temperature, pain, and joint receptors are also specific to the region of the body affected by the stimulus. It is obvious that joint receptors activated by moving an arm will be located in *that* arm. Similarly, receptors in the skin are activated only when the stimulus affects the region in which they are located.

The topographic response of the sense organs and receptors is maintained within the pathways entering the brain, and within the brain itself. For example, one area of a group of nerve cells will contain impulses that represent excitation of receptors in the right upper part of the retinal field, whereas another will carry impulses from the left side of the retinal image. Similarly, as the impulses are propagated from the optic nerve into the brain on their way to visual cortex, topographic representation is maintained throughout (this topic will be covered in more detail in the section on the brain).

II. PHYSIOLOGICAL/PSYCHOLOGICAL INTERACTIONS

Nowhere is the integration of physiology and psychology as apparent as it is with the senses. There is not enough space to cover all aspects in this book, but we shall cover the basic interrelations in this section and broader aspects in following sections.

Coexistence and Inseparability of Physiology and Behavior

The fact that the sense organs, sensory receptors, and sensory stimuli operate the way they do has an enormous influence on our behavior. *We are constantly behaving in a manner that will maximize the ability of the sense organs to function optimally.* The following diagrams illustrate this with most of the sense organs. Figure 6-8 (below) is a simple example involving approach behavior and the intensity of sound. Because the ears are shaped to best funnel sound waves

Figure 6–8. Continuity of physiology and behavior related to the intensity of sound. Note how the location and shape of the ears is integrated with behaviors and corresponding physiological responses that affect our experiences of the intensity of sound. Boxed material represents processes subject to conscious experience.

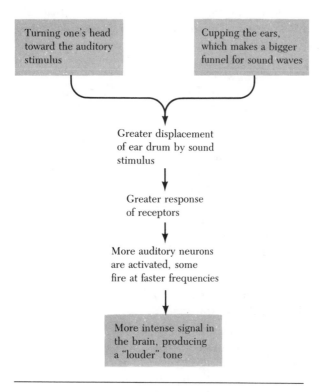

Property of sense organ: ears are located and shaped to best funnel sound waves from the front and side

Turning one's head toward the auditory stimulus

Cupping the ears, which makes a bigger funnel for sound waves

Greater displacement of ear drum by sound stimulus

Greater response of receptors

More auditory neurons are activated, some fire at faster frequencies

More intense signal in the brain, producing a "louder" tone

coming to the front and side of the head, we will turn our head toward the auditory stimulus and thereby increase the auditory signal in the brain. In addition, by cupping the ears, the funnel for sound waves becomes larger, again resulting in our perception of a louder tone.

Behavior that increases our ability to localize sounds in space is illustrated in Figure 6-9. As we turn our head, one ear is closer to the stimulus than the other. With low tones this maximizes phase differences between the two ears, causing the tone to displace the two ear drums at slightly different times. With high tones, the ear closest to the auditory stimulus will receive a more intense vibratory signal than the other ear, because the head is between the two ears and acts as a sound barrier for the ear farthest from the stimulus. The auditory receptors in the two ears therefore receive different signals, the difference being dependent on the position of the head relative to the source of the sound wave. The resulting differences in neural activity produced within the two ears are maintained in auditory pathways as neural impulses are propagated through the brain. These differences allow us to differentiate sounds according to their position in the auditory field. The behavior involved in localizing sounds is largely reflexive—happily so, for anyone who has worn a "collar" that prevents rotation of the head knows how bothersome it is to have to rotate the entire body to place a sound.

Another simple example, illustrated in Figure 6-10, involves touch, pressure, and joint receptors. In order to function, these receptors must be mechanically stimulated. Again, we activate their response through various behaviors—by touching or squeezing an object, for example, or by moving our limbs.

Two other examples, presented in Figures 6-11 and 6-12, involve taste and temperature sensations. Figure 6-11 illustrates the process of approaching food, putting it into our mouth, chewing it, and mixing it with the mouth's fluids in order to dissolve it (and give taste receptors maximal stimulation).

We also use behavior to gain information about the temperature of an object. Unless the object is very hot or very cold, we will not be able to perceive its temperature from a distance because the radiation of heat from it to us (if it is hot), or from us to it (if it is cold) is not intense enough to affect the temperature of our skin and its temperature receptors. Thus we will touch an object directly, or put our toes in the water to "see" how cold or warm it is. Also, as illustrated in Figure 6-12, we often touch an object to determine whether it is metal or plastic. If it is metal,

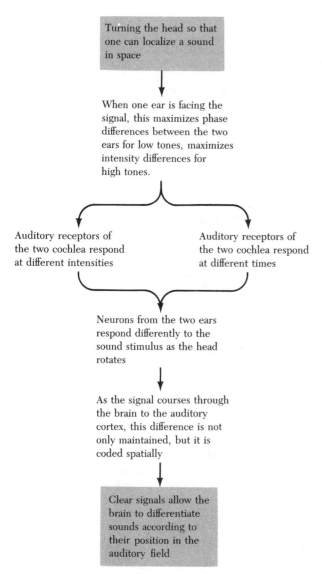

Property of sense organ: we have two ears, one on each side of the head

Turning the head so that one can localize a sound in space

When one ear is facing the signal, this maximizes phase differences between the two ears for low tones, maximizes intensity differences for high tones.

Auditory receptors of the two cochlea respond at different intensities

Auditory receptors of the two cochlea respond at different times

Neurons from the two ears respond differently to the sound stimulus as the head rotates

As the signal courses through the brain to the auditory cortex, this difference is not only maintained, but it is coded spatially

Clear signals allow the brain to differentiate sounds according to their position in the auditory field

Figure 6–9. Continuity of physiology and behavior related to the localization of sound. Note how the location of the ears is integrated with the behavior of rotating the head, a behavior which activates physiological mechanisms that affect our experiences of locating sounds in space. Boxed material represents processes subject to conscious experience.

heat will be quickly transferred to it from the skin, cooling the skin down (skin temperature is approximately 37° C, or 98.6° F, in contrast to room temperature, which is usually between 15.5 and 21° C, or 60 to 70° F). If it is plastic, the skin will not cool quickly because plastic is a poor conductor of heat.

Another property that is shared by all the senses is called **adaptation**. Adaptation refers to the fact that if a stimulus is applied, the response of the sensory receptors and neurons they serve is much stronger *at first;* after a short period of time the response is *less* even though the intensity of the stimulus has not changed. The properties of adaptation in each sensory system vary with the individual properties of each receptor and its neural connections. For example, touch receptors around hair, and Pacinian corpuscles —the pressure receptors that lie beneath the skin and also in tissues within the body (see Figure 6-6)— adapt completely (to "extinction") within a second; that is, although the pressure stimulus is still being applied, there is no longer a response in the sensory nerves.

Meissner's corpuscles (also illustrated in Figure 6-6) are pressure receptors that are particularly abundant in the fingertips, lips, and other areas of the skin where our ability to discriminate touch sensations is highly developed. These also adapt very quickly. Merkel's discs, pressure receptors that are found in all areas of the skin, adapt quickly at first, but after a prolonged period they are still responsive to the stimulus although only about half as much as initially. Other receptors adapt very slowly—such as Ruffini's endings in the skin, in the joints, and in other tissues in the body; vestibular receptors in the inner ear; pain endings; chemoreceptors in the carotid bodies, and baroreceptors in the walls of the carotid arteries and aorta. Thus, after a prolonged period they are still almost fully responsive to the stimulus.

Sound receptors in the ear also adapt very slowly, yet we will often cease hearing a repetitive tone after a short period of time. This reduced response does not occur solely because of the auditory receptors in the ear, but also because of activities occurring in the brain. This reduction in the sensory signal within the brain is called **habituation**. Although habituation occurs with all the senses, some are affected more than others. For example, there is very little habituation to pain, while there is a great deal of habituation to auditory signals, especially if they are repetitive. Mechanisms of habituation are discussed in more detail in Chapter 8, where we discuss a number of processes involved in *attention*. For now, we merely

Property of sense organ:
touch and pressure receptors
in the skin and joints must
be mechanically stimulated
in order to function

Property of sense organ:
a substance must be dissolved
in the fluids of the mouth
in order to activate taste
receptors

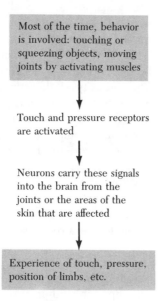

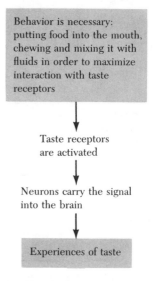

Figure 6–10. Continuity of physiology and behavior related to touch, pressure, and joint sensations. Note how the need to mechanically stimulate touch and pressure receptors is integrated with behaviors and corresponding physiological responses that affect our experiences of touch, pressure, and the position of our limbs.

Figure 6–11. Continuity of physiology and behavior related to sensations of taste. Note how the need to stimulate taste receptors is integrated with behaviors such as putting food into the mouth and chewing, both of which activate physiological responses that affect our experiences of taste.

wish to note that habituation is not the result of adaptation of receptors or receptor fatigue, but is one of a constellation of processes occurring in the brain.

Sensory systems serving taste, and olfactory receptors also show a rapid reduction in response to repetitive stimuli. In this case, although part of the reduction is due to decreased responsiveness of taste buds and olfactory cells (adaptation), at least half of the reduction is due to habituation mechanisms occurring within the brain. Similarly, reduced responsiveness to a constant visual stimulus is also a combined result of biochemical changes in the rods and cones of the retina, neural changes in the retina, and mechanisms of habituation occurring within the brain.

These two properties—the adaptation of the sense organs to a repetitive sensory stimulus and the further reduction the brain accomplishes through habituation

—are also connected to our behavior. As with previous examples, these behaviors we use are generally quite "automatic." We seldom stop to analyze the how and why of our actions—they simply work. For example, as illustrated in Figure 6-13, when we eat something we don't like whole and without interruption, without stopping, there will be maximal adaptation by the taste receptors in the mouth—in other words, a reduced sensation of taste. Conversely, if we wish to prolong the taste of something we like, we will often chew slowly and pause between mouthfuls—perhaps drinking liquid or switching to some other food; in this way, the taste receptors have very little chance to adapt, and little or no habituation of the taste signal will occur in the brain.

Another example involves the way we use our hands to determine the shape and texture of an object. The pressure receptors in the hands that are responsible for fine touch discrimination adapt very quickly. As a result, we must constantly move our fingers over an object, or roll it in our hands, in order to offset the blunting of sensations that would otherwise occur. This process is illustrated in Figure 6-14.

Figure 6-15 illustrates behaviors that heighten or reduce sensations of smell. Most sensory stimuli can be avoided easily; this is not the case with audition (hearing) and olfaction (smell). We cannot close "ear

Figure 6–12. Continuity of physiology and behavior related to the perception of objects through temperature sensations. The temperature of many objects in our environment does not differ sufficiently from skin temperature to activate temperature receptors in the skin unless we touch them. Note how this property of temperature sensation is integrated with behaviors that allow our skin to come close to, or touch, objects. In this example the perception that an object is made of plastic is not because it is warmer than metal, but because it does not feel cool. (The metal and plastic are both at room temperature, which is cooler than body temperature.)

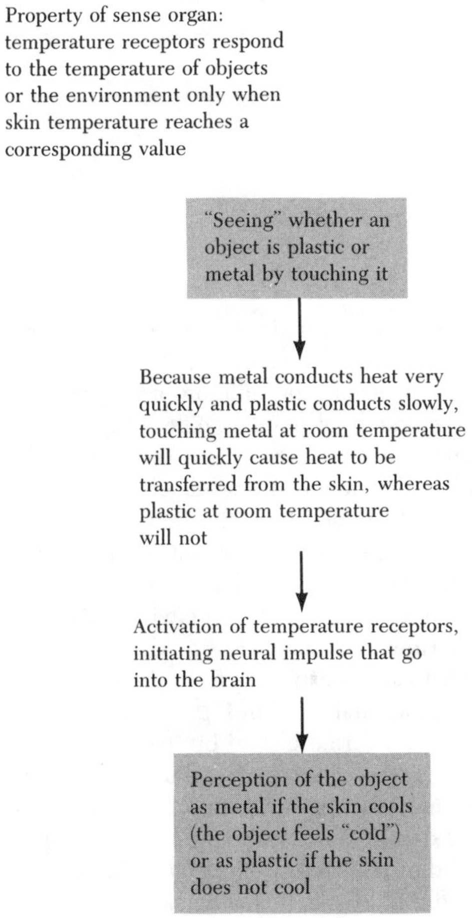

Property of sense organ: temperature receptors respond to the temperature of objects or the environment only when skin temperature reaches a corresponding value

"Seeing" whether an object is plastic or metal by touching it

↓

Because metal conducts heat very quickly and plastic conducts slowly, touching metal at room temperature will quickly cause heat to be transferred from the skin, whereas plastic at room temperature will not

↓

Activation of temperature receptors, initiating neural impulse that go into the brain

↓

Perception of the object as metal if the skin cools (the object feels "cold") or as plastic if the skin does not cool

lids" nor can we prevent aeration of the olfactory mucosa by not breathing. We can minimize stimulation of the olfactory receptors by pinching our nose, and reduce aeration of the olfactory epithelium by breathing through the mouth. Under some circumstances, we can avoid an olfactory stimulus by not getting too close to it. If we must stay in the vicinity of the olfactory stimulus and the situation makes it inappropriate to pinch our nose, we will find within a few minutes that our sensitivity to the unpleasant odor has decreased considerably—again, because of adaptation. Within a short period of time after that, we are likely not to notice it at all because neural mechanisms in the brain will have caused almost complete habituation to the stimulus. Conversely, as indicated in Figure 6-15, when we wish to heighten sensations of smell we can approach the olfactory stimulus more closely. In some cases, we can put our head very close to it and sniff, a behavior that increases aeration of the olfactory epithelium and allows more molecules to come in contact with olfactory receptors.

The intricacy of physiological and behavioral aspects of sensory awareness is particularly striking when it comes to vision. Figure 6-16 notes various physiological properties of the eye as they correlate with numerous behaviors, all designed to deliver a clear, sharp visual image (visual acuity). The area around the fovea, the "macula," contains photoreceptors that respond differentially to the slightest variations in the visual image, and it is this area of the retina that gives us the most detail. In terms of our behavior, we enhance this capability by turning our head and moving our eyes to face the visual stimulus and receive an image on the macula. In addition, because the photoreceptors in the macula require bright light in order to function well, we will turn on lights, or move to a light room or to a window so that these photoreceptors can function optimally.

Another compensation our body makes for insufficient light is to dilate the pupils to increase the amount of light entering the eye. There is a limit to this dilation, however, and, consequently, to the degree we can expect to increase the amount of light. (Remember, our eyes cannot make the light stimulus itself brighter.) Light that is too bright will also reduce the sharpness of our vision, in this case by depleting the cones of their photosensitive chemicals. (When light strikes these photochemicals, a series of chemical reactions are initiated that changes the structure of these molecules. To respond again to light, these molecules must first be reconverted to their original structure.) If the "automatic" constriction of the pupils is not sufficient to reduce the

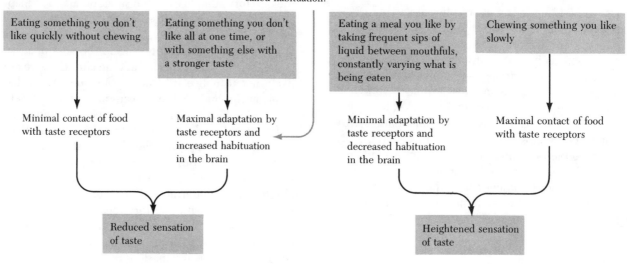

Property of sense organ: when a substance activates taste receptors, these receptors respond strongly for a few seconds, then continue to respond less powerfully. This decrease in sensitivity is called adaptation.

For the first few seconds neural transmission is strong; then, because of adaptation, it is reduced. Through a process distinct from that of adaptation by receptors, the brain itself continues to reduce the signal; this process is called habituation.

Eating something you don't like quickly without chewing

Eating something you don't like all at one time, or with something else with a stronger taste

Eating a meal you like by taking frequent sips of liquid between mouthfuls, constantly varying what is being eaten

Chewing something you like slowly

Minimal contact of food with taste receptors

Maximal adaptation by taste receptors and increased habituation in the brain

Minimal adaptation by taste receptors and decreased habituation in the brain

Maximal contact of food with taste receptors

Reduced sensation of taste

Heightened sensation of taste

Figure 6–13. Continuity of physiology and behavior related to decreased or increased sensations of taste. Taste receptors **adapt** to a given substance quickly. In addition, the taste signal undergoes **habituation** within the brain. Note how these properties are integrated with behaviors and corresponding physiological responses that affect our experiences of taste.

amount of light, we will again correct the problem by our behavior, whether it means shading our eyes with our hands, wearing a hat, or squinting.

The lens of the eye is also needed for sharp vision. Under normal circumstances the lens changes its shape to keep the visual image focused on the retina. If the lens cannot change its shape enough, the image will not be focused on the retina and the resulting image will be blurry. Again, behavior is usually necessary to offset this limitation: moving closer or farther from the object, moving the object so that it is closer or farther from the eyes, or wearing glasses (corrective lenses).

Even though the brain is obviously involved in all sensory function, as we will see in the section that follows, some of the brain's workings are included in Figure 6-16 to illustrate its direct influence on our ability to visually discriminate detail. As the neural signal goes from the optic nerve (behind the eye) to the cerebral cortex, it becomes "sharpened"; that is,

neurons become increasingly selective in their responses, whether to color, movement, place of the image in the visual field, orientation of the stimulus (vertical, horizontal, or at some specific oblique angle) or to differences in the image as it is received in the two eyes. (For a review of these effects, see Hubel and Wiesel, 1979.) In addition, through mechanisms largely unknown, the brain is very much involved in regulating our ability to be selectively attentive to specific areas of the visual field. This visual clarity is based on discriminatory mechanisms that are much finer than what can be expected from the eye alone. These processes are italicized in Figure 6-16, again to emphasize the active role played by the brain.

The last diagram in this section illustrates a complex integration involving visual stimuli and the visual perception of depth. This example not only involves movement of the head, but also involves *prior experience*. The required learning usually takes place when we are very young—a point to be further discussed later in this chapter. As indicated in Figure 6-17, when we move our head, visual images move across the retina. If an object is close to us, its retinal image will move rapidly, if it is far away it will move slowly. Thus, when we move our head the speed of motion of the visual image serves as a gauge for determining how distant it is.

Figure 6–14. Continuity of physiology and behavior related to the perception of the form of an object through pressure, touch, and joint sensations. Receptors in the skin responsible for sensations of fine touch and pressure adapt almost completely (to "extinction"). Note how this property is associated with movement of the hands, a behavior which activates physiological processes that increase sensations of fine touch and pressure.

Property of sense organ: although all the senses, with the possible exception of pain, show adaptation, touch and pressure receptors adapt especially rapidly and completely

The ability to perceive something with one's hands (get the "feel" of it) is greatly enhanced by a constant movement of one's fingers over the object or by rolling the object in one's hands

Touch, pressure and joint receptors are activated; the constant movement counteracts the blunting of sensation caused by adaptation

Neural input into the brain

Perception of the form of the object—a combination of tactile qualities such as roughness, hardness, and sharpness (touch and pressure), and position qualities that assess the form of the object relative to the position of the fingers in space (joint receptors)

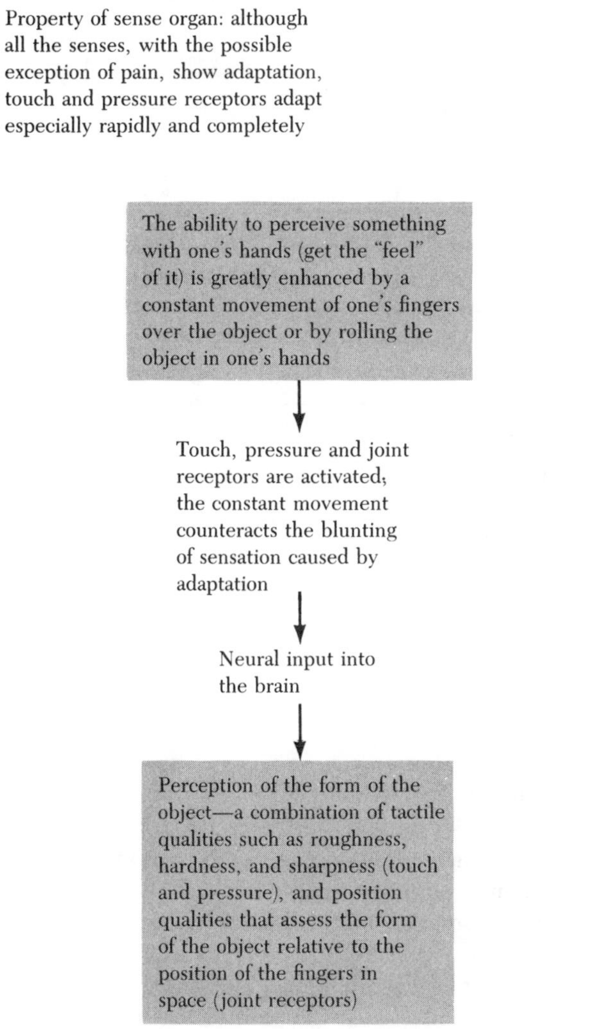

When the eyes are focused on an object, movement of the head allows us to perceive depth in an additional way: everything in front of the object will move in a direction opposite to the direction the head is moving, whereas everything behind the focused object will move in the same direction as our head is moving. (You can try this by holding both hands in front of your face, one hand in front of the other, with one finger of each hand pointed upwards. Now focus on the front finger and move your head to the right; the back finger will appear to move to the right. Now focus on the back finger and again move your head to the right; the front finger will appear to move to the left.) We can increase our depth perception, in other words, by moving our head, a behavior we often use to clearly perceive the distance of objects. These apparent movements of visual objects—called **motion parallax**—give us a tremendous amount of information about their distance from us.

In addition, we use prior experience, a process involving learning and memory. Through neural mechanisms that are still poorly understood, we have learned the size and shape of many objects. If anything is in front of an object, its shape will be incomplete; that is, part of its shape is obstructed by the closer object. From this we perceive the obstructed object to be behind the unobstructed object. Also, once we know the size of an object, we know automatically that when it appears small it is far away, when it appears large it is close.

The above examples make it amply clear that behavior and prior experience add a great deal to our visual perception of depth. It is important to realize that depth perception does not rely solely on the fact that we have two eyes—this accounts only for its stereoscopic aspects (see Figure 6-17). Stereoscopic depth perception greatly increases our ability to judge the relative distance of nearby objects, especially when the head is stationary. Yet while relative distance perception is reduced, people with one eye have as much ability as people with two eyes to use all the other mechanisms listed in Figure 6-17.

The Brain

In general, our sense organs are organized so that sensory stimuli directly affect the activity of the brain and have little direct influence on other organs of the body. Later in the chapter we will discuss some of the exceptions, but there is no doubt that sensory stimuli largely constitute the "food for the mind." As such, sensory input is needed not only to maintain normal

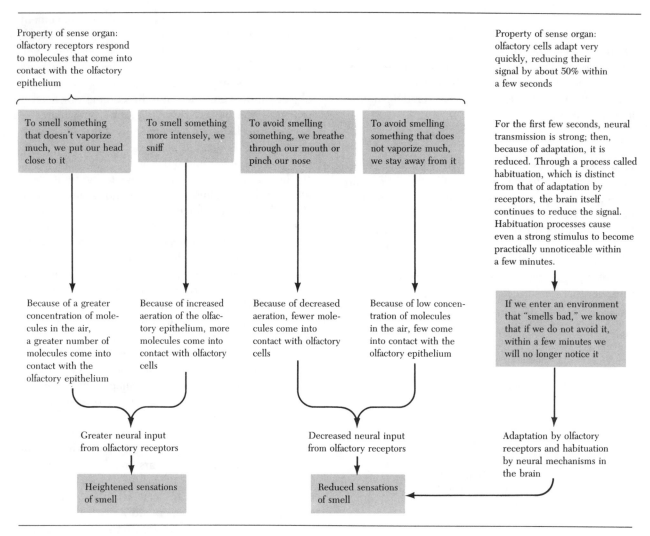

Property of sense organ: olfactory receptors respond to molecules that come into contact with the olfactory epithelium

To smell something that doesn't vaporize much, we put our head close to it

To smell something more intensely, we sniff

To avoid smelling something, we breathe through our mouth or pinch our nose

To avoid smelling something that does not vaporize much, we stay away from it

Because of a greater concentration of molecules in the air, a greater number of molecules come into contact with the olfactory epithelium

Because of increased aeration of the olfactory epithelium, more molecules come into contact with olfactory cells

Because of decreased aeration, fewer molecules come into contact with olfactory cells

Because of low concentration of molecules in the air, few come into contact with the olfactory epithelium

Greater neural input from olfactory receptors

Heightened sensations of smell

Decreased neural input from olfactory receptors

Reduced sensations of smell

Property of sense organ: olfactory cells adapt very quickly, reducing their signal by about 50% within a few seconds

For the first few seconds, neural transmission is strong; then, because of adaptation, it is reduced. Through a process called habituation, which is distinct from that of adaptation by receptors, the brain itself continues to reduce the signal. Habituation processes cause even a strong stimulus to become practically unnoticeable within a few minutes.

If we enter an environment that "smells bad," we know that if we do not avoid it, within a few minutes we will no longer notice it

Adaptation by olfactory receptors and habituation by neural mechanisms in the brain

Figure 6–15. Continuity of physiology and behavior related to the integration of approach and avoidance behaviors with sensations of smell. Olfactory receptors respond to molecules only when these molecules come into contact with the olfactory epithelium. In addition, olfactory receptors adapt very quickly, and the olfactory signal undergoes extensive habituation within the brain. Note how these properties are integrated with behaviors and corresponding physiological responses that affect our experiences of smell. Boxed material represents processes subject to conscious experience.

perceptual experiences of "reality," but also for normal growth and function of neurons within the brain, the development of normal perceptual skills (such as the ability to discriminate objects), and the development of language skills. Before discussing these processes, let's consider how the brain is specifically organized to serve the senses.

We are still far from having any complete understanding of how the brain contributes to our sensory experience. We do know that various regions of the brain are specialized with respect to the sense they serve. This knowledge has come from findings that localized damage—in one area of the cerebral cortex, for example—can cause blindness but not impair hearing or somatic sensations, such as pressure and touch. Similarly, damage in another area of the cerebral cortex will severely impair one's ability to localize sounds, but will have no ill effects on vision or somatic sensations. Finally, when still other areas of the cerebral cortex are damaged, fine touch and pressure

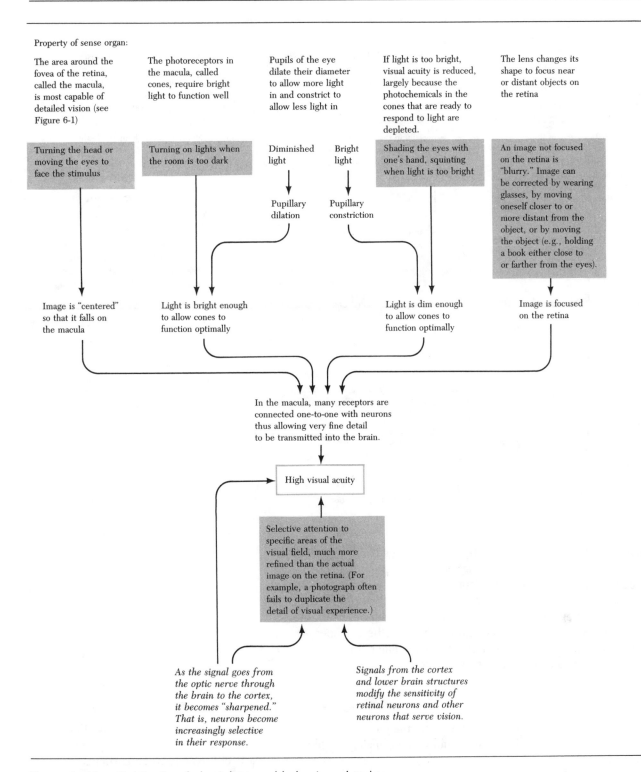

Property of sense organ:

The area around the fovea of the retina, called the macula, is most capable of detailed vision (see Figure 6-1)

The photoreceptors in the macula, called cones, require bright light to function well

Pupils of the eye dilate their diameter to allow more light in and constrict to allow less light in

If light is too bright, visual acuity is reduced, largely because the photochemicals in the cones that are ready to respond to light are depleted.

The lens changes its shape to focus near or distant objects on the retina

Turning the head or moving the eyes to face the stimulus

Turning on lights when the room is too dark

Diminished light

Bright light

Shading the eyes with one's hand, squinting when light is too bright

An image not focused on the retina is "blurry." Image can be corrected by wearing glasses, by moving oneself closer to or more distant from the object, or by moving the object (e.g., holding a book either close to or farther from the eyes).

Pupillary dilation

Pupillary constriction

Image is "centered" so that it falls on the macula

Light is bright enough to allow cones to function optimally

Light is dim enough to allow cones to function optimally

Image is focused on the retina

In the macula, many receptors are connected one-to-one with neurons thus allowing very fine detail to be transmitted into the brain.

High visual acuity

Selective attention to specific areas of the visual field, much more refined than the actual image on the retina. (For example, a photograph often fails to duplicate the detail of visual experience.)

As the signal goes from the optic nerve through the brain to the cortex, it becomes "sharpened." That is, neurons become increasingly selective in their response.

Signals from the cortex and lower brain structures modify the sensitivity of retinal neurons and other neurons that serve vision.

Figure 6–16. Continuity of physiology and behavior related to processes that affect sharpness of vision (visual acuity). Several different properties of the eye are listed. Note how these properties are integrated with behaviors and corresponding physiological responses that increase visual acuity. Visual acuity is also the result of processes occurring within the brain itself. This involvement of the brain is noted by the use of italic type.

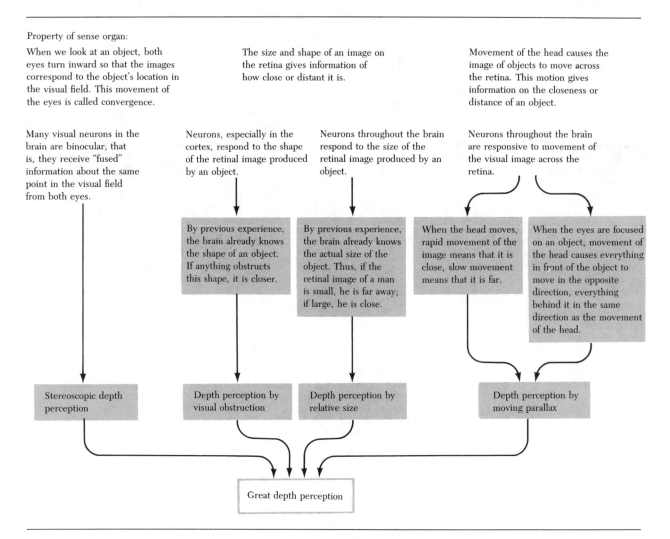

Figure 6–17. Continuity of physiology and behavior related to the visual perception of depth. Visual depth perception depends on the placement, size, shape, and motion of visual images as they are focused on the retinae of the eyes. Note how these properties of the image are integrated with the behavior of moving the head, the existence of neurons specialized to respond to these properties, and prior learning (previous experience). Boxed material represents processes subject to conscious experience.

sensations, and sensations we receive from the joints, are severely impaired, but hearing and vision remain normal.

As discussed in Chapters 1 and 3, the fact that damage in various regions of the brain leads to one or another impaired function is not, in itself, proof that the damaged region is uniquely involved in that function. However, when the results of brain damage are looked at in combination with other results, such as those obtained from electrical stimulation or electrical

recording, misinterpretation is less likely. For example, various somatic sensations are experienced to come from parts of the body when particular areas of the cerebral cortex are electrically stimulated, and these are the same areas of the cortex that, when damaged, result in impaired somatic sensations. Also, when a flash of light is presented to the eyes, electrical signals can be recorded from regions of the cortex that, when damaged, result in impaired vision. The flash of light will evoke electrical signals from other regions of the cortex as well, but these signals are less intense and appear later. Similarly, when clicks are presented to the ear, electrical signals are most immediate and intense when they are recorded from those regions of the cortex that, when damaged, result in impaired hearing.

There is much evidence of this kind, all pointing to the conclusion that areas of the brain are specialized in which senses they serve. How specialized these areas can be is seen most clearly from studies involving the activity of single nerve cells. When electrical recordings are made from single nerve cells, responses to various sensory stimuli can become extremely specific. In the region of the cortex that serves vision, some cells will respond to the color of the stimulus, some to its brightness, others to the location of the stimulus in the visual field, still others to the shape of the stimulus or whether the stimulus is moving or not. Many more cells within this region of the cortex respond to such visual cues than do cells in cortical areas serving other senses. Similarly, in the region of the cortex that serves audition, some will respond maximally to a tone of one particular frequency and others to tones of other frequencies.

Many regions of the brain that serve our senses are not only specialized in terms of which sense they serve, but also are *topographically organized*. That is, one cortical area that serves vision is largely devoted to neural input coming from the central part of our visual field, whereas other areas are more devoted to the visual field as it extends to the periphery. The cortical area that serves audition is also topographically organized. Here, the low tones, which principally stimulate auditory receptors located in just one part of the cochlea, evoke responses in nerve cells located primarily toward the anterior part of the auditory cortex (toward the front of the brain). Higher tones, which stimulate auditory receptors in a different part of the cochlea, evoke responses in nerve cells located more toward the posterior part (toward the back of the brain). Similarly, the somatic sensory cortex is organized so that each region is devoted more to one area of the body than to another.

These **topographic representations**—that is, these systematic, orderly representations within the brain of the receptor surfaces containing the sensory receptors (surfaces like the retina, the cochlea, the surface of the skin, and the "surface" defined by the muscles and the joints distributed over the body)—are undoubtedly a very important factor in the neurophysiology of sensation. For example, it is now clear that many regions contain topographic representations of the retina within the visual cortex, the cochlea in the auditory cortex, and the surface of the body in somatic

sensory cortex, and that these different, topographically organized areas, in a way not yet understood, appear to function together to contribute to our sensory experience (see Woolsey, 1981a, 1981b, 1982, for a detailed discussion).

The topographic representation of sensory receptors within the brain is not uniform. In general, *those parts of the body that give us the highest discriminatory ability also have the most brain area devoted to them.* For example, proportionately much more visual cortex is occupied by neurons that serve the central part of the retina—the part that gives us clear and precise visual information—than the far peripheral part. Similarly, the parts of our body that are most involved in furnishing us with precise somatic sensations are the parts that have the most area of somatic sensory cortex devoted to them. The lips, tongue, and throat, for example, have a disproportionately large number of cortical neurons devoted to them, as do the hands. In general, the number of nerve cells devoted to the face, arms, and hands is much greater than the number of cells devoted to the trunk.

In addition to these three ways in which the brain is organized to serve our sensory needs—a) containing regions that serve one sense organ but not another, b) containing within these regions topographic representations of the receptor fields as defined by the distribution of the sense organs, and c) giving those parts of the receptor field that have the highest discriminatory capabilities relatively more brain area than other parts—is one other critical feature: *The brain is organized to transmit sensory information to one or another region of the cortex, or to other structures of the brain, in well-defined neural pathways.*

Earlier, we mentioned that neural pathways are composed of many neurons, each pathway acting as a many-laned highway containing different patterns of traffic as it courses through the brain. This comparison, obviously, is a gross oversimplification, for neural pathways in the brain are tremendously intricate in their functioning. For example, the optic nerves, which transmit neural impulses generated in the eyes into the brain, consist of over a million nerve cells *each* of which is capable of propagating neural impulses at higher or lower frequencies, or in different temporal patterns, according to how they are activated. In turn, how these neurons are activated depends on the visual stimulus—whether the visual image on the retina is one or another color, whether it is moving or not, how bright it is, or how it influences other nerve cells in the retina that reduce or increase this cell's activity. In serving the senses, neural pathways such as the optic nerves connect the sense organs to various regions of the brain. One of these regions, the **thalamus**, is important not only because it receives signals from all of the sense organs, but also because it transmits a great deal of sensory information to other regions of the brain. Its role is discussed below.

The Thalamus.   As illustrated in Figure 6-18, the thalamus is situated in the middle of the brain, above the hypothalamus. The thalamus contains clusters of neurons, called "nuclei," "bodies," or "areas." These nuclei receive input from pathways that serve visual, auditory, touch, pressure, pain, temperature, taste, and joint sensations.

One nucleus of the thalamus, for example, called the **lateral geniculate body**, contains nerve cells that receive a large part of their input from neural impulses travelling in the *optic tract* (the optic nerves split after they enter the brain, and become the optic tracts as they go to the thalamus). Similarly, the **medial geniculate body** of the thalamus contains nerve cells that receive a large part of their input from neural impulses travelling in the *auditory tract*, a neural pathway that originates with the auditory nerve, coming from the cochlea of the ear. Another region of the thalamus, called the **ventral posterior nucleus**, receives neural input from pathways that serve touch, pressure, joint, temperature, and pain receptors. These receptors serve *somatic sensations*, so called because touch, pressure, pain, temperature, and sensations from the joints all come from receptors dispersed over or throughout the body. In addition, part of this nucleus receives neural input coming from taste receptors in the mouth.

As indicated in the brief explanation of thalamic function that accompanies Figure 6-18, the sense organs are represented topographically in the nuclei of the thalamus. In addition, the *thalamus appears to be directly responsible for some sensory experiences.* The perception of pain and temperature, as well as simple perceptions of tone, taste, touch, and pressure, continue when large areas of the cortex are damaged, provided the thalamus is left intact.

Aside from acting as a *receiving station* for neural input propagated along pathways that serve the sense organs, the thalamus acts as a *relay station* in that many of its cells send their axons to other parts of the brain, especially to the cerebral cortex. When neurons form a connection between one specific region, (in this case, the thalamus), and another region (the cortex, but it could be some other region), this connection is called a **projection** and the nerves are said to *project* from one region of the brain to another. Many nerve cells that originate in the lateral genicu-

late body project to the region of the cerebral cortex that serves vision. Similarly, nerve cells in the medial geniculate body project to the region of the cortex that serves audition. Many nerve cells in the ventral posterior nucleus of the thalamus project to regions of the cortex that serve somatic sensation, or, with taste, to those regions of the cortex that serve this sensation. The areas of the cortex that serve visual, auditory, somatic sensory, and gustatory (taste) sensations will be discussed in turn below. First, let's discuss the **primary olfactory area**.

The Primary Olfactory Area.   Olfaction (smell) also appears to be a sensory experience that does not require functioning of the cerebral cortex. In this case, however, most neurons serving olfaction don't enter the thalamus. As indicated in Figure 6-19, olfaction is represented in the **amygdala**, the **olfactory bulb**, the **olfactory tubercle**, the **prepiriform cortex**, and part of the **orbitofrontal cortex**. (For some comments on connections between the olfactory tract and the thalamus, see Giachetti and MacLeod, 1977.)

Extensive damage to the primary olfactory area can lessen an animal's ability to use olfactory stimuli for complex behaviors. In rats, for example, the ability to use olfactory stimuli for conditioned (learned) reflexes, and complex olfactory cues for finding food are impaired. Extensive damage, however, does not affect simple discriminatory abilities, nor does it affect responses such as eating, salivating, and licking when an olfactory stimulus is presented to the animal. Again, it is assumed that these abilities are maintained because of the numerous secondary connections—to the hypothalamus, thalamus, septum, hippocampus, and upper spinal cord—made by neurons serving olfaction.

Visual Cortex.   For vision, the nerve cells that comprise the optic nerves and optic tracts go to many areas of the brain, but a large fraction of them pass uninterrupted from the retina to the lateral geniculate body of the thalamus. In turn, neural impulses from the lateral geniculate body go to the **primary visual cortex**, located at the back of the brain. Most of the primary visual cortex lies along the medial surface of the brain, which is only visible when the brain is split in the middle (see Figure 6-19, areas 1 through 4). The primary visual cortex is organized topographically; note the disproportionately large area (area 1) devoted to the fovea of the retina, which, as noted earlier, serves detailed vision. (This area is also visible from the side of the brain, as illustrated in Figure 6-20.) The primary visual cortex appears to be responsible for the localization of images in the visual field.

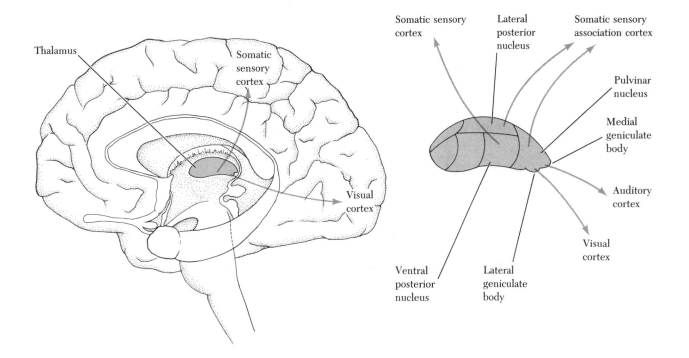

Vision: the lateral geniculate body receives neural input from the optic tract and projects it to primary visual cortex and visual association areas (see Figures 6-19 and 6-20). Within the thalamus, the retinal field is organized topographically, with a disproportionately large area devoted to the central part of the visual field.

Audition: the medial geniculate body receives neural input from the auditory tract and projects it to auditory cortex (see Figure 6-20).

Somatic sensation (touch, pressure, temperature, and pain) and taste: the ventral posterior nucleus receives neural input from touch, pressure, temperature, taste and pain receptors and projects it to somatic sensory cortex (see Figures 6-19 and 6-21). Within the thalamus, the body is represented topographically, with

disproportionately large areas devoted to the face and hands. The medial aspect of this nucleus receives input from taste receptors and projects it to an area that overlaps the somatic sensory representation of the tongue (see taste area, Figure 6-21).

The lateral posterior nucleus receives input, probably mostly somatic sensory, and projects it to somatic sensory association cortex in the parietal lobe (see somatic association cortex, Figure 6-21).

Many of the medial nuclei of the thalamus, not shown in the above illustration because they lie behind those nuclei that are drawn, have been shown to be involved with pain and, to a lesser extent, with temperature.

Vision, audition, and somatic sensation: the pulvinar nucleus receives sensory input and projects it to visual, auditory, and somatic association cortex in the parietal and temporal lobes (see Figures 6-20 and 6-21).

Figure 6–18.   Areas of the thalamus involved in sensory processes. This drawing is a medial view of the cerebral cortex and limbic system, showing a lateral view of the thalamus. In the figure to the left, arrows from the lateral geniculate body to visual cortex and from the ventral posterior nucleus to somatic sensory cortex indicate that nerve cells in various nuclei of the thalamus project to specific regions of the cerebral cortex. Other arrows could be drawn, as indicated in the figure to the right.

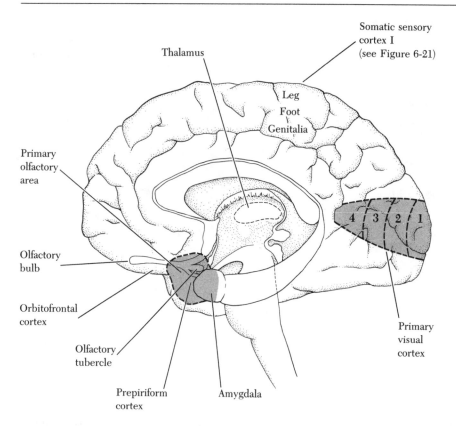

Primary olfactory area: includes the olfactory tubercle, prepiriform cortex, part of the orbitofrontal cortex, and amygdala. All of these areas are either part of the limbic system or are intimately connected to it.

Primary visual cortex: area 1 represents the central part of the visual field; areas 2 through 4 represent the retinal field as it extends to the periphery. The visual field is organized topographically, with a disproportionately large area devoted to the central part (area 1). Small areas of *damage* lead to spots of blindness in the visual field. Total *destruction* causes complete blindness to visual patterns, although the ability to detect crude differences in light intensity is maintained. *Stimulation* usually evokes unformed visual sensations, such as a flash of light or color.

Figure 6–19. Primary visual cortex (areas 1 through 4) and the primary olfactory area. Although the primary visual cortex is best seen from this medial view of the brain, much more visual cortex is seen from side views (see Figure 6–20).

Small areas of damage in the primary visual cortex lead to spots of blindness in the visual field, and total destruction causes complete blindness to visual patterns although the ability to detect crude differences in light intensity is maintained. Electrical stimulation of the primary visual cortex usually evokes unformed visual sensations, such as a flash of light or color. In itself, however, the primary visual cortex is not sufficient to give us detailed perception of shapes and forms. For this, the **visual association areas** are needed as well.

The term *association area* was originally created to denote the belief, prevalent in the early 1900s, that large areas of the cortex *associate* (connect) the primary sensory areas with the motor area. (The motor area is a region of the cortex that serves movement, as discussed in Chapter 9.) This view is no longer prevalent, but the term remains in use. Association areas are now known simply to be additional areas of cortex that further process sensory and other signals. As indicated in Figure 6-20, large areas of the cortex process visual information. The prestriate and parietal

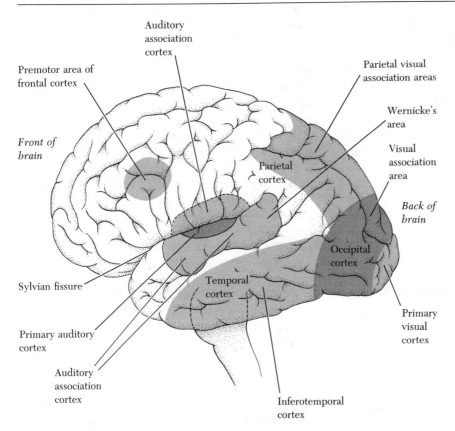

Figure 6–20. Lateral view of the cerebral cortex showing areas involved with vision and audition.

AUDITION

Primary auditory cortex: this area is topographically organized, with low tones represented in the anterior part (toward the front of the brain) and high tones in the posterior part (toward the back of the brain). *Damage* produces a severe loss of ability to localize sound in space, a loss that is more severe if auditory association cortex is also destroyed.

Auditory association cortex: this area includes a portion that extends into the insula and the parietal operculum; this portion can be seen only by spreading the Sylvian fissure (see Figure 7-13).

Wernicke's area: this area is usually dominant in the left hemisphere of the brain. *Damage* in Wernicke's area impairs one's ability to recognize words and other sounds uttered by oneself and other people; it also causes a loss in the ability to discriminate sounds that are phonetically close, such as "p" and "b" (see also Figure 6-22).

Both primary and auditory association cortex: *damage*, if complete or nearly so, greatly impairs one's ability to discriminate tonal patterns (e.g., high-low-high vs. low-high-low). Damage does not hinder one's ability to discriminate frequencies of simple tones or intensity of sound.

VISION

Primary visual cortex: see Figure 6-19 for comments on this area.

Visual association area: also called prestriate area. *Damage* leads to difficulty in perceiving shapes and forms. *Damage* greatly impairs one's ability to automatically "fixate" (keep one's eyes "locked" on an object); this area regulates "involuntary fixation." *Stimulation* sometimes evokes a visual image, such as a tree.

Parietal visual association areas: *damage* sometimes causes disruption of visual recognition of a familiar object, even though the parts that make up the object can be described.

Inferotemporal cortex: *damage* causes disruption of visual recognition and visual memory, and a deficit in one's ability to learn to discriminate among objects. *Stimulation* evokes visual images, sometimes of scenes perceived many years before.

Frontal cortex-premotor area: this area regulates "voluntary fixation." *Damage* greatly impairs one's ability to voluntarily fixate.

visual association areas and the **inferotemporal cortex**, for example, are necessary for complex perceptual experiences, such as detailed perception of shapes and forms, visual recognition, and visual memory. In addition, an area in the **frontal cortex** is involved with "voluntary fixation," which is the ability to voluntarily move one's eyes so that they are locked on an object, whereas visual association cortex is involved with "involuntary fixation"—the ability to automatically keep one's eyes locked on an object as it moves. Humans suffering from damage in one or another of these brain areas have visual disabilities consistent with the functions just described. Correspondingly, electrical stimulation of visual association cortex sometimes evokes a visual image, such as a tree, whereas stimulation of the inferotemporal cortex sometimes evokes images of scenes perceived many years before. Some visual information reaches the visual association cortex from the primary visual cortex, but the association areas also receive input directly from the thalamus (see comments on the pulvinar nucleus of the thalamus, Figure 6-18).

Auditory Cortex. With audition (hearing), neural impulses from the medial geniculate body of the thalamus project mainly to the **primary auditory cortex**, but also to the **auditory association cortex**. These regions of the brain are illustrated in Figure 6-20. The auditory association cortex receives a great deal of auditory input from neurons coming from the primary auditory cortex, but it also receives information from the pulvinar nucleus of the thalamus (see Figure 6-18). The primary auditory cortex is organized topographically, with high tones represented in the anterior part (toward the front of the brain), and low tones in the posterior part (toward the back of the brain). In addition, the primary auditory cortex contributes to our ability to localize sounds in space, although this function is more severely impaired if the auditory association cortex is damaged as well. When both primary and association cortex are damaged, one's ability to discriminate tonal patterns (like distinguishing high-low-high from low-high-low patterns) is severely impaired, but the ability to discriminate simple tones and the intensity of sound still remains. It is generally believed that the cerebral cortex is not required for such simple auditory perceptions, which probably are served by the thalamus and other subcortical structures.

The functioning of one part of the auditory association cortex, called **Wernicke's area**, appears to be necessary for our ability to recognize words and other sounds, whether uttered by ourselves or by other people. When this area is damaged, not only do we lose this ability, but our ability to discriminate sounds that are difficult to separate, such as "p" and "b" is also impaired. Wernicke's area is part of a neural system that serves our ability to use and understand *language*—a topic covered in some detail later in the chapter.

Somatic Sensory Cortex. Neural impulses from sense organs in the skin, muscles, joints, and internal organs that serve touch, pressure, temperature, and pain, enter into the spinal cord and then travel along specific neural pathways into the ventral posterior nucleus of the thalamus (see Figure 6-18). In addition, somatic sensory information travels to the lateral posterior nucleus, the pulvinar nucleus and, in the case of pain and temperature, to the medial nuclei of the thalamus as well. (The lateral posterior and pulvinar areas are shown in Figure 6-18; this figure does not show the medial nuclei.) Somatic sensory information is projected from the thalamus to **somatic sensory I**, **somatic sensory II**, and **somatic association cortex**. These regions of the cerebral cortex are illustrated in Figure 6-21.

Somatic sensory I occupies the postcentral gyrus of the cortex (see Figure 6-21). This region is topographically organized, with one region serving the arm, another the face, and so forth, as indicated in the figure. This region goes over the top of the brain and continues in the medial postcentral gyrus, as shown in Figure 6-19. Again, each area of the body is not equally represented. Instead, the hands, face and mouth have disproportionately large areas devoted to them. When a small part of somatic sensory I is damaged, there is severe impairment of one's ability to perceive fine touch and pressure sensations—and sensations of the joints—coming from the part of the body served by this part of the brain. Perception of pain and simple sensations of temperature are not severely impaired, however. This observation is generally believed to indicate that the thalamus and other subcortical structures are capable of serving our perception of pain and temperature.

Somatic sensory II is also topographically organized but, unlike somatic sensory I, damage to this region does not impair simple touch and pressure discrimination. This region might receive proportionately more temperature and pain input than somatic sensory I, but its contribution to sensory experience remains largely unknown (for detailed comments, see Woolsey, 1981a).

The role played by the somatic association cortex (see Figure 6-21) appears to be a little more clear.

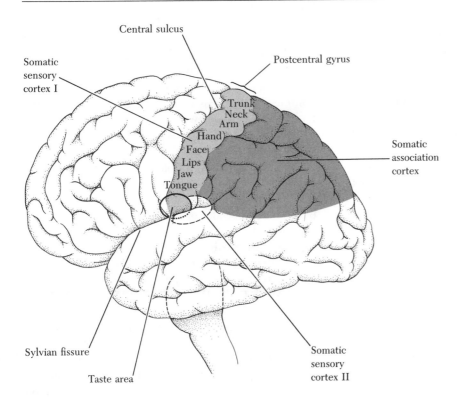

SOMATIC SENSATION

Somatic sensory cortex I: this area is in the postcentral gyrus of the cortex. It is topographically organized, with the hands, face, and tongue occupying large areas. The lower part of the body is represented in the medial portion of the postcentral gyrus (see Figure 6-19). *Stimulation* causes sensations of touch, warmth, cold, pain, and sometimes movement. These sensations are experienced to come from the parts of the body that correspond to the area of the cortex being stimulated. *Damage* severely impairs fine touch and pressure sensations and sensations from the joints. The lack of sensation is restricted to an area of the body that corresponds to the area damaged in the cortex. *Damage* decreases temperature sensations to some extent, but pain sensations are only slightly affected.

Somatic sensory cortex II: this area lies below and behind the base of the postcentral gyrus. It is topographically organized, but this organization appears to be much cruder than for somatic sensory I. *Damage* has little or no effect on simple sensory discrimination.

Stimulation causes tingling, warmth, vibration, tightness, and numb sensations in various parts of the body.

Somatic association cortex: this area is in the parietal cortex behind somatic sensory I and above somatic sensory II. *Damage* impairs a person's ability to recognize complex forms by "feel." *Damage*, especially in the nondominant hemisphere (usually the right side), sometimes causes a person to be oblivious to the contralateral side of the body (usually the left side). One "forgets" that it is there. *Stimulation* sometimes evokes a "feeling" of an object, such as holding a ball in one's hand.

TASTE

Taste area: overlaps the area representing somatic sensations from the tongue. The taste area is at the base of the postcentral gyrus, in the Sylvian fissure, and extends into the insular region (seen when the Sylvian fissure is spread apart—see Figure 7-13). *Damage* impairs taste discrimination, but some discrimination remains even when the entire taste area is destroyed.

Figure 6–21. Lateral view of the cerebral cortex showing areas involved with somatic sensations (touch, pressure, pain, temperature, and sensations from the joints) and taste.

This region is important for complex perceptual processes involving touch, pressure, visual, auditory, and joint sensations. When this region of the cortex is damaged, the ability to recognize complex forms by "feel" is sometimes impaired. In addition, damage to the somatic sensory association cortex, usually on the right side of the brain, sometimes causes a person to be oblivious to sensations coming from the muscles and joints of the left side of the body—in other words, one "forgets" that it is there. These, of course, are complex sensory processes that require integration of a great deal of sensory input as well as prior learning. We will discuss one example of complex integration— an example involving language functions—when we discuss language later in the chapter.

Gustatory (Taste) Cortex. The taste area of the cortex (see Figure 6-21), overlaps the area of somatic sensory cortex that serves sensations of the tongue. Neural impulses travel to this region from the ventral posterior nucleus of the thalamus after they have entered the upper spinal cord via neurons that serve the taste receptors in the mouth. When the taste area of the cortex is damaged, there is some reduction in one's ability to discriminate various foods by their taste, but some discrimination remains even if the entire taste area is destroyed. Again, these findings indicate that other (subcortical) areas of the brain are capable of giving us experiences of this sensation. (For more comments, see Norgren, Grill, and Pfaffmann, 1977.)

Body and Self

Earlier, we stated that nowhere is the integration of physiology and psychology as apparent as it is with the senses. This integration is especially evident when we compare known physiological workings of the brain, which we have just covered in some detail, to our perceptual experiences. Although the details are not fully understood, there is no doubt that the brain itself is responsible for our sensory experiences. For example, the fact that specific neural pathways serve one or another sense as they propagate neural impulses from the sensory receptors all the way to the cortex and other regions of the brain is surely related to the fact that we experience different sensations separately from each other. On the other hand, the fact that the brain devotes large areas to sensory input coming from more than one sense is somehow related to our ability to assimilate information coming from many different sensations all at once. Also, the fact

that the brain devotes large areas, for example, to the fovea, or the hands, is no doubt related to why our vision is best in the center of the visual field, or that our ability to discriminate by touch is best when we use our fingertips. Just as we are sensitive to the position and shape of images in the visual field, neurons in the visual cortex respond to these parameters. Likewise, we discriminate tones by their frequency, just as neurons in the auditory cortex respond to the frequency of a tone.

Another obvious example of integration between physiological and psychological mechanisms is the fact that one or another movement of any part of the body, but especially of the head, makes it more (or less) likely for us to receive sensory information from various sensory stimuli. When we move our head in order to see something, or use other behaviors and sensory-related processes (shown in boxes in Figures 6-8 through 6-17), the fact is that we are *not* always aware of doing so. In other words, although many sensory processes are classified as belonging to our conscious experiences, *much of the time sensory-related behaviors and the effects of activation (or inactivation) of the sense organs occur without our conscious participation.* When we rub a sore spot on the body to reduce sensations of pain, or move our legs because of discomfort associated with hydrostatic pressure, or move our head to better hear a sound, or begin to breathe through our mouth instead of our nose to avoid a bad odor, we usually do so automatically. On the whole, this is fortunate, because otherwise we would be constantly preoccupied with such behaviors. At the same time, it is absolutely necessary that these behaviors and sensory effects be consciously accessible. We will list some of the reasons why.

1) As noted earlier, the sense organs provide a means for us to *apprise* the external world. Without the ability to consciously perceive external events, we would have no means of adjusting our actions to the ever-changing conditions we face.

2) Many "automatic" behaviors and experiences involving sensory perception need to be learned through repeated, consciously perceived events. As children, we had to *learn* to look to our right and to our left before crossing the street. We had to *learn* to avoid the pain of touching a hot stove. We had to *learn* the size of objects and what that meant in terms of judging their distance from us. We had to *learn* the sounds associated with a need for attentiveness, such as the sounds of sirens, alarms, brakes, and horns.

3) Pain sensations let us *know* when an organ, muscle, or bone is being (or has been) damaged. Many people do not use this capacity fully, only "tuning in" to body sensations when asked by a clinician to describe an ailment or respond to a specific manipulation of the body (Does that hurt? Can you feel that? etc.) At the simplest level, without pain sensations we would probably continue standing or sitting in postures that are hurting our back, or holding or gripping sharp objects that are cutting us, or wearing shoes that don't fit.

4) Joint sensations anchor our bodies in reality by letting us *know* where our limbs and head are in space. These sensations are often ignored, but they quickly must (and do) come to our attention as we grope, for example, to walk from one place to another in the dark.

Obviously, that these processes are subject to our conscious experience, but not always, allows us to adapt to a wide range of circumstances.

In attempting to explain how the brain is organized to serve conscious experiences, researchers generally accept that those functions governed by the lower portions of the brain are less subject to conscious influence (more automatic) than those governed by the upper portions. However, *conscious and automatic processes are not necessarily restricted to specific brain locations.* For example, we have just seen that damage to certain areas of the cerebral cortex impairs our ability to recognize patterns such as melodies (tonal patterns), visual shapes and forms, and objects placed in the hands to be recognized by "feel." Simpler perceptions, on the other hand, such as recognizing the frequency and intensity of a sound, discriminating among simple tastes, and gross tactile sensibilities (touch and pressure) are still maintained in the absence of cortex. Similarly, although pain and temperature are represented in the cortex, it seems that the absence of cortex has almost no effect on our ability to experience either, and especially pain. Research to date points to the thalamus and other subcortical structures as being responsible for this awareness. Extensive damage to the olfactory area does not affect simple olfactory discrimination, but because most olfactory input does not go through the thalamus but, instead, enters the limbic system directly via the olfactory bulb, subcortical areas other than the thalamus probably participate in this awareness. The converse case, that some "automatic" processes have their representation in higher portions of the brain rather than in lower portions, is also evi-

dent. For example, the function of automatically keeping our eyes "locked" on an object appears to be largely regulated by the visual association cortex (see Figure 6-20). Clearly, the fact that we have many types of sensory processes—automatic and/or subject to conscious experience—has its physiological correspondence in the fact that many regions of the brain contribute to these functions.

Another example of physiological/psychological interactions involves experiences connecting the activities of two or more senses at the same time. For example, when a breeze comes up, not only are *touch* receptors activated by the movement of hair on our skin but also *temperature* receptors are activated as the skin is cooled by increased evaporation. Even when the breeze is extremely slight, we can clearly "feel" it blow across our face or limbs, especially on a warm day. Given that both touch and temperature are somatic sensory, it is not surprising that these two modalities cooperate so closely in giving us information on this gentle movement of air. We can, however, connect other modalities, such as *watching* how an object falls after we have thrown it into the air, or looking at the motion of plants, or *listening* to the rustling of leaves, wetting our finger and sticking it into the air, and many other things. Clearly, we have a large repertoire of sensations and behaviors that can inform us of the breeze. Moreover, many parts of the brain can participate in this function, including those areas that serve somatic sensory, auditory, and visual sensations.

Similarly, the areas of the brain that serve the function of taste are not well understood, but it is clear that *visual* and *olfactory* stimuli are very important in the diversity of "tastes" that we perceive. A person who is blindfolded or who has a stuffy nose from a cold has a greatly reduced sense of taste. Somehow these "connections" must have their physiological correspondence in the workings of those parts of the brain that serve taste, olfaction, and vision.

Language is a particularly important example of a function that relies on many sensory modalities. In general, language proficiency involves reading, writing, speaking, and listening, and, as such, involves *vision* (for reading), *touch, pressure,* and *joint sensations* (for writing), and *audition* (for listening). However, it is even more complex, for in addition to the involvement of the motor cortex, which controls the movement of muscles (see Chapter 9), we need to hear our voice in order to speak normally, see what we are recording in order to write properly, and say a word—either to ourselves or out loud—in order to read. Furthermore, all of these language skills must be learned. In fact, *how* they are learned determines *which* senses are integrated. For example, people who are blind learn to "read" by touch and people who are deaf learn to "listen" by reading lips and sign language.

The physiological processes that relate to language functions have been studied more extensively than other functions that make use of more than one sensory modality. Many areas of the brain are known to participate in language functions. The sensory and motor processes involved are located mostly in the association areas of the left hemisphere of the cerebral cortex, as illustrated in Figure 6-22. These areas are well situated to receive input from all sensory modalities, and damage in this region produces a wide range of symptoms, all indicating impairment of one or another of the language functions mentioned above. For instance, a person might be able to understand spoken words perfectly and be unable to read, even though not blind. (Other examples of impaired

Figure 6—22. Areas of the cerebral cortex involved with language.

Broca's area: part of motor cortex and premotor cortex. *Damage* severely impairs one's ability to speak fluently. *Damage* does not impair one's ability to comprehend the speech of others, nor does it impair the ability to comprehend one's own speech.

Wernicke's area: part of auditory association cortex. *Damage* severely impairs one's ability to comprehend the speech of others and one's own speech. Spoken sentences are devoid of meaning. *Damage* does not impair one's ability to articulate words. There is often fluent speech, but no meaning.

Arcuate fasciculus: connects Wernicke's area and Broca's area. *Damage* impairs one's ability to repeat words that are associated with sound. *Damage* does not severely impair one's ability to speak or comprehend words.

Inferior parietal lobe: located between somatic sensory, visual, and auditory cortex (also includes the posterior part of the temporal lobe). *Damage* in areas close to the visual cortex (see Figure 6-20) severely impair one's ability to read or understand written words. This area is probably responsible for most of the integration of visual, auditory, somatic sensory, and motor processes involved in language.

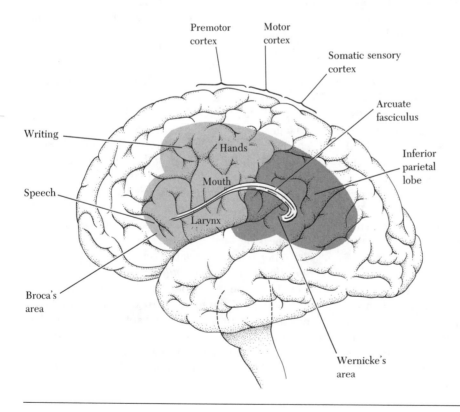

language function are listed in Figure 6-22.)

The importance of sensory modality in the learning of language skills is apparent from studies showing that damage produces different results depending upon the *type* of sensory stimuli used for learning. That is, a person with damage in Wernicke's area often has trouble writing words that *sound* alike: "tip" might be spelled instead of "dip," for example. Deaf persons with similar damage in Wernicke's area, however, will often have no difficulty with this spelling because their acquisition of language skills depended on *sight*, not sound. Similarly, people who have damage in the arcuate fasciculus (Figure 6-22) often have difficulty repeating words, except for those associated with *visual* images, such as are numbers. This is because most people learn numbers through visual stimuli, in contrast to other words which are usually learned through sound (for a more detailed discussion, see Geschwind, 1965).

One should not conclude from the above discussion that all integration of the senses occurs in the association cortex. In fact, all of the senses also meet in the **reticular system**, that part of the brain which, as mentioned in the previous chapter, projects from the upper spinal cord, and the **thalamus**. These areas of the brain are important in arousal and attention, functions that also require the integration of many types of sensory input. (We will discuss the reticular system in some detail in Chapter 8 in relation to the mechanisms of arousal, sleep, and attention.)

Another important aspect of sensory function is that it provides us with a wide range of *emotional* experiences. Unfortunately, the physiological workings associated with these experiences are not known. Nevertheless, we will briefly discuss some possible connections. To begin, we can identify three general types of emotional experiences related to sensory function:

1) Sensory-related experiences that are centered totally around oneself. These "emotional" experiences convey information only about our own physical condition—"I" feel pain or cold. (Some would argue that these experiences are not "emotional" because they involve no feelings or attitudes beyond the sensate. There is no general agreement on this point; it involves highly speculative disputes over the definition of "emotion.")

2) Sensory-related experiences that are centered around our relation to "primary objects." Primary objects are those agents or conditions external to ourselves that are vital for us to perceive, either because we must assimilate them (solid foods, water, air) or because we must adjust to them (ex-

cessively hot or cold environments, objects that hurt when we contact them). These "emotional" experiences convey information about the physical "value" of the primary object—I "like" or "dislike" the food I am tasting or smelling, or the temperature of the room.

3) Sensory-related experiences that extend beyond our immediate environment and exist independently of our physical needs. For example, I am "moved" by a beautiful, panoramic view.

We will discuss, in turn, each of these general types of experiences in relation to (1) the types of sensory stimuli involved, (2) the sense organs affected, (3) the areas of the brain that are implicated, and (4) the results of self-stimulation experiments.

Sensory-Related Experiences That Are Centered Totally Around Oneself. Pain, *touch*, *pressure*, and *temperature* have a number of qualities that are similar:

a) Most of the receptors for these senses are in the skin and, with pain and temperature, in the internal organs as well.

b) These senses almost always reflect conditions in our *immediate* environment. In other words, to receive an impression of an object through touch, pressure, pain, or temperature, the object must be in contact with our skin (unless, as indicated earlier in the chapter, it is very hot or very cold, in which case the heat gained or lost by the skin is sufficient to activate temperature or pain receptors without direct contact).

c) Neurons serving these senses go to the ventral posterior nucleus of the thalamus (see Figure 6-18) and from there to the somatic sensory cortex (see Figure 6-21). It is interesting to note that when electrodes are implanted into the somatic sensory cortex, they do *not* generally cause an animal to self-administer stimulation.

d) As just mentioned, emotional experiences involving these modalities are almost always self-centered; that is, they convey information about our own state—"I" feel pain, touch, pressure, hot, cold. Because they give us information about the state of our own body in relation to itself, these sensory experiences have little object-related emotional value. In fact, unless they are associated with processes such as pain, sex, and affection, sensations of touch and pressure seem to be quite void of emotional content, as are sensations of limb position and the joints.

Sensory-Related Experiences That Are Centered Around "Primary Objects." Although *taste* can be regarded as self-centered in that it, too, conveys information of our own immediate environment and, in physiologic terms, also projects to the ventral posterior nucleus of the thalamus and from there to somatic sensory cortex, taste is more importantly related to its primary "object," food, as is *smell*. As we have stated, sensations of taste and smell are much greater when we are hungry than when we are full. Moreover, the primary olfactory area, in contrast to somatic sensory cortex, has strong connections with the hypothalamus and the limbic system, both of which have a great deal to do with hunger and eating (see Chapter 3). In addition, when implanted in almost every part of the primary olfactory area, animals will repeatedly press the lever to receive a stimulatory reward. The same is true for the orbitofrontal cortex, which also has strong connections to the limbic system and hypothalamus (see Figure 6-19). In fact, when monkeys are hungry they will respond to electrodes placed in the orbitofrontal cortex by self-administering electrical stimulation more frequently than when they are sated (see Mora, Avrith, Phillips, and Rolls, 1979).

Our experiences of taste and smell fall easily into "likes" and "dislikes." Perhaps these emotional qualities have some physiological correspondence in the fact that those regions of the brain most involved in regulating food-related processes—the hypothalamus, limbic system, upper spinal cord, and orbitofrontal cortex—appear to be the most rewarding (when "reward" is measured by the technique of self-stimulation). (However, the converse is not correct: self-stimulatory reward is *not* necessarily related to objects or goals, as discussed in Chapter 4 where we mentioned that self-stimulation sometimes occurs separate from any food-, water- or sex-related processes.)

Although *pain* and *temperature* sensations have been listed as belonging to the first category of emotional experience because they often are solely centered around the individual, these sensations can also be related to primary objects. For example, if we are too hot we will be uncomfortable and will seek a cooler environment. Having entered the cooler environment, we will experience a reward (it will feel good, for example, as we enter the swimming pool). In this case, the primary object is the environment, and brain mechanisms include those having to do with temperature regulation. Again, as discussed in Chapter 4, temperature regulation, aside from relying on thalamic and cortical function, also relies heavily on hypothalamic and upper spinal cord function. Much the same can be said of sensations of pain.

Although the physiology associated with the reward represented by the *absence* of pain is largely unknown, sensations of pain are not only associated with neural activity within the thalamus and the somatic sensory cortex, but also with activity in almost every subcortical region of the brain, including the spinal cord. (Pain will be discussed again in Chapter 11 in specific relation to neural chemicals such as the "endorphins," which activate the same neural receptors as do opiates such as morphine.)

As with the somatic sensory cortex, electrodes placed in the visual and auditory cortex of experimental animals do *not* usually evoke self-stimulation. In most cases, visual and auditory "likes" and "dislikes" are associated with experiences that are integrated with the functioning of *other* senses, such as those accompanying eating, drinking, sex, and the absence of pain. In many cases, the emotional experiences that accompany "pure" visual or auditory experiences extend beyond our immediate environment and exist quite independently of any immediate physical needs.

Sensory-Related Experiences That Are Centered Around Events Far-Removed from Our Immediate Needs. Visual and auditory stimuli often inform us of conditions far removed from our immediate environment, as do olfactory stimuli. Everyone has been inspired by certain pieces of music or certain paintings, by the beauty of a sunrise or sunset, a view of the mountains or of the stars, a song of a bird, or has had his or her compassion aroused by seeing injury to other life. Although the physiology that accompanies these emotions is largely unknown, there are a few interrelations worth describing.

When we enter a museum or gallery to see art, go to our local "symphony hall" to hear a concert, or view the beauties of nature, usually our "appreciation" of the art, music, or natural scenery before us is aided when there are few or no distracting stimuli. In other words, for maximum "enjoyment," there must be a minimal excitation of somatic sensations such as pain, temperature, pressure, and touch, and usually a minimal excitation of those senses that serve hunger, eating, and so forth. In a different example, the "smell" of early morning air or flowers in a field often helps us to appreciate nature, but it is significant that these aromas do *not* elicit sensations of hunger. Similarly, all of us are familiar with suddenly recalling a long-forgotten childhood experience because of some associated smell, but note that this experience, while perhaps triggered by our immediate environment, is often quite separate from it.

The emotional experiences described above might

have a physiological correspondence in the fact, already mentioned, that electrodes placed in many areas of the cerebral cortex (including visual and auditory areas) do not usually evoke self-stimulation when an animal is allowed to press the lever, nor does electrical stimulation of these regions often evoke behaviors associated with object-reward, such as eating or drinking. Perhaps this finding means that self-stimulation, for the most part, serves as a measure of reward as it relates to physiological and behavioral mechanisms connected to our immediate survival, and that, to a large extent, the sensory cortex is not organized to serve these functions (except when cortical activities connect to activities in subcortical regions, as when we look for food because we are hungry). Again, this interpretation does not negate the possibility that self-stimulatory reward might serve other purposes, or that it might sometimes serve no purpose other than the "reward" itself.

In sharp contrast to the remote environments described above, a conducive environment for eliciting emotions centered around oneself or primary objects often involves input from many sensory modalities at once. The taste, smell, appearance, texture, temperature, and seasoning of food all contribute to its appeal, for example. Interestingly, most "hot" spices activate pain receptors in the mouth; in this context, it has been found that gently pinching a rat's tail causes it to eat more. In fact, if a rat is made aphagic (made to stop eating) by damage to the lateral hypothalamus (see Chapter 3), pinching its tail can increase its eating to near-normal levels. Thus *taste, olfaction, vision, touch, pressure, temperature,* and *pain* all contribute to the satisfaction we derive from solid food. In this connection it is worth noting that the hypothalamus not only receives input from all of the sensory modalities, it contains many reward areas as well.

As a final topic, let's briefly discuss the organization of the cerebral cortex as this organization relates to *verbal and nonverbal functions.* We have already discussed the fact that large areas of our association cortex are devoted to language functions, and that these areas are almost always in the *left* hemisphere of the brain. Although it is premature to draw any firm conclusions until more research is done, it appears that the association areas in the *right* hemisphere are likewise devoted to complex integrative functions involving the senses, but these functions have more to do with tactile, spatial, visual, and auditory patterns. In clinical studies, patients suffering damage in the right hemisphere are often unable to recognize and discriminate shapes and melodies, whereas patients with similar damage in the left hemisphere usually

have difficulty only with language functions. For example, a person with damage to the left hemisphere can often discriminate between two patterns of the same word without recognizing the word's meaning. Similarly, a person with left hemispheric damage may have little difficulty singing songs but be barely able to speak. Even though these data give some support to the conclusion that the right side of the brain is more concerned with emotional experience than is the left side, we note them here because it may be more significant that one side of the brain is involved more with verbal information and the other side with nonverbal information. On the other hand, there is even uncertainty about this relatively long-standing interpretation. For example, there is recent evidence that the critical difference in the functions served by the left and right hemispheres is not based on whether the stimulus is verbal or nonverbal but whether the task to be performed requires that information be *processed* verbally or nonverbally. (For a detailed discussion of the two sides of the brain, see Springer and Deutsch, 1981.)

III. INVOLVEMENT OF MANY ORGANS AT ONCE

Although we have appropriately emphasized the brain as the most important organ for sensory functions, the sensory system actually requires the participation of many other organs. The sense organs themselves, of course, involve many other organs: the skin, the eyes, the ears, muscle, bone joints, the tongue, and the nasal cavity are some. In fact, pressure, pain, and temperature receptors are present in almost every organ of our body. (A notable exception is in the brain itself, where electrical stimulation or destruction does not elicit pain; the only pain receptors in the brain are those that surround blood vessels). The gastrointestinal tract, bile salts, and the lymphatics are also required for sensory functioning. For instance, when the intestines are unable to absorb vitamin A or other molecules similar to it (called provitamins for vitamin A), a severe vitamin A deficiency can occur and cause "night blindness," which is an inability to see in dim light. This inability to see is because vitamin A is needed to produce the visual pigment of our eyes. Because vitamin A and its provitamins are fats, they require proper functioning of the intestines, gall bladder, and lymphatics to assure that fats are absorbed into the blood. The most common cause of vitamin A deficiency is nutritional (although dietary lack of vitamin A is rare in the United States), but conditions that obstruct or bypass the small intestines, obstructions of the bile ducts, and ulcerative colitis can also cause such a deficiency and result in impaired vision.

IV. RELATION TO HEALTH

In general, the senses are absolutely necessary for survival; without them, we would be unable to function in relation to the external world, and we would not receive vital information concerning the state of our body. There is, however, another, more subtle, relationship between the functioning of the sense organs and our state of health. To appreciate this relationship, let's consider the effects of **sensory isolation**.

John Lilly, who has done considerable work in this area, has found that when people are placed in an environment designed to eliminate the stimulation of light, sound, gravity, heat flow, pressure, touch, and physical vibration—as in his "isolation tank"—they will at first be filled with curiosity about their new environment, thoughts of the day, and considerations of the general state of their body. Within a short period of time, however, they will begin to lose their sense of time and undergo a series of dream-like experiences. Although results vary according to the length of time one is in the tank and the personality of the person undergoing the experience, most people suffer various types of visual and auditory hallucinations and delusions, a sense of drifting in space, recurrent thoughts, and loss of the ordinary sense of self (see Lilly, 1978). The emotional reactions to such isolation range from panic and fear to euphoria and calmness. From these experiments, it is clear that in addition to their vital function of allowing us to survive in the external world, the senses are also necessary to keep us in "touch" with our ordinary sense of "reality." Sensory "food" actually seems to prevent the occurrence of a dissociation between oneself and ongoing mental, emotional, physical, and environmental processes. (Reports of prisoners who have been in solitary confinement certainly confirm the struggle it poses in terms of remaining "connected" with reality.)

As an additional comment, it is interesting that a person's suggestibility markedly increases during the time spent in the isolation tank. The hypnotic state—commonly induced by invoking sensory isolation through techniques such as staring at one object, listening to one voice, or lying quietly with minimal movement—is also characterized by its enhancement of suggestibility. These techniques are commonly used to promote the deep relaxation that is the appropriate state for hypnosis to be effective. Similarly, for many people, a short stay in an isolation tank is extremely relaxing. To a far lesser extent than in

Lilly's experiments, we all undergo some type of sensory isolation when, intent on relaxation, we find a quiet spot, lie down, close our eyes, or sit quietly in meditation.

There are numerous reasons why sensory isolation affects our experiences of reality. One reason might be that without sensory stimulation, we cannot be conscious of reality. On the other hand, one might regard our consciousness of reality as being, at least in part, *defined* by sensory experience, and see the technique of sensory isolation as allowing us to be conscious of a different, but equally legitimate, reality. This topic will be discussed more fully in the next section.

The role of experience and learning in perceptual processes was already emphasized when we discussed the relation between visual depth perception and prior experience, (see Figure 6-17), and when we discussed sensory modality and the learning of language functions (see page 103). Prolonged sensory isolation, called **sensory deprivation**, occurs in those who were born blind because of congenital cataracts. Having had virtually no visual experience for some years, then having sight restored by surgical removal of the cataracts, the person may be left with an inability to discriminate shapes and/or difficulties in perceiving motion.

Impaired perceptual ability resulting from prolonged sensory deprivation has been studied most extensively in animals. When tactile sensations (touch and pressure sensations of the hands) were restored in monkeys deprived of these sensations from birth, the ability to respond to tactile cues (for example, turning the head to the right if the right hand is squeezed) was seriously impaired. In all cases, these impairments were somewhat relieved through prolonged training, but certain defects appeared to be permanent. The most detailed findings come from studies in cats, where it has been shown that early visual deprivation not only produces perceptual defects, but also degeneration of cells in the lateral geniculate body of the thalamus and abnormalities in the functioning of cortical neurons (see Wiesel and Hubel, 1963a, 1963b; Dews and Wiesel, 1970; Hubel and Wiesel, 1970; Hirsch and Spinelli, 1971).

Because the greatest impairments of perceptual abilities and abnormalities in neural function occur when the sensory deprivation originated very early in life, researchers have concluded that exposure to appropriate sensory stimuli must begin at an early age if one is to develop normal discriminatory abilities. The well-known fact that language skills are much more easily learned early in life than when we are adults is probably related to this phenomenon. Adults who suffer extensive damage in Wernicke's area and the surrounding cortex have severe impairment of all types of "interpretive thought," and these deficiencies rarely improve. If this area is destroyed in a child under six years of age, however, the opposite side of the brain (usually the right side) is able to "take over" and, in many cases, obtain full restoration of these capabilities. In other words, just as exposure to sensory stimuli early in life is most likely to aid the development of normal sensory function, so it is that being deprived of this exposure at this critical time is likely to be most harmful.

Of course, without sensory stimulation a great number of physiological processes cease functioning, whether we are infants or adults. Without light, for instance, our visual pigments cease decomposing; without sound, the hair cells in the cochlea cease being activated. As discussed in the second section of this chapter, we make use of these facts when we take action to reduce sensory input. Also, when sunlight hits our skin, certain provitamins are converted into vitamin D, which facilitates the absorption of calcium from the gastrointestinal tract and promotes calcium deposition in bone. Inadequate intake and/or lack of sunshine can lead to a deficiency of vitamin D, leading to softening and bending of bones—one of the symptoms associated with rickets. In other words, sensory stimuli are necessary not only for stimulating the physiological processes that are directly related to sensory experience, but also for stimulating some physiological processes that are not related.

It should now be clear that a severe disorder of any of our sensory systems will have profound effects on our psychology and behavior. Even relatively mild handicaps, such as difficulties with hearing or aberrations in our vision that require we wear glasses, can lead to a variety of compensatory behaviors and emotional reactions concerning ourselves in relation to others and to the external world. Whether we are young or older, the compensations we need often affect our self-esteem and image. What is often not so obvious to most people is that the converse also holds true—our psychological state can have a profound influence on our sensory function. Such effects can be subtle or quite dramatic. Everyone is familiar with the experience of "feeling itchy" upon simply entering an environment where we know (or believe) mosquitoes to thrive; even thinking about common itch-provoking situations is sufficient to start us scratching our bodies (or hearing insects that are not there). A little less commonplace experience but one that is nevertheless familiar to many is that of visual trouble

associated with stress, or even that of seeing especially clearly or seeing particularly bright colors after some unusually profound or insightful event. (Some people report this experience after sessions of deep relaxation, meditation, or intense psychotherapy.) Most dramatic in this context are the hysterical conversion reactions described at the beginning of the chapter. In these cases, you will recall, a patient may experience total blindness or deafness with no associated organic defect, and can recover spontaneously or through counselling.

Before we leave the topic of health, it is important to mention that although the sense organs keep us in touch with the external world and, in many cases, our internal world, *they do not necessarily give us reliable information*. We experience many types of *illusions*. The example given in the beginning of this chapter having to do with the movement of one train past another, is an illustration of such an illusion. Two additional examples are illustrated in Figures 6-23 and 6-24. In Figure 6-23, the illusion depends on the angle formed by the "wings"—whether they are acute (in which case the line is underestimated) or obtuse (in which case the line is overestimated). In Figure 6-24, the illusion is based on the fact that the pattern is ambiguous; that is, the cubes can be seen to project in three dimensions either toward the viewer or away from the viewer. Although our retinal image does not

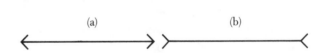

Figure 6–23. Visual illusions regarding line lengths. The length of the lines (a) and (b) are the same although (b) appears to be longer than (a).

Figure 6–24. Visual illusions regarding shapes. If one stares at the cross-bar in the center, the two cubes spontaneously reverse their perspective.

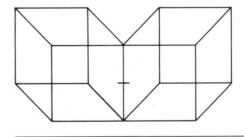

change, many different shapes can be perceived, as depicted in Figure 6-25.

As one might expect, damage to the brain will affect these illusions, depending on the brain region involved. Damage to the right hemisphere decreases the number of spontaneous "reversals" of the cubes shown in Figure 6-24 moreso than does damage to the left hemisphere. Damage in some areas actually increases the number of reversals (see Cohen, 1959). Although the physiology involved with illusions is still largely unexplored, it is apparent that:

a) Illusions are experienced with every sensory modality

b) Illusions are based on a tremendous variety of factors, including the sensory stimuli and the sensory receptors involved

c) Prior experience and learning have a great influence on the perception of illusions (for example, if we did not have prior experience, we might see in Figure 6-24 only a bunch of lines in two dimensions—instead of three—and the illusion would not appear).

Although sensory illusions are a part of our everyday experience, it would be incorrect to conclude that sensory information is likely to be false and, as such, is unhealthy. You will recall that the baroreceptors and chemoreceptors of the carotid bodies and aorta, and the stretch receptors of the lungs, are sensitive to mechanical and chemical stimuli, and that these sense organs are intimately connected to processes that regulate our blood pressure, blood volume, thirst, respiratory rate, and the rhythmicity of breathing (see Chapters 4 and 5). The fact that sensory information

Figure 6–25. Four shapes that spontaneously appear as one continues to fixate on the cross-bar in Figure 6–24.

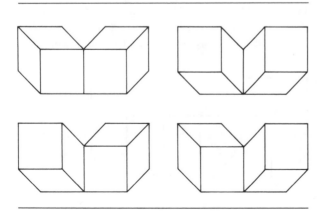

from these organs is integrated mostly in the hypothalamus and upper spinal cord parallels the fact that these processes usually occur automatically, without conscious participation, thus guaranteeing that these vital functions are maintained unimpeded by any modification resulting from learning, prior experience, voluntary control, or conscious interpretation. Illusion plays virtually no role in these mechanisms.

In general, taste, olfaction, pain, and temperature serve our health. Temperature and pain signals tell us whether there is a need to regulate body temperature or do something to prevent damage to tissues. For example, pinching a limb will often lead to "reflexive" withdrawal of that limb (flexor response). These types of reactions to pain occur at the level of the spinal cord and require no conscious involvement. However, because these modalities are also very much subject to conscious experience and interpretation, the possibility of incorrect perception (illusion) is greater with these signals than with those noted in the previous paragraph. For example, even though taste and olfaction strongly reinforce the body's real need for solid food, we could be in need of food and therefore experience an increased sense of smell, yet reject the food that is available because its smell reminds us of a particularly unpleasant experience.

Many of us are frequently "fooled" by visual and auditory stimuli. That we experience such a great number of visual and auditory illusions has to do with the fact that auditory and visual stimuli are used much more for learning—not only for the development of discriminative abilities, but also for education in the home and at school—than are other sensory stimuli. Many of us have participated in the illusion that a big, colorful fruit displayed at the grocery store, or on the TV screen is ripe and delicious. Only if we have the chance to actually bite into the fruit do we have the additional information of taste and smell that tells us reliably whether or not we can allow this fruit to enter our body. In this example, our association of visual appearance with taste is, of course, learned. Note, however, that although the vision and its associations might be sufficient to stimulate all of the processes the body undergoes in anticipation of eating such a fruit, the fact that it is "illusory" is not likely to be harmful because the fruit will not taste good and we will reject it.

Most of us are also familiar with other types of false perceptions we can have by relying on connections we automatically make between our sensory responses and our past experience. For example, someone frowns and we may infer he doesn't like us when, in fact, he is frowning from something he has read in the newspaper or from a passing thought totally unrelated to us. And we all know the effectiveness of a movie's background music in manipulating our emotions from lightheartedness to sadness to fear to romantic feelings. On a different plane, consider the illusion that something seen in the mountains is near when in fact it is miles away. Such impressions and illusions influence our psychology and our behavior (and may even accelerate our heart rate) yet, in most cases, they have little to do with our immediate health or the regulation of vital processes. In fact, sensory experiences that are essential to interpret accurately and quickly, like seeing a car coming at us so we can move out of its way, not only require minimal effort, but call upon behaviors that are easily learned. A warning shouted by a parent when we were children, or perhaps a close call, was all that was required.

V. THE WORKINGS OF REFINED SYSTEMS: DIFFERENT TYPES OF SENSORY "AWARENESS"

Throughout the chapter we have used the term "sensory experience" to mean that our sense organs provide us with information that can be perceived consciously; that is, we can be "aware of" or "know about" the existence of sensory stimuli. Sensory awareness has, of course, mental and emotional components. As expressed at the beginning of the chapter, the purpose of this book is not to discuss similarities and differences in the meaning of terms such as "consciousness," "experience," "awareness," or "sensation." However, it *is* our purpose to look at the associated workings of the body to expand our understanding of emotional and mental processes.

For one, it should now be clear that we are looking at the workings of very refined systems. *"Sensation," or "sensory awareness," comprises a set of processes that involve many different factors, ranging in scope from physical to physiological to behavioral.* Sensation involves many types of stimuli, each with different physical properties; it calls upon millions of receptors scattered throughout the body; fundamentally different sense organs such as the cochlea, retina, and Pacinian corpuscles; numerous neural pathways and areas of the brain, both cortical and subcortical; and a diversity of behaviors, some of them learned. Similarly, perhaps it is best to consider also that *"consciousness" is not a single state but an ongoing function of whatever processes are involved at the time.* In many respects, consciousness is defined by the capacity and use of our sense organs. This fact can

be most easily understood when we compare our perceptual abilities to those of animals. For example, we are not conscious of the millions of tiny bugs flying in the sky when we are walking at night, but a bat (for which they represent food) easily responds to such bugs by using echolocation, a process whereby the bat sends out bursts of frequencies from 40,000 to 100,000 vibrations a second from its larynx, then picks up these frequencies with its ears as the soundwaves are reflected from objects (in this case, bugs). Similarly, a dog responds to things detected with its nose that are totally beyond our awareness. In part, this canine response is due to its nasal cavity being much more developed than ours.

That consciousness is a varied function is also confirmed by the finding that sensory processes are organized to serve sensory experience in a variety of ways within the brain. When a person suffers from extensive damage to the area of the cerebral cortex that serves hearing, he or she may lose the ability to recognize complex auditory patterns such as melodies but still be able to perceive simple differences in frequencies and intensities of sound. In this case, *not only has a specific sensory ability been abolished, but so has a specific conscious experience.* Impairments ranging from the loss of very specific abilities, like being able to recognize numbers but not words, to the loss of an entire range of experiences, as when a person becomes totally blind, have been observed time and again in brain-damaged patients. Along the same lines, smell and taste are organized differently from the other senses in that they are intimately connected to the objectives of eating and drinking. Correspondingly, the areas of the brain that serve the sensation of smell are rewarding when electrically stimulated, and moreso when the animal is hungry than when it is sated, whereas the areas of the brain that serve vision, audition, and somatic sensations (e.g., touch and pressure) are not particularly rewarding under electrical stimulation.

There is a logical extension of the fact that consciousness, like sensation, is not a singular process: *Were we to develop additional sensory ability, we would also develop additional conscious ability.* Many people are endowed with or develop "extra-ordinary" sensory perception. This capacity need not be especially extraordinary for the person, of course, who, like a blind person, might possess or acquire increased sensitivity or increased dexterity either as a matter of course or as a matter of conscious effort. Blind people, out of necessity, develop echolocation far beyond what the sighted experience (or need to experience).

If a blind person were to correctly guess where an object is by reaching for it, or had the ability to discriminate different visual patterns by consistently guessing correctly, would this not be rather "extraordinary?" In fact, this "capability" sometimes occurs when there is damage to the primary visual cortex. In humans, damage to the primary visual cortex causes a blind spot in the corresponding part of the visual field. Even though not aware of seeing anything, affected persons sometimes remain able to respond to different visual stimuli with *correct* responses (they "guess" perfectly). In this case, *attentive discrimination is maintained without a corresponding conscious experience* (see Weiskrantz, Warrington, Sanders, and Marshall, 1974). This example simply indicates that conscious experience is not, in itself, a necessary criterion for determining that sensory processes are taking place, even sensory processes that we can act on. In other words, the concept that perceptual experiences can be as varied as the mechanisms that serve them can be useful in reminding us that "extraordinariness," generally and in specific relation to sensory experience, may merely represent differences among people—or, in the case mentioned above, even impaired function.

Along the same lines, we developed additional conscious ability when we learned to make interpretive sense of the words we saw on a page (i.e., when we learned to read)—we were allowed to become conscious of human thoughts and history which, in most cases, would not otherwise be available to us.

That consciousness is not a unique, singular phenomenon explains why it is not possible to completely abolish it by destroying just one area of the brain. It does not, however, mean that consciousness doesn't exist. Rather, consciousness is a diverse process which is defined by particular interactions of systems operating at one time. This is the same assertion that we made toward the end of Chapter 4 when we discussed "thirst" and "hunger," and we will come back to this assertion in later chapters when we discuss "attention," "sleep," "dreams," and other so-called "singular" processes. It is important to grasp that consciousness is not a singular process because insisting that it is can obscure our understanding of ourselves and other people. We are quite willing, for example, to accept that a blind person has developed hearing and other capabilities that are "extraordinary," yet we are largely unwilling to accept that some people, sighted as well as blind, are capable of "seeing" the moods of other people with extraordinary clarity, or that one can train oneself to higher levels of "consciousness." Yet most of us do acknowledge in our day-to-day interactions with others that some people know us better than others, regardless of how well we are actually acquainted—in other words, that a person need not be "extraordinary" to have exceedingly keen powers of perception.

VI. CONCLUSIONS

The information in this chapter has been presented to give the reader an appreciation of the vast extent to which physiology and psychology are integrated with respect to sensory functions. (Very little has been covered concerning the vestibular senses and the sense organs serving muscle, both of which will be discussed in Chapter 9.) As we hope has been made clear, the integrative processes outlined in this chapter occur at *all* levels—physical with respect to the properties of sensory stimuli, physiological with respect to the properties of sensory receptors and the brain, and psychological with respect to behavioral, emotional, and mental processes. Permitting us to function optimally in relation to our external and internal worlds, sensory stimuli serve our health in a variety of ways: a) They keep us apprised of the external world and provide us with vital information concerning the state of the body, b) They keep us in touch with our ordinary sense of "reality," preventing hallucinations and the loss of a sense of time and of a sense of self that often occur otherwise, c) They allow the development of discriminative abilities, ranging from depth perception to the discrimination of shapes to reading to the perception of motion, d) They permit the normal development of some neurons in the brain, and e) They are necessary for some physiological processes not dependent on the brain, such as the conversion of provitamins into vitamin D.

This chapter marks the end of our discussion of the basic systems involved in our assimilation and use of solid, liquid, gaseous, and sensory "foods." The next chapter covers our defense mechanisms—a very important topic if we are to protect ourselves against the myriad and ever-present conditions capable of upsetting our health.

Recommended Reading

GESCHWIND, N. "Specializations of the human brain." *Scientific American*, 241, 3, 180-199, 1979. *This article provides a brief review of the specialized functions of the brain. Language skills, the right and left hemispheres of the brain, and recognition of faces are among the interesting topics discussed.*

HEILMAN, K. and VALENSTEIN, E. (editors). *Clinical Neuropsychology*. New York: Oxford University Press, 1979, 644 pages. *A comprehensive presentation of human disorders resulting from brain damage. There are 18 articles, each written by authors who are experts in the areas covered. Included are articles on aphasia (impaired language functions), alexia (impaired reading), agraphia (impaired writing), acalculia (impaired ability to perform numerical calculations), and impaired abilities to identify one's body parts and to recognize or synthesize visual, auditory, and touch sensations. Recommended for readers who already have some familiarity with the anatomy of the cerebral cortex.*

LASSEN, N., INGVAR, D., and SKINHOJ, E. "Brain function and blood flow." *Scientific American*, 239,4, 62-71, 1978. *A nicely written and well-illustrated article describing the functions of the cerebral cortex.*

LILLY, J. *The Deep Self: Profound Relaxation and the Tank Isolation Technique.* New York: Warner Books, 1978, 334 pages. *This paperback describes the sensory isolation tank and contains the reports of many subjects who have used it.*

MERSKEY, H. *The Analysis of Hysteria.* London: Bailliere Tindall, 1979, 310 pages. *This book covers the historical development of concepts of hysteria, outlines many of the symptoms of hysteria, examines the relation between the personality and the symptoms of conversion reactions, and discusses its diagnosis. Included are over 500 references.*

REGAN, D., BEVERLEY, K., and CYNADER, M. "The visual perception of motion in depth." *Scientific American*, 241,1, 136-151, 1979. *An interesting discussion of various types of visual input that contribute to our perception of depth. This paper mostly deals with psychophysical experiments, although there are some references to the workings of the brain.*

SPRINGER, S. and DEUTSCH, G. *Left Brain, Right Brain.* San Francisco: W.H. Freeman, 1981, 243 pages. *This paperback discusses the relative contributions of the left and right hemispheres of the brain to language functions, visuo-spatial functions, left and right handedness, information processing, and other functions. Split-brain surgery is discussed in some detail. Many references are given and the illustrations are excellent.*

WEINTRAUB, M. A. *Clinician's Manual of Hysterical Conversion Reactions.* New York: Interdisciplinary Communications Media, Inc., 1978, 118 pages. *This monograph offers a concise definition of hysterical conversion reactions, lists criteria for their diagnosis, and suggests methods for treatment. The broad range of symptoms that classify as conversion reactions is elucidated.*

ZUBEK, J. (editor). *Sensory Deprivation: Fifteen Years of Research.* New York: Meredith Corp., 1969, 522 pages. *An excellent review and discussion of numerous investigations on the effects of sensory deprivation. Recommended for readers looking for detailed information on this topic.*

Defense Mechanisms: The Clinical Reality

Medical Disorder: Asthma

Read this "overture" carefully before you read Chapter 7. The connections between the medical reality of asthma and the basic underlying physiological and psychological processes that regulate normal defense mechanisms are developed in this chapter. (For more information on asthma, see Daniele, 1982; Creer, 1979; Maher-Loughnan, 1976; Knapp, Mathe, and Vachon, 1976.)

Asthma is a condition characterized by difficulty or distress in breathing, often accompanied by wheezing and coughing. During an asthmatic attack, there is widespread but reversible narrowing of the airways, caused by excessive reactivity of the smooth muscle of the trachea and bronchi, swelling of lung tissue, and excessive mucus secretion, alone or in some combination. Symptoms may be mild, moderately severe, or incapacitating depending upon the degree of bronchial constriction, the duration of the attack, and the frequency of its occurrence. In the United States, about 9 million persons suffer from asthma.

Two known physiological events that directly produce the symptoms of asthma are: a) the release of certain chemicals by white blood cells and b) the activation of nerves of the autonomic nervous system.

Allergic responses, infections, and cold temperatures are responsible for asthma in some patients. In these cases, the attack comes on because of an excessive response of the immune system. White blood cells release certain chemicals that irritate the smooth muscle of the lungs and make them hyperactive.

When nerves of the parasympathetic and sympathetic branches of the autonomic nervous system are activated, both immune and nonimmune responses are affected. Acetylcholine, a chemical released by nerves of the parasympathetic branch of the autonomic nervous system, has been shown to increase the immune response. As a nonimmune response, acetylcholine release directly stimulates the lungs to secrete mucus and the bronchial smooth muscle to contract.

Epinephrine, released by the adrenal glands, and norepinephrine, released by nerves of the sympathetic branch of the autonomic nervous system, usually inhibit the symptoms of asthma, partly by decreasing the response of white blood cells and thereby reducing the immune response. There is good evidence that some asthmatics suffer from a defect in the normal immuno-suppressive effects of sympathetic stimulation. Under normal conditions, the direct (nonimmune) effect of epinephrine released by the adrenal glands and norepinephrine released by neurons of the sympathetic nervous system is to dilate the bronchi. It appears, however, that these chemicals can also cause constriction. The type of response depends on the type of receptor that is activated. Beta receptors in the lungs respond to sympathetic stimulation by causing dilation and opening of the airways, whereas alpha receptors respond by causing constriction and closing of the airways. Many investigators believe that asthmatics suffer from an abnormally low response of beta receptors and/or an abnormally high response of alpha receptors in the lungs.

In asthmatics, emotional reactions such as anxiety, anger, panic, fear, frustration, impatience, nervousness, restlessness, and other states of emotional arousal or stress, sometimes trigger an attack. These emotional reactions can be associated with increased activity of the autonomic nervous system and increased secretion by the adrenal glands, causing, in turn, an increase or decrease in the activity of the white blood cells and the smooth muscle in the lungs, as previously described. Alternatively, emotional responses such as laughing, crying, and hyperventilating, and responses such as coughing or taking a sudden deep inhalation, can cause an attack because of their direct effects on the respiratory tract. Clearly, various psychological states and physiological mechanisms can influence the onset of asthmatic breathing.

That psychological states are involved in asthmatic reactions is further validated by the considerable body of evidence indicating that asthmatic symptoms can be learned and conditioned, especially through suggestion. This finding is supported by numerous reports that hypnosis can sometimes alleviate symptoms (see Maher-Loughnan, 1976). Attempts to discover a personality that characterizes asthmatic children and adults (see Creer, 1979) have failed to uncover an "asthmatic personality." Thus, investigators are looking more closely at the specific characteristics of individual patients and their responses.

Concerning the relative contributions of allergic, infectious, and psychological factors, it is clear that no one of these factors is uniquely responsible for the occurrence of asthmatic attacks. They seem to interact with each other to produce this complex disorder. Accordingly, asthma has many treatment modalities. If the problem is primarily an allergic reaction, for example, avoidance of the foreign agents and the environment that creates them is most effective. Exercise-induced asthma is sometimes alleviated by restriction of strenuous exercise, and sometimes by medications that increase the broncho-dilating effects normally induced by stimulation of sympathetic nerves. Emotional states can sometimes be managed through relaxation therapy and/or through consultation with a psychotherapist. In all cases, the effects of one factor, such as the person's emotional state, are enhanced or reduced by the effects of another, such as the person's allergic sensitivity. For example, even if a respiratory infection cannot be treated, relaxation therapy and/or reduction of anxiety or other emotional states can often greatly reduce the frequency and severity of attacks.

7

Defense Mechanisms

The processes outlined in the previous four chapters all involve "food" that enters our body from the external world. There is always the possibility, however, that these foods will produce harmful effects in our body. The body is sterile within, but it lives in an unsterilized world.

Solid foods, water, and air contain many organisms and particles, including viruses, bacteria, pollutants, and toxins, that can be injurious to the body. In some cases, the body has no means to defend itself when exposed to something harmful, in which case we get sick, sometimes even die. *In many cases we can avoid these agents*—for example, by handling food carefully, washing hands when appropriate, not eating certain mushrooms, being careful not to drink polluted water, eat rotten food, or breathe in toxic fumes. There are also many agents that are harmful if they penetrate our skin, and it is for this reason we are careful about our contact with bees, spiders, and snakes, why we avoid rubbing our fingers over a sharp knife blade, or stepping on a nail, and why we thoroughly clean all cuts, especially a puncture wound, to avoid infection. In general, we are well able to avoid those agents we cannot otherwise defend ourselves against. Accidents do occur, but they are quite rare, especially when we consider the increasing number of potentially dangerous situations we face each day. Again, we are looking at integrated processes involving physiology and behavior. Many of these avoidance behaviors are learned, but they are also closely connected to, and coexist with, defensive processes such as gagging, quick withdrawal (flexor response to pain), and alerting responses (quick orientation toward the source of danger, accompanied by a sudden cessation of behavior and increased alertness —see page 137).

There are two basic ways we defend ourselves against harmful agents. One is by avoiding them, as discussed above. This defense is extremely unworkable, however, with such vital functions as eating, drinking, and breathing. Furthermore, we simply do not have the sensitivity that would be required to be constantly alert to the contaminants in our foods, nor would it be psychologically healthy to do so. Thus the second type of defense, *destroying harmful agents once they have invaded our bodies*, is an essential protective mechanism we use; this mechanism is called **immunity**.

A detailed discussion of the physiology of immunologic responses is not appropriate for this book. Nevertheless, we will devote an entire section of this chapter to a discussion of the fundamental workings of the immune system because it is important to realize that the protective mechanisms of our body are very much integrated with our psychological states and our behavior. Although most of the mechanisms contributing to this process are not understood, their workings are undoubtedly responsible for a large part of what is called **psychosomatic medicine**.

In contrast to conversion reactions, where the abnormal symptoms merely *imitate* the signs of physical illness (see Chapter 6), psychosomatic disorders are disorders in which emotional or mental processes influence or directly cause an *organic* disease. In many cases the disease can be related to an altered functioning of the immune system. As we have noted, if the immune system becomes too active, the excessive protective response can produce symptoms such as those of asthma. By the same token, if the immune system does not react enough, the reduced protective response can increase our susceptibility to germs, toxins, or other agents that, under normal conditions, would not be harmful. Peptic ulcers are an example of a decreased resistance of the stomach walls to the stomach's secretions, and tuberculosis is an example of a decreased resistance of the lungs to *myobacterium tuberculosis*, an organism also known as *tubercle bacillus*. There is no question that these symptoms of extremely increased or decreased responsiveness of the body's protective mechanisms are sometimes brought about by emotionally troublesome life situations.

In order to understand the body's defense mechanisms more fully, not only must we take into account the workings of the immune system, but also we must attempt to understand how the body itself, independent of invasion by harmful agents, is equipped to alter immune responses. In so doing, we must discuss the **autonomic nervous system**, a part of the nervous system that originates in the brain and influences the activity of most organs and tissues in the body, including those that serve the immune system. We will also look at the functions of the **adrenal glands**, two glands that are found just above each kidney. This discussion will lead us to look at certain emotions and behaviors that are especially important in altering responses of the autonomic nervous system and the immune system. In so doing, we will also note those regions of the **brain** that appear to be most involved in regulating both the autonomic nervous system and these emotions and behaviors. Next, we will relate all of this information to our health, especially as it is affected by **stress**. Finally, we will attempt to understand the **variability** of these responses, which is great from one individual to another as well as within a single individual. We will begin with the immune system.

I. THE IMMUNE RESPONSE

There are two ways that the body responds to such harmful substances as bacteria, viruses and toxic agents, once it is exposed to them. Both involve **white blood cells**, which are produced mainly in the bone marrow and lymph tissue. The first is called **natural** or **innate immunity**, which involves protective mechanisms that are *inborn*. The second is called **acquired** or **adaptive immunity**, which involves specific alterations in the immune system that are *induced* by encounters with specific foreign agents.

Natural or Innate Immunity

Natural or innate immunity involves inborn mechanisms that are present in all healthy people. One such mechanism is called **phagocytosis**, which is a process that occurs when a white blood cell envelops the foreign particle, ingests it, and finally "digests" it by releasing enzymes and bactericidal agents that destroy the ingested particle. Many bacteria, particles of degenerating tissue, particles not related to living organisms (such as turpentine and ink particles), and even some parasites are destroyed in this manner. The white blood cells most responsible for phagocy-

tosis are **neutrophils** and **monocytes**. **Macrophages**, which are derived from monocytes, are especially active scavenger (phagocytic) cells that vigorously ingest and destroy numerous foreign agents. In addition, chemicals released during the encounter with "phagocytes," which are the cells that perform phagocytosis, attract other white blood cells, including **basophils** and **eosinophils**. Basophils appear to become **mast cells** once they enter the tissue, although it is not yet known exactly where mast cells originate. Basophils and mast cells secrete **histamine** and other chemicals that attract more white blood cells to the area that contains the foreign agent. Eosinophils appear to be especially effective in attacking large foreign agents, such as parasites.

Neutrophils, basophils, and eosinophils are all white blood cells found in the blood, whereas macrophages and mast cells are found in connective tissue throughout the body. Monocytes are found both in the blood and in connective tissue. Through their concerted actions, these white blood cells constitute an "inborn army" that is ready to recognize and destroy foreign agents.

The mechanisms of natural or innate immunity are schematically illustrated in Figure 7-1. As indicated in this diagram, in addition to activating those processes mentioned above, foreign agents or damaged tissue also activate **clotting factors**—chemicals that "wall off" the damaged area either by forming a blood clot if a blood vessel is damaged, or a fibrin clot for tissue damage.

Taken together, the response of this army of white blood cells is called an **inflammatory response**. The most obvious symptoms of inflammation are local swelling, itching, redness, warmth, and sometimes soreness and the formation of pus. All of these reactions are caused by white blood cells. Histamine and other chemicals, released especially by basophils and mast cells, cause the small blood vessels surrounding the area to become leaky to the fluid of the blood. This leaky condition is called **increased vascular permeability**, and it allows fluid and blood cells to move more freely into the area, thus causing swelling. In addition, the blood vessels become dilated (enlarged) to carry more blood, and the tissue then becomes red and warmer. Some of these chemicals also lower pain thresholds and cause itching by acting on nerve endings that serve these sensations. (The exact mechanisms involved in this process are not understood.) Sometimes there is a formation of pus, a fluid product consisting of white blood cells, the debris of dead cells, and other particles liquified by phagocytic and chemical processes. To a large extent, pus is the

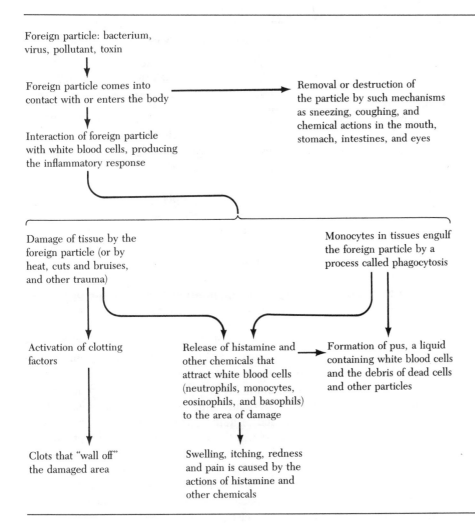

Foreign particle: bacterium,
virus, pollutant, toxin

Foreign particle comes into
contact with or enters the body → Removal or destruction of
the particle by such mechanisms
as sneezing, coughing, and
chemical actions in the mouth,
stomach, intestines, and eyes

Interaction of foreign particle
with white blood cells, producing
the inflammatory response

Damage of tissue by the
foreign particle (or by
heat, cuts and bruises,
and other trauma)

Monocytes in tissues engulf
the foreign particle by a
process called phagocytosis

Activation of clotting
factors

Release of histamine and
other chemicals that
attract white blood cells
(neutrophils, monocytes,
eosinophils, and basophils)
to the area of damage

Formation of pus, a liquid
containing white blood cells
and the debris of dead cells
and other particles

Clots that "wall off"
the damaged area

Swelling, itching, redness
and pain is caused by the
actions of histamine and
other chemicals

Figure 7–1. Mechanisms of natural or innate immunity. (A more
complete diagram of these mechanisms is presented in Figure 7–1A in
the appendix.)

result of the intense infiltration of phagocytes that
ingest and destroy the "invader."

Figure 7-1 also indicates that removal or destruction of a foreign agent occurs through innate mechanisms which, because they do not require white blood
cells, are not regarded as inflammatory responses.
These mechanisms are sometimes *behavioral*, as
when foreign particles are ejected from the nose,
throat, or lungs through sneezing or coughing, or
they can be *chemical*, as when foreign agents are
destroyed in the stomach by stomach secretions or in
the mouth by salivary secretions. Vomiting and diarrhea are also protective responses the body uses to rid
itself of foreign agents. (For those who are interested,
a more complete diagram of natural or innate immune
responses is presented in Figure 7-1A in the appendix.)

We will now look at immune responses that are not
innate but, rather, occur as the result of previous
encounters with specific foreign agents.

Acquired or Adaptive Immunity

The acquired immunity system is extremely important; it provides a powerful means of coping with
foreign agents to which our body has little or no natural or innate immunity. (It is also the system that is
activated when we are vaccinated to become resistant
to particular diseases.) In contrast to the responses of
the innate or natural immunity system, the body does
not strongly oppose invasion by the foreign particle
upon initial exposure to it. Rather, within a short
period of time (a few days to a few weeks) an extremely strong resistance develops that is highly specific for that particular particle and not for others.

Thus, when the invader is encountered *again*, it is destroyed very quickly. This adaptive property of the immune system is based on the fact that the population of white blood cells capable of responding to a particular agent becomes larger once the agent has been encountered. The cells that make up this population are called **memory cells**, and they are part of a larger population of white blood cells called **lymphocytes**, as described below.

The protective mechanisms of acquired immunity involve all of the innate mechanisms, but, as just noted, the principal white blood cells that initiate acquired or adaptive immunity are lymphocytes. While we are still developing as a fetus, lymphocytes differentiate from cells in the bone marrow, liver, and yolk sac. Shortly before birth, and for a few months after birth, these lymphocytes are "preprocessed" by the thymus to become **"T" lymphocytes**, or they are preprocessed by other organs (possibly bone marrow) to become **"B" lymphocytes**. These lymphocytes then migrate in the blood and lymph fluid, finally inhabiting lymphoid tissues in the nasal epithelium, mouth, stomach, intestines, lungs, skin, lymph nodes, thymus, spleen, and bone marrow. That is, the lymphocytes in lymphoid tissue do not originate in these tissues but are white blood cells that have migrated there very early in life.

When the foreign particle comes into contact with lymphoid tissue, it *sensitizes* the "T" and/or "B" lymphocytes inhabiting this tissue. These sensitized lymphocytes then proliferate to form a **clone** of "T" and/or "B" lymphocytes, all specifically sensitized to the particular foreign particle involved. A clone of lymphocytes is a colony or group of lymphocytes that have arisen from one or a few original lymphocytes. As replications of the same cell, these cells are all exactly alike. Some of these lymphocytes remain dormant in the lymphoid tissues, thereby greatly increasing the number of lymphocytes that can be activated if the foreign agent is encountered again (these are the memory cells mentioned earlier). Others are ready to encounter the specific foreign agent that activated them in the first place. The details of this encounter are explained below and are illustrated schematically in Figure 7-2.

The sensitized "T" lymphocytes destroy the invader either directly—by attacking it—or by attracting large numbers of white blood cells that destroy it mostly by phagocytosis. "T" lymphocytes can therefore attack and destroy the invader, but their main function is to release **lymphokines**, chemicals that have a variety of actions, including:

a) causing the small blood vessels in the vicinity to become dilated and carry more blood (vasodilation)

b) making these blood vessels leaky so that fluid and blood cells move into the surrounding tissue and cause swelling (increased vascular permeability)

c) attracting other white blood cells, especially monocytes and macrophages, to intensify phagocytosis.

Also, sensitized "T" lymphocytes often mobilize "B" lymphocytes, whose actions are discussed below.

The sensitized "B" lymphocytes destroy the invader that activated them by first differentiating to become **plasma cells** that secrete **antibodies**. Antibodies are large proteins secreted by the plasma cells into the lymph, and from there into the blood. The antibodies destroy the foreign particles either by direct attack or indirectly by releasing chemicals into the blood. The indirect mechanisms involve the **complement system** and the **anaphylactic system**, both of which destroy or incapacitate the foreign invader.

The complement system involves a host of enzymes that are normally found circulating in an inactve form in the body's fluids. When activated by antibodies, these enzymes destroy the invader by direct attack as well as by attracting large numbers of phagocytes.

The anaphylactic system does not involve enzymes found in the blood and tissue fluids. Rather, it involves a specific interaction of antibodies with basophils and mast cells, an interaction that causes these cells to release a large number of chemicals called **mediators**, which attract or activate other parts of the immune system. Some of these mediators are involved in allergic inflammation (see below). Others either directly destroy the invader or promote intense phagocytosis of the invader by other white blood cells. (For those who are interested, a more complete diagram of acquired and adaptive immunity mechanisms is presented in Figure 7-2A in the appendix).

Although extensive comment must wait for the results of additional research, recent studies suggest the existence of a third group of lymphocytes, called **natural killer cells** (NK cells). These cells are large lymphocytes, estimated to constitute as much as 3 percent of all white blood cells (10 to 15 percent of lymphocytes). When activated by suitable target cells, including some cancer cells, NK cells appear to produce the chemical, **interferon**. The released interferon appears to augment the NK cell's ability to destroy tumor cells, virus-infected cells, and other

Foreign particles come into
contact with lymphoid tissue
containing T and B lymphocytes

T and B lymphocytes become
"sensitized" by the foreign
particle; sensitized lymphocytes
proliferate to form a clone

Sensitized B lymphocytes enlarge
and differentiate to become plasma
cells. These plasma cells secrete
antibodies. Antibodies either
directly attack the invader or indirectly attack it by activating
other white blood cells or the
complement system.
The complement system involves
enzymes in the fluids that directly
destroy the invader or mobilize
white blood cells which then attack
it, producing the inflammatory
reactions illustrated in Figure 7-1.
The anaphylactic system involves a
direct activation of mast cells and
basophils by antibodies, causing
these cells to produce inflammatory
reactions including those of allergic inflammation described in
Figure 7-3.

Sensitized T lymphocytes either
destroy the invader directly or
release chemicals that attract
other white blood cells (monocytes, eosinophils and basophils).
These white blood cells participate
in the same inflammatory reactions
as those illustrated in Figure 7-1.
In addition, the sensitized T
lymphocytes often attract and
mobilize B lymphocytes.

Because some sensitized
T or B lymphocytes
become memory cells, there
are many more T or B
lymphocytes ready to
respond to the foreign
particle should it in-
vade the body again.

Figure 7–2. Mechanisms of acquired or adaptive immunity. (A more complete diagram of these mechanisms is presented in Figure 7–2A in the appendix.)

cells; it also appears to mobilize "pre" NK cells, causing these cells to mature, and to inhibit the activity of
some "T" lymphocytes whose action is to suppress the
activity of NK cells (Kiessling, 1978; Saksela, 1981).
We will now explore allergic reactions.

Allergy

As much as twenty percent of our population, approximately forty million Americans, suffers from
some type of allergy. Sometimes our body becomes so
sensitive to a foreign agent that its protective responses are excessive. *These hypersensitive immune
reactions are called allergies*, and are illustrated in
Figure 7-3. Allergic reactions usually involve a spe-

cific interaction of the "allergen" (foreign particle)
with an antibody or a sensitized "T" lymphocyte. The
allergic response can therefore be regarded as a special case involving mechanisms of adaptive or acquired immunity.

One of the main mechanisms that makes us hypersensitive (allergic) involves the memory cells. These
lymphocytes can remain in the body for as long as ten,
perhaps even twenty years—especially the "T" lymphocytes. The role of prior experience with (exposure
to) a foreign agent is complex. In some cases a person's sensitivity seems to be determined by genetic
factors; that is, some persons, for no apparent reason
other than their genetic make up, have, for example,
a strong reaction to a bee sting after only a few exposures. Others, however, show such sensitivity only

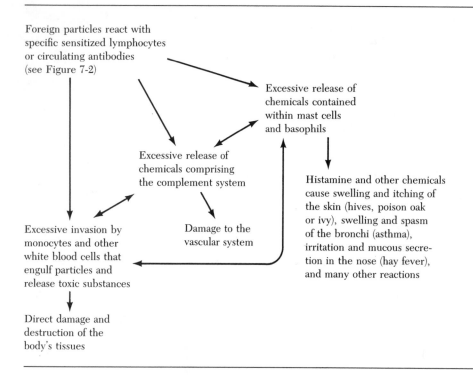

Foreign particles react with specific sensitized lymphocytes or circulating antibodies (see Figure 7-2)

Excessive release of chemicals contained within mast cells and basophils

Excessive release of chemicals comprising the complement system

Histamine and other chemicals cause swelling and itching of the skin (hives, poison oak or ivy), swelling and spasm of the bronchi (asthma), irritation and mucous secretion in the nose (hay fever), and many other reactions

Excessive invasion by monocytes and other white blood cells that engulf particles and release toxic substances

Damage to the vascular system

Direct damage and destruction of the body's tissues

Figure 7–3. Allergic reactions, also called "hypersensitive immune reactions." Note that instead of the normal beneficial effect of the immune response, allergic reactions are excessive and cause harm to the body. (A more complete diagram of these reactions is presented in Figure 7–3A in the appendix.)

after many exposures. Regardless of the number of exposures preceding, when a hypersensitive reaction does occur, it is because the now larger population of sensitized lymphocytes are ready to attack immediately and more forcefully than they did previously. In many cases, this response is beneficial because the invader is destroyed quickly. Sometimes, however, the immune reaction is so intense that it does harm.

Many of the antibodies involved in allergic reactions belong to different classes of globulins, called **immunoglobulins**. Globulins are large proteins that are dissolved in the fluid portion of the blood, and immunoglobulins are a special kind of globulin, called "immuno" because antibodies belong to this family of proteins. Of particular interest is immunoglobulin E (IgE), which is attached to mast cells and basophils. When IgE interacts with specific allergens contained in pollen, certain foods, drugs, venom, etc., the mast cells and basophils release their chemicals and can produce hay fever or bee sting reactions, some types of asthma and hives, and such abdominal symptoms as diarrhea, vomiting, and cramps. Where in the body the allergic reaction occurs depends on where these

chemicals are released. They are usually released in the eyes, nose, throat, lungs, intestines, or skin.

The chemicals most responsible for the symptoms of allergy are histamine, bradykinin, prostaglandins, and the slow-reacting substance of anaphylaxis. These chemicals cause the smooth muscle of the organs to contract, the tissues of the eyes, nose, throat, and skin to swell, itch, redden and become sore, and, often, the glands lining the respiratory and digestive organs to secrete excessive amounts of mucus. These chemicals with their respective actions are shown in Figure 7-3A in the appendix.

The universally prescribed "cure" for all allergic reactions—whether they involve plants (pollen, fungal spores, poison oak, poison ivy), animals (especially cats, dogs, and venom from insects), food (usually eggs, milk, nuts, shellfish and berries) or any other source (including drugs or industrial products)—is *avoidance*. In other words, as discussed previously in relation to those agents against which the body has no means of defending itself, here, too, avoidance behavior is most effective for maintaining a state of health. In this case, however, one is avoiding the harmful effects of *excessive* protective reactions rather than the harmful effects of little or no protective action.

II. INTERNAL MECHANISMS THAT MODIFY THE IMMUNE SYSTEM

Perhaps at this point the reader is wondering why we have paid so much attention to immune mechanisms. This defense system is often bypassed in psychology texts because it appears to be a complex, largely medical topic. However, it is an extremely powerful system that clearly involves behavioral as well as physiological responses. Furthermore, our immune system is exquisitely sensitive not only to bacteria, viruses and other foreign agents, but also to our emotional and physical states.

Unless one wishes to include sneezing, coughing, and vomiting as behavioral responses, the defensive behaviors described so far in this chapter mostly involve avoidance. There are many, more subtle, behaviors, however, such as being physically active or inactive, that can affect immune responses. In order to understand how various behaviors, as well as physical and emotional states, might influence immune mechanisms, we must first understand how the body is equipped to modify immune responses *on its own;* that is, how the body can intensify or suppress immune reactions through *internal* activities that are not directly associated with invasion by foreign agents. The **adrenal glands**, which secrete *hormones*, and the **autonomic nervous system** exert precisely such actions. In this section, we will discuss how the autonomic nervous system and the adrenal glands are organized and, in a general way, what their functions are. We will discover that the actions of the autonomic nervous system and the adrenal glands affect not only immune responses but also many other bodily functions that are connected to protective mechanisms. Afterwards (in Section III) we will discuss emotions and the involvement of the brain. First, let's briefly define the word "hormone."

The word "hormone" is a general term that denotes any chemical produced by one or another organ and released into the *blood* to be carried to other organs where it then exerts specific stimulatory or inhibitory effects. In this chapter we will emphasize the hormones secreted by the adrenal glands, and discuss these hormones in the context of the body's protective mechanisms. (The role of hormones in reproduction is covered in Chapter 10 in some detail.)

The Autonomic Nervous System

The autonomic nervous system is composed of two separate branches: the **parasympathetic branch** and the **sympathetic branch**. (In discussing this system, we will use PNS to refer to the parasympathetic nervous system, and SNS for the sympathetic nervous system.)

Figure 7-4 illustrates the parasympathetic nervous system. As shown, the neurons that comprise the PNS leave the spinal cord at the level of the medulla, pons, or midbrain (upper spinal cord) or at the sacral level (bottom of the spinal cord). The axons of these neurons are arranged in bundles that are held together by connective tissue. These bundles are called **nerves**. The nerves that contain the axons of neurons that leave from the upper spinal cord are all **cranial nerves** (relating to the cranium, or skull). These are the oculomotor nerve, the trigeminal nerve, the facial nerve and the glossopharyngeal nerve, which innervate the eyes, face, sinuses, jaws, mouth and tongue, tonsils, and pharynx; and the vagus nerve, which innervates the pharynx and larynx, trachea, bronchi and lungs, heart, stomach, gall bladder, pancreas and intestines, liver, and kidneys. The pelvic nerve (not a cranial nerve) contains the axons of neurons that leave from the bottom of the spinal cord and innervate the large intestines, the urinary bladder, and the reproductive organs. As is evident, the nerves comprising the parasympathetic nervous system innervate almost all of our organs. In general, blood vessels are not innervated by parasympathetic nerves.

The nerve endings of neurons that comprise parasympathetic nerves all release a chemical called **acetylcholine**. The chemical structure of acetylcholine is given in the figure. When parasympathetic nerves are stimulated, this causes acetylcholine to be released by neurons comprising these nerves. *It is acetylcholine that influences the activity of the organs innervated by the PNS.* We will discuss the effects of acetylcholine a little later in this section.

Figure 7-5 illustrates the sympathetic nervous system. The nerves that comprise the SNS contain neurons whose axons leave the spinal cord between the first thoracic segment, at the bottom of the neck, and the second lumbar segment, toward the bottom of the back. As with parasympathetic nerves, sympathetic nerves innervate most of the organs of the body. However, their anatomical distribution is different. For one, they originate in the middle sectors of the spinal cord whereas parasympathetic nerves originate either above or below. (In Greek,

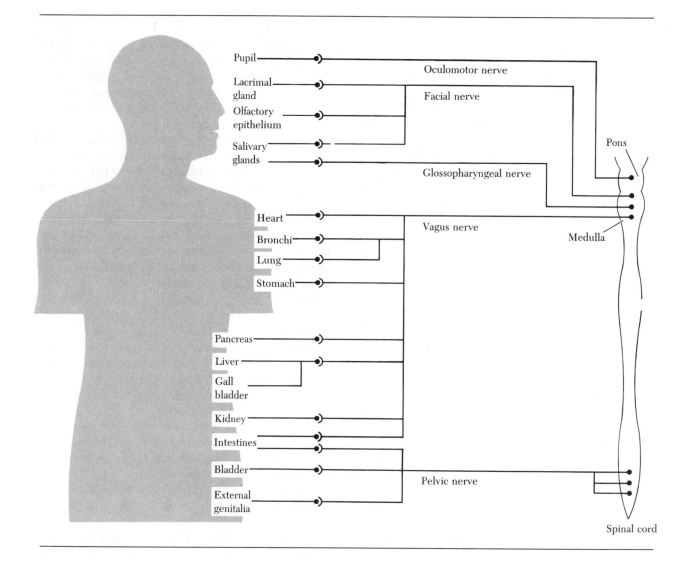

(1) The nerve endings that terminate in the various organs of the body all release acetylcholine.

$$H_3C-\overset{\displaystyle CH_3}{\underset{\displaystyle CH_3}{\overset{|}{\underset{|}{N^+}}}}-CH_2-CH_2-O-\overset{\displaystyle O}{\overset{\|}{C}}-CH_3$$

Acetylcholine

(2) The nerves that comprise the PNS leave the spinal cord at the level of the medulla or pons (upper spinal cord) or at the sacral level (bottom of spinal cord). The nerves that leave from the upper spinal cord are all cranial nerves (but not all cranial nerves are part of the autonomic nervous system).

(3) Blood vessels are poorly innervated by the PNS. The autonomic nervous system influences blood flow mostly through sympathetic nerves.

Figure 7–4. Organs innervated by the parasympathetic nervous system (PNS).

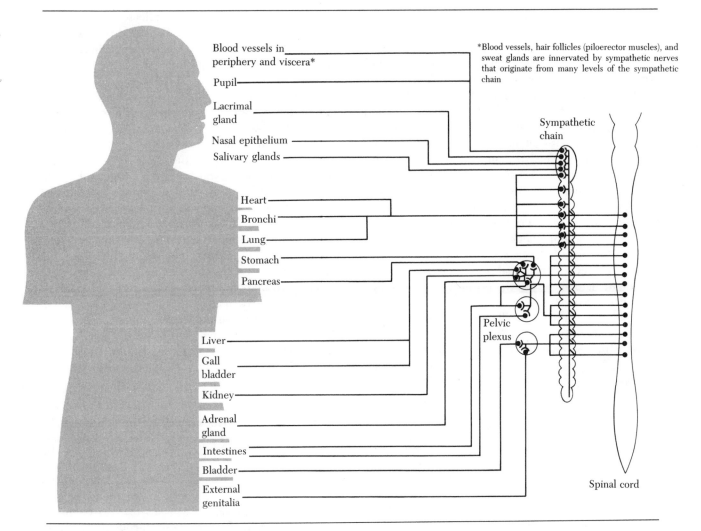

(1) Most of the nerve endings that terminate in the various organs of the body release norepinephrine, some also epinephrine, but in smaller amounts. The sympathetic nerves that innervate sweat glands release acetylcholine; those that innervate blood vessels of the skin and skeletal muscle release norepinephrine or acetylcholine.

Norepinephrine (also called noradrenalin)

Epinephrine (also called adrenalin)

(2) The nerves that comprise the SNS leave the spinal cord between the first thoracic segment (T_1) and the second lumbar segment (L_2).

(3) The nerve endings that terminate in the adrenal glands cause the adrenal medulla to release epinephrine and norepinephrine into the blood. The secretion from the adrenal medulla is 80% epinephrine, 20% norepinephrine. The norepinephrine (and slight amounts of epinephrine) released by sympathetic nerves in the organs remains active only for a few seconds. In contrast, when these chemicals are released by the adrenal glands, they remain active in the blood for a long time (up to 30 seconds).

Figure 7–5. Organs innervated by the sympathetic nervous system (SNS). Because they are widely dispersed in the body, blood vessels, hair follicles (piloerector muscles), and sweat glands are innervated by many sympathetic nerves.

"para" means alongside or near. Thus, parasympathetic means alongside—in this case on top of or under—the sympathetic.) Also, sympathetic nerves contain the axons of neurons that leave the spinal cord and then go to spinal **sympathetic ganglia** that lie on each side of the spinal column. Many of these ganglia are connected to neighboring ganglia above and below to form what is called the **sympathetic chain**. Ganglia are groups of neural cell bodies that are covered with connective tissue and are located outside the central nervous system. In turn, the neural cell bodies that comprise the ganglia of the sympathetic chains send their axons to different organs of the body where they terminate as sympathetic nerve endings. (Parasympathetic nerves also go to ganglia, called parasympathetic ganglia, but, rather than forming a chain outside the spinal cord, they are located in the immediate vicinity of the organs they innervate.)

In general, nerves leaving the upper portion of the sympathetic chain go to all parts of the head, the larynx, and the trachea. Nerves leaving progressively lower portions innervate the bronchi and lungs, the heart, and all the other organs of the body, including its blood vessels.

Almost all sympathetic nerve endings release a chemical called **norepinephrine** at the point where they terminate at one or another organ. The chemical structure of norepinephrine (also called **noradrenalin**) is given in Figure 7-5 together with that of **epinephrine** (also called **adrenalin**) which is also released, although in much smaller amounts than norepinephrine. When sympathetic nerves are stimulated, its neurons release norepinephrine. *In general, it is norepinephrine that influences the activity of the organs innervated by the SNS.*

There are a few notable exceptions to the workings described above. The sympathetic nerves that innervate the adrenal glands do not go to sympathetic ganglia before innervating this organ. Instead, they go directly to the inner portion of the adrenal gland, called the **adrenal medulla**, where they innervate special cells that secrete large amounts of epinephrine (80%) and also some norepinephrine (20%) into the blood. These chemicals remain active in the blood for a much longer period than when they are released by sympathetic nerve endings that terminate in the organs of the body. The adrenal glands are discussed in the next section.

Another exception to the workings presented in Figure 7-5 involves the chemicals released by sympathetic nerves that innervate sweat glands and blood vessels of skin, and the blood vessels of skeletal muscle. The sympathetic nerves that innervate sweat

glands contain neurons that release *acetylcholine*. Those that innervate some of the blood vessels of skin and skeletal muscle also release acetylcholine, but some release norepinephrine instead. As one would expect, when sympathetic nerves release acetylcholine the effects are different from those occurring when they release norepinephrine. These effects will be discussed when we cover the effects of stimulation of the autonomic nervous system.

Although the sympathetic nervous system and the parasympathetic nervous system are defined by their anatomical differences, it is important to note that they both have their origin within the brain and, as such, are part of the nervous system as a whole. Responses resulting from activation of sympathetic and parasympathetic nerves can be elicited by stimulating almost any area of the brain, but especially the upper spinal cord, hypothalamus, certain parts of the limbic system, and certain areas of the frontal cortex, as will be discussed later in the chapter.

In the end organs and tissues of the body, the PNS and SNS differ significantly in the reactions they elicit. In general, parasympathetic responses are those which:

1) AID THE DIGESTION OF SOLID FOOD. This digestive effect applies to the actions of the salivary glands, esophagus, stomach, intestines, gallbladder, and pancreas.

2) INCREASE PROTECTION AGAINST THE INGESTION OF FOREIGN PARTICLES. This protective effect applies to lacrimal secretions by the eyes, salivary secretions, mucous secretions of the mouth, nose, throat, esophagus, stomach, intestines and bronchi, and secretions of the stomach, all of which help to trap foreign particles and wash them away or destroy them.

3) DOMINATE WHEN WE ARE QUIET, RELAXED OR ASLEEP. These responses probably are due more to a decrease in the activity of the SNS when one is quiet than to any increase in PNS activity.

In contrast, sympathetic responses are those which:

1) GENERALLY PREPARE OUR BODY TO MEET AN EMERGENCY. This is popularly known as the "fight or flight syndrome." Many responses are involved in this response of the SNS, ranging from an increase in the contractility of the heart and an increase in the heart rate to an increase in the mobilization of chemicals that the skeletal muscles use for energy. While blood flow

in skeletal muscle usually increases, partly because of dilation of vessels in skeletal muscle and partly because there is more blood made available due to its reduced flow in the gut, blood flow to the kidneys and the gastrointestinal organs is reduced. Relaxation of the smooth muscle of the digestive organs and the urinary bladder help conserve energy which can be used by skeletal muscle, and relaxation of bronchial muscle and decreased secretion of mucus by the lungs helps us to breathe in more air.

2) GENERALLY DIMINISH THE EFFECTIVENESS OF PROTECTIVE MECHANISMS WITHIN THE BODY.

This result is mainly due to effects on the immune system. Non-immune effects, like reduced secretions of saliva, mucus, and gastric acid, make it more likely that a foreign particle will be ingested; however, in a normal emergency situation, one is preoccupied with the crisis and has little appetite for food. (The relation between the SNS and immune mechanisms in our body is covered more fully later in this section.)

3) DOMINATE WHEN WE ARE ALERT, EXCITED, OR ENGAGED IN MUSCULAR EXERCISE.

Many people emphasize the opposing nature of the parasympathetic and sympathetic nervous systems. As a generalization, however, this can be misleading, for even though these systems often have opposing effects, at any given time only one system is likely to dominate any given organ. Also, because both the PNS and SNS stimulate some organs and inhibit others, the generalization can't be made that one system is inhibitory and the other excitatory. Furthermore, the PNS and SNS are both continually active in the body. The "tone" of the gastrointestinal tract, for example, is usually dictated by the PNS: increased PNS activity increases peristaltic activity and promotes secretion, whereas decreased PNS activity decreases these responses. Although the digestive tract is also innervated by the SNS, the stomach and intestines are usually not dominated by it. Most of the "tone" of the blood vessels, the activity of sweat glands, and the activity of the adrenal glands, on the other hand, are dominated by the SNS. Increased SNS activity usually constricts blood vessels (a notable exception is in skeletal muscle) and leads to secretion of sweat from the skin and hormones from the adrenal glands, whereas decreased SNS activity diminishes or stops these responses. The PNS plays almost no role in this regulation. In fact, the adrenal

glands, sweat glands and piloerector muscles of the skin (the muscles that cause hair to "stand on end" or that give us "goose bumps"), do not even have PNS innervation.

In short, the autonomic nervous system is largely concerned with the regulation of visceral function. It influences the contraction of smooth muscle found in blood vessels, the eyes, the walls and sphincters of the esophagus, stomach, intestines, gall bladder, bronchi of the lungs, and urinary bladder. It also influences the contraction of the heart and the secretion of glands such as the salivary glands, lacrimal glands, and sweat glands. In addition, the autonomic nervous system affects the secretion of mucous cells found throughout the gastrointestinal tract, mouth, nose, throat, and lungs, the secretion of acid by the stomach, and the secretion of insulin and digestive enzymes by the pancreas. These processes and others are summarized in Tables 7-1 and 7-2. These tables also list some of the common effects we all experience when the autonomic nervous system is activated. It would be well worth the time to study these tables for a few minutes.

The Adrenal Glands

The role of the adrenal glands in defense reactions is so important that we will discuss this topic in some detail. The adrenal gland is actually composed of two different organs, an outer *cortex* and an inner *medulla* (see Figure 7-6).

The **adrenal medulla** is activated by sympathetic nerves and responds by secreting **epinephrine** and **norepinephrine** into the blood (the same chemicals released in the organs by most sympathetic nerve endings).

The **adrenal cortex** is not activated by nerves, but by a hormone, **ACTH** (adrenocorticotrophic hormone), which is released into the blood from the pituitary gland. In other words, when the pituitary gland releases ACTH into the blood, the adrenal cortex is stimulated to secrete a number of different chemicals into the blood. Of these, the most important are **cortisol** and **aldosterone**. In order to better understand the effects of adrenal secretions on protective mechanisms in the body, we will first discuss the effects of activation of the adrenal medulla, then the effects of activation of the adrenal cortex.

Activation of the Adrenal Medulla. Since the hormones released by the adrenal medulla into the blood are the same chemicals as those released by SNS nerve endings that innervate the organs of our body, the effects of activation of the adrenal medulla

Organ	Physiological effects of parasympathetic stimulation	Some common experiences associated with activation of the parasympathetic nervous system (PNS)
Eye: pupil lacrimal gland	Pupillary constriction Secretion of fluid	Tears in the eyes, a runny nose, and a congested throat, symptoms of weeping, are eliminated by cutting the cranial nerves that carry both the parasympathetic impulses to the nose, throat, and eyes and the impulses that innervate the facial muscles involved.
Nasal and pharyngeal glands	Secretion of fluid from mucous membranes	
Salivary glands	Secretion of watery fluid filled with enzymes	Salivation is a response to desirable foods, but also to unpleasant odors or undesirable foods (usually a prelude to vomiting).
Lungs: bronchial muscle bronchial glands	Contraction of smooth muscle Secretion of fluid from mucous membranes	Increased resistance to breathing, sometimes with wheezing, are symptoms especially common in asthma. When a person goes to sleep, the PNS becomes more dominant. Asthmatics frequently experience much more difficulty breathing in bed at night than while active during the day.
Heart: pacemaker cells atria	Decreased heart rate Decreased force of contraction in atria only (not the ventricles)	No obvious experiences are associated with this response.
Esophagus, stomach, and intestines: muscle glands	Increased motility and tone Increased secretion of gastric and intestinal juices	Resting after a meal facilitates digestion. When a person is digesting food or is anticipating a meal, the activity and secretions from the stomach, intestines, pancreas, and gallbladder increase. These parasympathetic responses are more intense when a person is relaxed.
Gallbladder *Pancreas*	Increased contraction of the gallbladder Increased secretion of insulin and enzymes from the pancreas	No obvious experiences are associated with these responses (although an insulin-induced lowering of blood glucose levels can lead to sensations of hunger).
Bladder: detrusor muscles trigone muscles	Contraction of the body of the bladder Relaxation of the internal sphincter	Urination is more easily accomplished when a person is relaxed. (Contraction of the bladder and relaxation of the internal sphincter allow the bladder to empty.)
Sexual organs: male: female:	Erection of penis Erection of introitus and clitoris; vaginal secretion by mucous glands	The erotic aspects of sexual arousal are most dominant when anxiety, fear, or other emotions that activate sympathetic responses (and inhibit parasympathetic responses) in the sexual organs are absent or only minimally present.

Table 7–1. Effects of acetylcholine release resulting from stimulation of the parasympathetic nervous system (PNS): physiological effects on various organs and common experiences associated with these effects.

Organ	Physiological effects of sympathetic stimulation	Some common experiences associated with activation of the sympathetic nervous system (SNS)
Eye: pupil lacrimal gland	Pupillary dilation[a] Constriction of the blood vessels supplying this gland, thereby reducing its ability to secrete fluid[a]	Although pupillary dilation is not usually associated with an obvious experience (except when a person's eyes are dilated for an eye examination, in which case light is experienced as too bright), the enlarged pupils are visible to someone else. We do sometimes experience dryness and irritation of the eyes during emergencies or other stressful situations.
Nasal and pharyngeal glands	Constriction of the blood vessels supplying these glands, thereby reducing their ability to secrete mucus[a]	When a person with a cold undergoes a stressful experience, there is often a temporary relief of symptoms of congestion because less mucus is secreted in the nasal cavities and throat.
Salivary glands	Constriction of blood vessels, causing reduced secretion of watery fluid; increased production of a thick, viscous secretion[a]	A "thick," "pasty," "dry" mouth is sometimes experienced when a person is defending himself/herself or is reacting to a threatening situation.
Lungs: bronchial muscle bronchial vessels and glands	Relaxation of smooth muscle[b] Mild constriction of vessels, reducing secretions[a]	A decreased resistance to breathing is sometimes experienced by people with asthma. In an emergency situation where the SNS is strongly stimulated, an asthmatic will often feel much better. (However, once the SNS activity is reduced again, the asthmatic often feels worse because of the relative increase in PNS activity—see Table 7–1.)
Heart: muscle and conduction system	Increased heart rate, increased force of contraction in atria and ventricles[b]	"Pounding" of blood, usually felt in the chest, neck, and head and usually accompanied by a rise in blood pressure.
Esophagus, stomach, intestines, gall-bladder: muscle vessels & glands	Relaxation and inhibition of gastrointestinal muscles[b] Constriction of blood vessels, reducing secretions[a]	Loss of appetite is a common experience associated with decreased stomach contractions. In addition, if a person becomes very active or excited, the decreased contraction of smooth muscle and reduced secretion throughout the gastrointestinal system inhibits digestive processes and results in feelings of discomfort, particularly if one has just eaten. (The occurrence of prolonged periods without bowel movement during emergencies is also a result of suppressed gastrointestinal activity.)

continued on next page

[a] A response elicited by norepinephrine released by sympathetic nerve endings.
[b] A response elicited by norepinephrine released by sympathetic nerve endings, but more so by epinephrine released by the adrenal glands.

Table 7–2. Effects of norepinephrine, epinephrine, and acetylcholine release resulting from stimulation of the sympathetic nervous system (SNS): physiological effects on various organs and common experiences associated with these effects.

Organ	Physiological effects of sympathetic stimulation	Some common experiences associated with activation of the sympathetic nervous system (SNS)
Pancreas	Decreased insulin secretion[c]	No obvious experiences are associated with the decreased secretion of insulin. The increased secretion (see footnote c) in a crisis situation sometimes makes one feel "energized" because insulin promotes glucose uptake by cells.
Liver	Stimulation of glycogenolysis and the release of glucose[b]	Glucose provides quick, usable energy for the body, and is partly responsible for feeling "energized." Increased glucose levels also contribute to a loss of appetite.
Kidneys	Constriction of blood vessels, reducing filtration of blood [a]	One reason why a person in a prolonged emergency situation can go a long time without urinating is because the sympathetic stimulation decreases the formation of urine.
Bladder:		
detrusor muscles	Relaxation of the body of the bladder[a]	Another reason why a person in a prolonged emergency situation can go a long time without
trigone muscles	Constriction of the internal sphincter[a]	urinating is because the sympathetic stimulation suppresses the emptying of the bladder. (Relaxation of the bladder and constriction of the internal sphincter inhibit urination.)
Spleen capsule	Contraction of capsule[a]	No obvious experiences are associated with this response.
Skin:		
blood vessels	Constriction of blood vessels[a] Dilation of blood vessels[b]	In a situation where there is a sudden, pronounced threat, a person will become "pale." This reaction is due to SNS stimulation of blood vessels in the skin.
sweat glands in most areas of the body	Increased secretion of sweat[d]	One may also react with an increase in sweat secretion, called a "cold sweat," which may or may
sweat glands in the palms and feet	Increased secretion of sweat[a]	not be accompanied by "goose bumps" (due to activation of piloerector muscles).
piloerector muscles	Piloerection[a]	
Skeletal muscle:		
blood vessels	Constriction of blood vessels[e] Dilation of blood vessels[d]	These effects impart feelings of energy during a crisis. As part of a response to a sudden threat, or when startled, blood flow to the skeletal muscles
muscle cells	Increased glycogenolysis, increased force of contraction[b]	(and skin) decreases and the blood is shunted to the inner organs. When "action" is required, however, the activation of the SNS increases the strength and activity of skeletal muscles, increases the release of nutrients from muscle cells (glucose), and causes dilation of blood vessels (allowing more oxygen for muscle). These mechanisms are partly responsible for the general feeling of being "energized."

[c] A response elicited by norepinephrine released by sympathetic nerve endings. In contrast, epinephrine (from the adrenal glands) increases insulin secretion.

[d] A response elicited by acetylcholine released by sympathetic nerve endings. With sweat glands, this response is usually associated with the regulation of body temperature; with blood vessels of skeletal muscle, with the contraction of the muscle.

[e] An intense response elicited by norepinephrine released by sympathetic nerve endings. In contrast, epinephrine only mildly constricts and often dilates the vessels in skeletal muscle.

Table 7-2. (continued)

Organ	Physiological effects of sympathetic stimulation	Some common experiences associated with activation of the sympathetic nervous system (SNS)
Male sexual organs	Ejaculation[a]	A man experiencing anxiety or tension sufficient to activate his SNS can sometimes experience "premature" ejaculation.
Adipose tissue	Increased lipolysis[b]	This physiological response also promotes feelings of energy during a crisis. The mobilization and breakdown of fats produces more usable energy for the body. This mechanism also contributes to the general feeling of being "energized."

Table 7-2. (continued)

are not that different from the effects of activating the SNS as a whole. Several differences do exist, nevertheless: a) When these chemicals are released by SNS nerve endings, the composition is almost entirely norepinephrine. In contrast, the composition of chemicals from the adrenal medulla is largely epinephrine; b) The chemicals released by the adrenal medulla last about ten times longer in the body than do those released by SNS nerve endings in the organs; c) Norepinephrine exerts its influence largely by acting on **alpha receptors** in the organs, whereas epinephrine exerts its influence by acting on *both* **alpha and beta receptors** in the organs. This is discussed below.

Because the words "alpha" and "beta" are used to distinguish a variety of processes in the body, these terms must be further defined according to the context in which they appear. For example, in Chapter 8 we will see that certain patterns, called "brain waves," of the electroencephalogram (abbreviated EEG) are referred to as "alpha" rhythms or "beta" rhythms. In this chapter, "alpha" receptors and "beta" receptors mean something quite different.

When epinephrine and, to a lesser extent, norepinephrine are released by the adrenal medulla, they exert their actions in the body by interacting with cells in the blood and in various organs. The part of the cell that responds to these chemicals is called the **receptor**. The receptor is believed to be a site on the surface of the cell where the chemical (in this case epinephrine or norepinephrine) becomes attached. As the result of complex, largely unknown interactions between a chemical and its receptor, specific cellular processes are initiated that further define what is called the **receptor response**. For example, in attaching itself to blood vessels in skeletal muscle, epinephrine can cause them either to become narrow (*vasoconstriction*) or to relax, or become wide (*va-*

sodilation). These different actions of epinephrine have been determined through tests conducted with certain drugs. For example, the drug **phentolamine**, which selectively *blocks* the "alpha" receptor, will cause blood vessels to dilate in response to epinephrine (a "beta" receptor response), whereas the drug **propranolol**, which selectively blocks the "beta" receptor, will cause blood vessels to constrict in response to epinephrine (an "alpha" receptor response). When the "alpha" receptor is blocked, the "beta" receptor is free to respond and vice versa. *Both* of these

Figure 7-6. The adrenal gland, showing the adrenal medulla being activated by the SNS—indicated by the single arrow—to release epinephrine and norepinephrine, and the adrenal cortex by ACTH—indicated by the dashed arrow—to release mineralocorticoids and glucocorticoids. (We have two adrenal glands, one above each kidney.)

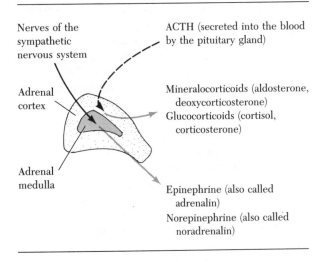

Nerves of the sympathetic nervous system

Adrenal cortex

Adrenal medulla

ACTH (secreted into the blood by the pituitary gland)

Mineralocorticoids (aldosterone, deoxycorticosterone)
Glucocorticoids (cortisol, corticosterone)

Epinephrine (also called adrenalin)
Norepinephrine (also called noradrenalin)

receptors to epinephrine exist in the blood vessels.

The fact that one receptor is called "alpha" and the other "beta" is purely arbitrary. We know they are *different* from each other, however, because certain drugs influence one but not the other. For this reason, all effects exerted by epinephrine that are blocked by phentolamine are called effects exerted through alpha receptors, and all of those effects blocked by propranolol are referred to as effects exerted through beta receptors. Many more drugs than the two mentioned here influence these receptors, either blocking them or stimulating them. These workings are discussed in more detail in Chapter 11.

Although epinephrine and norepinephrine are both capable of activating alpha and beta receptors, they do not activate these receptors equally. *Norepinephrine, which is mainly released by sympathetic nerve endings, activates alpha receptors much more than beta receptors*. Epinephrine, which is mainly released by the adrenal medulla, activates alpha and beta receptors about equally. Therefore, *epinephrine stimulates beta receptors much more than does norepinephrine*.

In most circumstances the effects of epinephrine are much more pronounced on the heart, lungs, liver, and adipose tissue (fat) than are the effects of norepinephrine, a finding used to infer the dominant presence of beta receptors in these organs. In contrast, the piloerector muscles in the skin, the sweat glands in the palms, and the blood vessels of the salivary glands and mucous membranes are highly sensitive to norepinephrine, thus suggesting the dominant presence of alpha receptors in these organs. The receptors in the blood vessels of skeletal muscle and the abdominal organs, the pancreas, and lymphocytes respond to both norepinephrine and epinephrine (although the effects often differ depending upon which receptor is activated), thus suggesting that these organs or tissues have a mixture of responsive alpha and beta receptors.

The effects of activation of alpha and beta receptors by norepinephrine and epinephrine are summarized in Table 7-3. As shown, when the adrenal medulla is activated, there is a pronounced **calorigenic** effect from the heat generated by the increased metabolism associated with activation of beta receptors in liver and fat cells (see the responses listed under "D"). This increase in metabolic rate is characterized by increased levels of blood sugar, increased fatty acids in the blood, and increased conversion of these foods into usable energy. There is also a pronounced **anti-inflammatory** effect, reflected by a decrease in the activity and proliferation of lymphocytes that leads to

a *decreased immune response* (see under response "C"). ("Suppression" of the immune system and "anti-inflammatory effects" are two ways to say the same thing.) Although epinephrine and norepinephrine also increase the activity and proliferation of lymphocytes through their action on alpha receptors (see under response "B"), in a normal situation the anti-inflammatory response is much more dominant. This dominance is because the hormones released into the blood, and therefore most likely to influence lymphocytes, come almost exclusively from the adrenal medulla rather than from SNS nerve endings.

In the above discussion, we have talked about alpha and beta receptors as if they are activated solely by epinephrine and norepinephrine from the adrenal medulla. This is not the case. The norepinephrine and epinephrine released by SNS nerve endings throughout the body also affect these receptors. Since norepinephrine is by far the more prevalent chemical released by SNS nerve endings in the organs, the effects largely involve stimulation of alpha receptors. However, since the norepinephrine that is released by SNS nerves is very quickly neutralized (it is either destroyed or it goes back into the cells), it has very little influence except on the organs that are directly innervated by these nerves. In contrast, the norepinephrine released by the adrenal medulla is secreted into the blood where its actions last much longer.

Activation of the Adrenal Cortex. The adrenal cortex is stimulated to produce and release its chemicals by ACTH (adrenocorticotrophic hormone) released by the pituitary gland. In turn, the production and release of ACTH by the pituitary gland is under the control of the *hypothalamus*. The adrenal cortex is therefore regulated by the brain, as is the adrenal medulla, which is regulated by the sympathetic nerves that innervate it. (See Figure 10-8, Chapter 10.)

When the adrenal cortex is activated by ACTH, it responds by secreting **steroid hormones** into the blood. Steroid hormones are derived from cholesterol and from ergosterol (also called provitamin D). Steroids all share the same basic structural ring system composed of three hexane rings (six carbons per ring) and one pentane ring (five carbons). The function of the different steroid hormones is based on how various chemicals are attached to these rings. There are many steroids secreted by the adrenal cortex, and the sex glands secrete steroids as well. (The sex steroids will be discussed in Chapter 10.) The most important steroids secreted by the adrenal cortex are cortisol,

Table 7–3. Effects of norepinephrine and epinephrine on alpha and beta receptor responses. When epinephrine is released by the adrenal glands, the main effects are those listed in A, C, and D. The responses listed in A result from epinephrine's stimulation of alpha receptors as well as beta receptors. When norepinephrine is released by the adrenal glands or by SNS nerve endings, the main effects are those listed in A and B.

*Effects of activating **alpha receptors**. These effects are caused by both norepinephrine (SNS nerve endings and 20% of adrenal medullary secretion) and epinephrine (80% of adrenal medullary secretion).*

*Effects of activating **beta receptors**. These effects are mostly caused by epinephrine (80% of adrenal medullary secretion).*

Responses in organs almost exclusively enriched with alpha receptors	*Responses in organs having both alpha and beta receptors*		*Responses in organs almost exclusively enriched with beta receptors*
A. alpha receptor responses:	B. alpha receptor responses:	C. beta receptor responses:	D. beta receptor responses:
Piloerection	Constriction of blood vessels throughout the body	Dilation of blood vessels in skeletal muscle and abdominal organs	Increased contractility of heart muscle and increased heart rate
Increased sweat secretion in the palms	Decreased insulin secretion by the pancreas	Increased insulin secretion by the pancreas	Relaxation of smooth muscle of bronchi
Constriction of blood vessels in the salivary glands and mucous membranes (nose, throat, bronchi, gastro-intestinal tract)	Increased activity and proliferation of lymphocytes—a **pro-inflammatory** effect caused by stimulation of the immune system	Decreased activity and proliferation of lymphocytes—an **anti-inflammatory** effect caused by suppression of the immune system	Increased liver glycogenolysis (conversion of glycogen into glucose, causing high blood sugar levels)—a **calorigenic** effect
Thick, pasty secretion from the salivary glands	Relaxation of intestinal smooth muscle	Relaxation of intestinal smooth muscle	Increased lipolysis in adipose tissue (conversion of fats into fatty acids which can be metabolized)—a **calorigenic** effect

corticosterone, aldosterone and deoxycorticosterone. The structure of these chemicals is given in Figure 7-7 to emphasize their structural similarities and differences.

In many respects the adrenal glucocorticoids (cortisol and corticosterone) act similarly to epinephrine in that they have both *calorigenic* and *anti-inflammatory* effects. In addition, they seem to have a "permissive action" on epinephrine and norepinephrine; that is, without glucocorticoids the calorigenic effects of epinephrine do not occur. On the other hand, these steroids do not affect the organs innervated by the SNS as widely as does epinephrine.

The adrenal mineralocorticoids (mostly aldosterone) have their most important effects on the kidneys, where they increase the reabsorption of sodium into

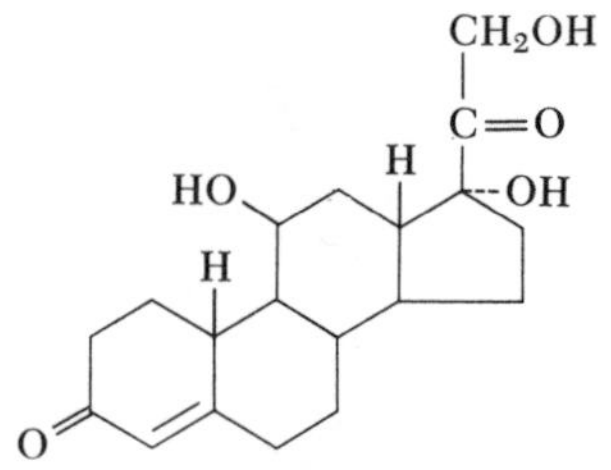

Cortisol

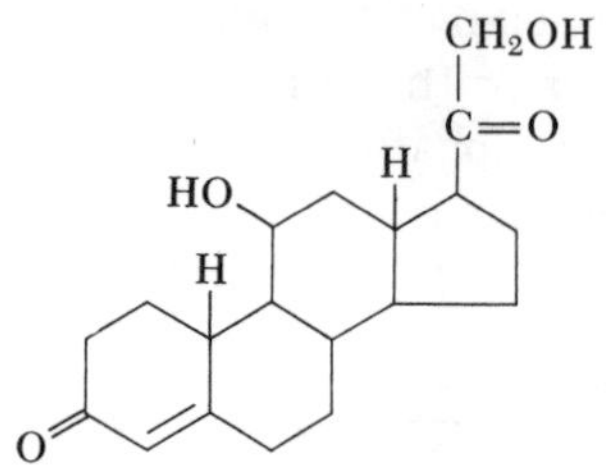

Corticosterone

Glucocorticoids

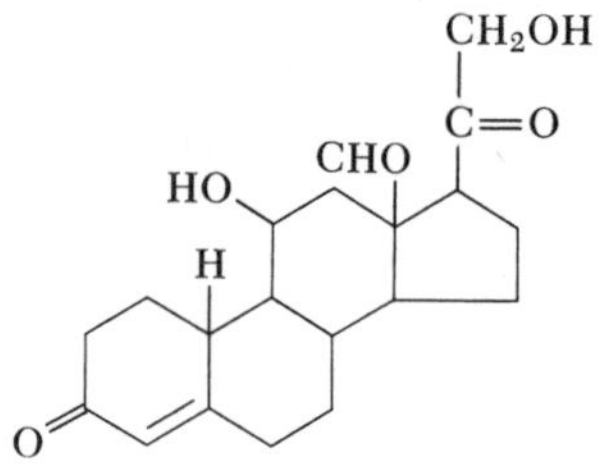

Aldosterone

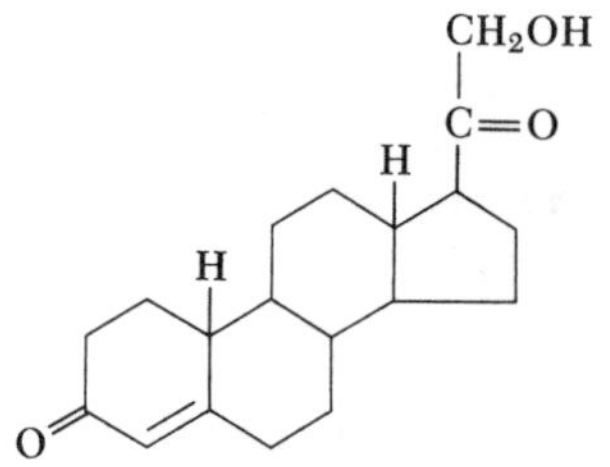

Deoxycorticosterone

Mineralocorticoids

Figure 7–7. The chemical structure of the major steroids secreted by the adrenal cortex. Note that although all of these molecules are similar in their basic structure (which is that of all steroids), each differs from the other.

the body and, to a lesser extent, increase the excretion of potassium out of the body. Related to this regulation of "minerals" (i.e., sodium and potassium), aldosterone is released by the adrenal cortex not only when levels of ACTH from the pituitary gland increase, but also when plasma potassium levels rise, plasma sodium levels fall, or when the arterial pressure in the kidneys falls. These stimuli do not necessarily increase glucocorticoid secretion from the adrenal cortex.

Although the physiological mechanisms are not clearly known, it has been shown that the mineralocorticoids are **proinflammatory**; that is, they *intensify* inflammatory responses by stimulating the immune system and they antagonize the anti-inflammatory effects of the glucocorticoids, which suppress the immune system. Whatever the significance of this finding may be, it is quite clear that the overall effect of activation of the adrenal cortex by ACTH leads to anti-inflammatory responses.

The Adrenal Glands, the Autonomic Nervous System and the Immune System

The effects of epinephrine and norepinephrine on alpha and beta receptors, as well as the effects of glucocorticoids on calorigenesis and anti-inflammatory mechanisms are summarized in Figure 7-8. This diagram shows that when the adrenal glands are stimulated, immune reactions are inhibited or reduced. This is one reason why glucocorticoids are sometimes given to patients with severe allergic reactions.

On the other hand, there are also a variety of proinflammatory effects that can be elicited with adrenal secretions. Activation of alpha receptors causes an increase in the number of lymphocytes. Also, as mentioned previously, the mineralocorticoids secreted by the adrenal cortex appear to be proinflammatory, and these steroids can actually neutralize the anti-inflammatory effects of the glucocorticoids.

At first glance, findings that adrenal secretions are

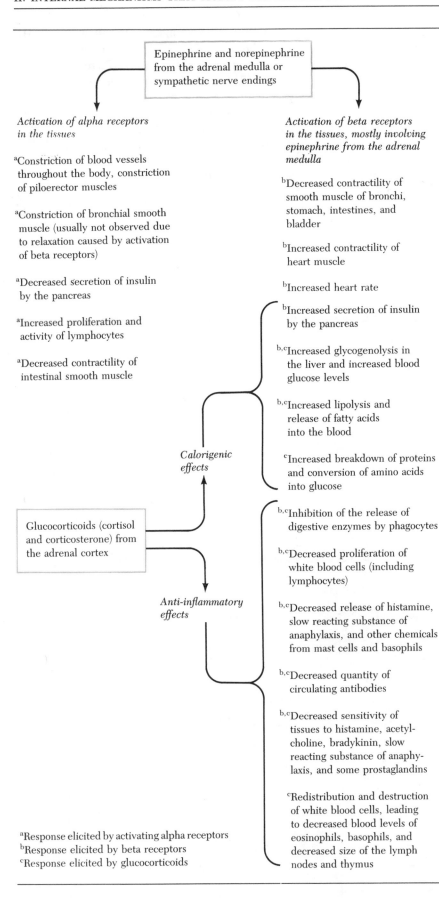

Figure 7—8. Effects of adrenal secretions on various tissues, emphasizing anti-inflammatory and calorigenic effects.

Epinephrine and norepinephrine from the adrenal medulla or sympathetic nerve endings

Activation of alpha receptors in the tissues

[a]Constriction of blood vessels throughout the body, constriction of piloerector muscles

[a]Constriction of bronchial smooth muscle (usually not observed due to relaxation caused by activation of beta receptors)

[a]Decreased secretion of insulin by the pancreas

[a]Increased proliferation and activity of lymphocytes

[a]Decreased contractility of intestinal smooth muscle

Activation of beta receptors in the tissues, mostly involving epinephrine from the adrenal medulla

[b]Decreased contractility of smooth muscle of bronchi, stomach, intestines, and bladder

[b]Increased contractility of heart muscle

[b]Increased heart rate

[b]Increased secretion of insulin by the pancreas

[b,c]Increased glycogenolysis in the liver and increased blood glucose levels

[b,c]Increased lipolysis and release of fatty acids into the blood

[c]Increased breakdown of proteins and conversion of amino acids into glucose

Calorigenic effects

Glucocorticoids (cortisol and corticosterone) from the adrenal cortex

Anti-inflammatory effects

[b,c]Inhibition of the release of digestive enzymes by phagocytes

[b,c]Decreased proliferation of white blood cells (including lymphocytes)

[b,c]Decreased release of histamine, slow reacting substance of anaphylaxis, and other chemicals from mast cells and basophils

[b,c]Decreased quantity of circulating antibodies

[b,c]Decreased sensitivity of tissues to histamine, acetylcholine, bradykinin, slow reacting substance of anaphylaxis, and some prostaglandins

[c]Redistribution and destruction of white blood cells, leading to decreased blood levels of eosinophils, basophils, and decreased size of the lymph nodes and thymus

[a]Response elicited by activating alpha receptors
[b]Response elicited by beta receptors
[c]Response elicited by glucocorticoids

strongly anti-inflammatory and yet, that adrenal secretions and a host of other chemicals can also be shown to be proinflammatory, may seem bewildering. A tremendous amount of research has been done (and continues to be done) in order to understand the mechanisms at work here. The simplest explanation involves the hypothetical existence of **second messengers**, substances which function as mediators within the cells. These second messengers appear to be activated by "first messengers," such as epinephrine, norepinephrine, glucocorticoids, etc., that are circulating in the blood. Two second messengers seem to be especially important in determining the opposing effects observed in the immune system. In general,

an intracellular second messenger called **cyclic AMP** *inhibits* the responses of white blood cells, and another messenger called **cyclic GMP** *stimulates* their responses. The known effects of this second messenger system are summarized in Figure 7-9.

Figure 7-9 shows that acetylcholine, the chemical released by parasympathetic nerve endings, is also a first messenger. It has been shown that acetylcholine activates the second messenger cyclic GMP and increases inflammatory responses (in other words, it enhances the immune response). The significance of this finding is not yet fully clear (see Szentivanyi and Williams, 1980), yet there is no doubt that increased output of acetylcholine by the vagus nerve (part of the

Figure 7–9.   The regulatory effects of the second messengers, cyclic GMP (cyclic guanosine monophosphate) and cyclic AMP (cyclic adenosine monophosphate), on white blood cells. Note that the second messengers are affected by the activity of the autonomic nervous system and the adrenal glands. (In this context, epinephrine, norepinephrine, acetylcholine, and glucocorticoids are called "first messengers.")

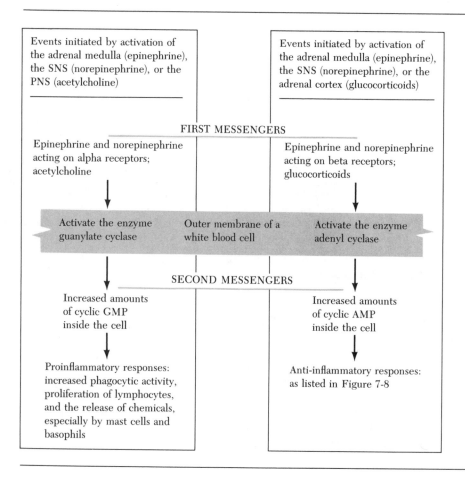

parasympathetic nervous system—see Figure 7-1) causes constriction of the airways, that histamine participates in this response, and that this mechanism contributes to the imbalance in parasympathetic and sympathetic influences that can produce the symptoms of asthma. Furthermore, recent evidence suggests that acetylcholine or parasympathetic nerves contribute to a variety of proinflammatory responses, including facilitating histamine release, and intensifying responses to inhaled antigens. These effects are reviewed by Gold (1978).

Thus it is apparent that the autonomic nervous system plays a very important role in eliciting defense mechanisms, not only by regulating the activity of various organs of the body, but also by regulating the responsiveness of the immune system, described in the first section of this chapter.

Other Hormones and the Immune System

There are a number of other hormones that influence the immune system. For example, growth hormone, thyroid hormone, parathyroid hormone, and insulin all increase the immune response and therefore are proinflammatory. For more information on these effects, the reader is referred to a review article by Morris and Selner (1980).

The information presented in this section makes it amply clear that a host of internal mechanisms, but especially the autonomic nervous system and the adrenal glands, participate in regulating our immune response. The significance of this finding lies in the fact that *emotions have a strong influence on the activity of the autonomic nervous system and the adrenal glands.*

III. THE RELATION OF EMOTIONS TO THE ACTIVITY OF THE ADRENAL GLANDS, THE AUTONOMIC NERVOUS SYSTEM, AND THE BRAIN.

The Effects of Emotions on the Autonomic Nervous System and the Adrenal Glands

Almost every emotional state we experience involves activation of one or another part of the autonomic nervous system. This fact is the reason why we often describe our emotions in "autonomic terms." For example, when someone speaks of being deeply touched by an event in his life, he or she will often use such expressions as "it gave me goose bumps all over," or "it sent a chill up my spine," or "I broke out in a sweat," or "I had butterflies in my stomach," or a

"lump in my throat," or a "pounding chest," or "tears in my eyes." All of these effects can be traced to one or another organ being stimulated either by parasympathetic or sympathetic nerves (see Tables 7-1 and 7-2), and thus we might conclude that an understanding of emotional reactions could be obtained simply by matching emotional states with specific autonomic responses. Needless to say, many people have tried to do this. For a number of reasons, however, it turns out not to be this straightforward!

1). Not all people (or animals) respond to the same situation with the same autonomic response. In a group of people undergoing a series of stress-evoking experiences, some will react with one response (for example, increased blood pressure), and others will respond with a different response (such as sweaty palms).

2) When a group of people is subjected to a variety of stimuli that evoke emotional responses—being subjected to pain, having to perform mental-arithmetic or word-fluency tests, being provoked into anger or fear—the tendency is much greater for an individual to give the *same* autonomic response to *any and all* of these stimuli than there is for the entire group being tested to produce the same autonomic response. In other words, many different autonomic responses can be elicited from a group of people yet any one person is likely to respond similarly regardless of the stimulus. This repeated experimental finding has been embodied in a principle called "autonomic response stereotypy" (see Lacey and Lacey, 1958).

3) Autonomic responses are clearly subject to learning and conditioning. For example, when autonomic responses like salivation, heart rate, contractility of intestinal smooth muscle, blood flow, and blood pressure are coupled with reward or punishment, they can be conditioned to go either up or down. In other words, our individual backgrounds and our prior experiences contribute to how our autonomic nervous system responds to any given situation.

That autonomic responses can be conditioned has been put to use with biofeedback procedures. In such a procedure, a person is connected to a device that "feeds back" clear, obvious information about the intensity of various autonomic activities occurring in the body. For example, a person's hands may be connected to an instrument that monitors skin temperature. When the temperature of the skin changes as little as .02° F, the instrument is designed to record this change and display it visually (e.g., the brightness of a lamp may change). Such changes in skin temperature actually reflect changes in blood flow resulting from an altered functioning of sympathetic nerve endings. The person, observing the display, is asked to either increase or decrease hand temperature, deliberately using the changes in light intensity as an indication of success. Such biofeedback procedures are used in various ways to assist people to manage various bodily processes. (See Taub and School, 1978, for more comments on biofeedback training.)

Although the above properties make it impossible to define emotional reactions strictly by the autonomic responses they evoke, this does not mean that emotions lack a firm connection with the autonomic nervous system but simply that the connections are different for different people. For example, in studying the autonomic responses to situations that evoked either anger or fear, it has been noted that even though strong reactions uniformly occur, they are markedly unique for each individual (see Ax, 1953). Similar findings have been reported with other emotional states—the anticipation of pain or the performance of difficult mental tasks, for example (see Lacey and Lacey, 1958).

The variability of responses from individual to individual has to do with the differing degrees of responsivity of specific organs rather than a lack of response by the autonomic nervous system or the adrenal glands. When the response of the adrenal medulla, as evidenced by changes in the level of epinephrine in the blood, is measured in persons exhibiting emotional reactions to such varied stimuli as pain, mental or physical exertion, avoiding or accepting a shock, or having to perform a boring task, there appear to be marked and consistent elevations regardless of the quality of the stress. Furthermore, the more intense the stress, the greater the amount of epinephrine secretion. Increases in norepinephrine levels were also noted in this study, but much less consistently (see Frankenhaeuser, 1971). Similarly, the release of adrenal steroids by the adrenal cortex appears to be related more to the intensity than the quality of the emotional response. (However, certain types of emotional reactions might influence the sympathetic nervous system, the adrenal medulla, and the adrenal cortex in different ways; the evidence is still scanty and should be taken as merely suggestive—see Lundberg, 1980; and Henry, 1980.)

Emotional states such as anger, rage, excitement, resentment, fear, anxiety, depression, desperation, and terror share two basic properties: a) As just mentioned, they are associated with activation of the autonomic nervous system and/or adrenal glands, and b) They are related to *defense*, which becomes obvious when we look at the *behaviors* associated with these states.

Behavioral responses include attack, aggression, fight, flight (escape), avoidance, and inactivity ("freezing," giving up, withdrawal). In all cases, the behavioral patterns can be viewed as defensive responses; that is, a potentially harmful encounter is made less harmful by attacking and thereby abolishing the source of danger, by fleeing and thereby removing oneself from the source, or, in some cases, by submission, thereby reducing the potential threat of the encounter itself. In attempting to distinguish among these defensive responses and to understand how they relate to the functioning of the autonomic nervous system, you might find useful the following classifications developed to describe animal behavior.

1) SHAM RAGE. This behavior is characterized by an intense but short-lived display of aggression. In the cat, it involves growling, hissing, baring teeth, arching the back with piloerection (hair standing on end), and clawing. Physiologically, although sham rage is sometimes associated with general activation of the SNS, often there is almost no stimulation of the autonomic nervous system. After an intense display of aggression for a second or two, the animal suddenly stops and goes on with whatever it was doing before (such as eating).

2) RAGE. The visible display of aggressive behavior in rage is the same as in sham rage, except that it often culminates in attack. It is always associated with activation of the autonomic nervous system (especially SNS). In this case the animal is "really angry" instead of "bluffing" as with sham rage.

3) QUIET ATTACK, also called PREDATORY ATTACK. This type of aggression is characterized by its intent to harm or kill, and it does not involve the intense display of rage behaviors described above. In animals, it is most often seen when the need arises to kill for food. In humans, expressions of this type of aggression emerge when one is hunting or boxing, or actually killing an enemy in battle. That we regard this type of aggression as "cold-blooded" and "efficient" is in keeping with the fact that it is associated with little or no emotional expression. Predatory attack is associated with only slight activation of the autonomic nervous system.

4) FEAR. This behavior is characterized by cringing, crouching, withdrawal, and the *lack* of expressions of aggressiveness. It is well known that one way to keep people submissive and timid is to instill fear in them. In many respects fear is the antithesis of rage. An enraged animal, for example, will show no fear at all. As the saying goes, an angry mouse will attack even an elephant! Fear is always associated with activation of the autonomic nervous system (SNS, but also, to a lesser extent, the PNS).

5) FLIGHT (OR ESCAPE). This behavior involves a clear attempt by the animal (or by humans) to run away from the source of danger. It also involves activation of the SNS.

6) DOCILITY. In animals, docility is associated with expressions of affection such as a desire to be groomed or petted. In general, docile animals (or humans) endure conditions that would otherwise evoke aggression. Docile responses do not appear to involve specific activation of the autonomic nervous system, except for such oral behaviors as salivation and licking, which are associated with activity of the PNS.

7) ALERTING RESPONSE. This response occurs when an animal (or a human) is "surprised" by a novel or unusual stimulus. There is a sudden cessation of movement or involvement with what one is doing, and a quick "orientation" or turning toward the stimulus with heightened attention. This response usually lasts only a few seconds. In most cases, it is not accompanied by changes in autonomic activity, although sometimes there is SNS involvement (see comments about the alarm reaction in the next section of this chapter).

When the SNS is activated, the adrenal glands usually are activated as well. As noted earlier, the adrenal cortex is usually stimulated by ACTH, but this activation is especially evident in the adrenal medulla, which itself is innervated by SNS nerves.

It is difficult to develop clear-cut terms for differentiating the human emotional states which accompany the kinds of behaviors described above. While feelings like anger, hostility, resentment, annoyance, and irritability appear to be somewhat different from one another, they are all commonly associated with rage. It is easier to develop terms for the behavioral expressions that accompany these emotions. They may all be classified, for example, as defensive behaviors, since they usually involve aggression and attack. Similarly, while feelings of apprehension, anxiety, dread, and terror differ from each other, they

are similar to those that accompany fear. Again, it is easier to classify the behavioral expressions of these emotions as primarily defensive; they are usually associated with cowering and cringing behavior, startle and alarm responses, and withdrawal reactions. Even so, the behaviors themselves do not always fall into clear categories. The behavioral terms used for animals are more objective, yet even in their world the same behavior can mean entirely different things. For example, the "emotional" correlates of the attack of a cornered animal are not the same as those involved in the attack of a hungry animal. Furthermore, even though the behaviors that we have just listed are clearly distinguishable, in many respects they are related to each other. For example, if a "frightened" animal is prevented from "escaping," it will almost always "attack" or display "sham rage" to its pursuer. Limited as it may be, this classification of behaviors will nevertheless simplify our discussion of the involvement of the brain in defensive responses, which is the next topic.

The Involvement of the Brain

Many parts of the brain are consistently involved in the above behaviors, as they are in modifying the responses of the autonomic nervous system and the adrenal glands. In general, the physiological and the behavioral responses are well integrated; that is, if stimulation of an area of the brain evokes rage, it also evokes pupillary dilation, piloerection, and other signs of SNS activation. For example, in the cat, if the medial area of the hypothalamus or parts of the amygdala are stimulated with a current made progressively more intense, the behavior elicited sometimes progresses from alerting and attention, to turning the head, to pupillary dilation, to flattening of the ears, to hissing, snarling, clawing, and then to attack. Accompanying these responses is an increase in blood pressure, increased cardiac output, constriction of the blood vessels of the kidneys, intestines, and skin, a decrease in motility of the stomach and intestines, and an increase in skeletal muscle blood flow (vasodilation of the blood vessels in skeletal muscle). It is clear from these experiments that the observed responses vary according to the intensity of the stimulation.

Many investigators who study the brain's involvement have found the intensity of the stimulation to be a significant variable in determining whatever physiological and behavioral responses occur. Although stimulation of the ventromedial hypothalamus usually elicits rage reactions and attack in animals, a more intense current will usually shift the response to one of intense flight. The accompanying organ responses are now likely to include urination and defecation. Although behavioral and physiological responses differ according to the areas of the brain being stimulated, the intensity of the stimulation remains a significant variable regardless of the specific brain area involved. Stimulation of the hypothalamus at a low intensity will cause the adrenal medulla to release epinephrine and norepinphrine (or will cause the release of ACTH which stimulates glucocorticoid release from the adrenal cortex) without any other visible sign of SNS activation (such as piloerection). However, if the intensity of the stimulation is increased, visible signs of SNS activation appear. Also, when some areas of the brain are stimulated at a low intensity there is a drop in blood pressure but, at a higher intensity, blood pressure rises. Moreover, as the intensity of the stimulus increases, not only are there more visible effects, but electrical stimulation of brain areas that previously gave no response might now increase adrenal secretions, alter blood pressure, evoke aggressive behavior, and many other responses.

As we discuss the involvement of specific areas of the brain in the following pages, it might appear that almost any area of the brain is capable of modifying PNS and SNS responses, as well as flight, fight, sham rage, and docile behaviors. Indeed, this multiplicity of effects has led some investigators to view the brain's role as being rather nonspecific. This is incorrect. The more we understand how the brain works, the more we realize that just the opposite is the case: *The neural circuits involved in behavioral responses and responses of the organs and tissues are perhaps too discrete and specific to be properly studied by such crude procedures as electrical stimulation and physical destruction.* For example, moving a stimulating electrode just one millimeter within the hypothalamus can change the response from a distinct rise in adrenal secretions to no response at all. Similarly, the neural circuits that regulate SNS-evoked *constriction* of blood vessels in skeletal muscles (whose nerve endings release norepinephrine) are represented widely throughout the brain, including some areas containing neurons that regulate SNS-evoked *dilation* of skeletal blood vessels (whose nerve endings release acetylcholine—see Table 7-2). Even here, it is now clear that sympathetically-induced vasodilation and sympathetically-induced vasoconstriction of skeletal blood vessels—both of which involve the frontal cortex, the hypothalamus, and the upper spinal cord—involve different neural circuits coursing through the brain.

The Hypothalamus. The hypothalamus can be divided into an **anterior portion** and a **posterior portion**. Although, as discussed above, there is a tremendous variability in the type of responses that can be evoked, in general the anterior portion seems to regulate PNS responses and the posterior portion, SNS responses. This distinction is most clearly seen with heart rate and blood pressure; stimulation of the posterior portion increases arterial pressure and heart rate (a SNS response), whereas stimulation of the preoptic area often decreases arterial pressure and heart rate (a PNS response). In terms of behavioral responses, the strongest defensive reactions are associated with the medial portion of the hypothalamus and the strongest quiet-attack responses with the lateral areas of the posterior portion of the hypothalamus.

The Anterior Portion. The anterior portion of the hypothalamus is illustrated in Figure 7-10. We already mentioned that the anterior portion of the hypothalamus appears to be involved in activating the parasympathetic branch of the autonomic nervous system. Electrical stimulation of this region frequently produces a decrease in heart rate and blood pressure and an increase in the motility of the gastrointestinal tract and in urinary bladder contractions. All are PNS responses which are frequently observed when either the **preoptic area** or the **anterior hypothalamic area** are stimulated, although effects on heart rate and blood pressure are more consistently observed in the preoptic area. This reduced activity is often accompanied by a decrease in behavioral responses. Electrical stimulation of the preoptic area usually leads to a state of somnolence, characterized by decreased respiration, increased drowsiness, and sleep (decreased arousal and sleep are discussed in some detail in Chapter 8). In addition, there is often a reduction in the release of thyroid-stimulating hormone by the pituitary gland, which lowers metabolism (because thyroid-stimulating hormone activates the thyroid to release thyroid hormones, and thyroid hormones stimulate metabolic processes).

Electrical stimulation of the anterior portion also elicits responses that have to do with *temperature regulation*. These responses are mediated by the SNS and include peripheral vasodilation (the enlargement of the blood vessels of the skin), and sweating, both of which involve SNS nerves that secrete acetylcholine (see Table 7-2). In animals, there is also panting. (For more details on temperature regulation generally, see pages 47–49, Chapter 4.)

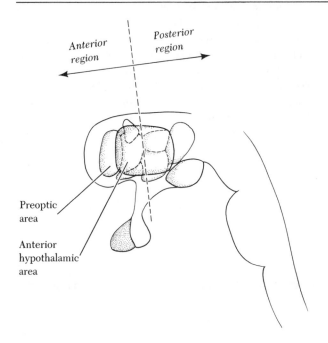

Anterior region

Posterior region

Preoptic area

Anterior hypothalamic area

Preoptic area of the hypothalamus: *stimulation* causes peripheral vasodilation, panting, and sweating (these three responses lower body temperature—see Chapter 4), bladder contraction, decreased heart rate and blood pressure, increased gastrointestinal motility, and decreased secretion of thyroid hormone. *Stimulation* also causes somnolence (sleepiness), decreased skeletal muscle tone (see Chapter 9), fear, anxiety, and escape behavior. *Stimulation* of this area for more than two weeks (2–4 times per day) causes ulcers in monkeys. *Destruction* causes insomnia, and damage to this area has been reported to cause gastric ulceration and pulmonary edema (accumulation of fluid in the lungs).

Anterior hypothalamus: *stimulation* causes most of the responses listed for the preoptic area, although it does not seem to consistently decrease heart rate and blood pressure. *Stimulation* of the lateral borders of the anterior hypothalamus can elicit rage, whereas stimulation of the medial borders can elicit fear, anxiety, escape behavior, and active vasodilation in skeletal muscles (via acetylcholine—see Table 7-2).

Figure 7–10. The anterior portion of the hypothalamus and its involvement in regulating the autonomic nervous system as well as defensive and other behaviors. Note the large number of effects that have been reported when portions of the anterior region (the preoptic area and the anterior hypothalamus) are electrically stimulated or destroyed in test animals. Many of the organ responses listed above are due to activation of the parasympathetic branch of the autonomic nervous system (see Table 7–1).

Of interest is the finding in monkeys that electrical stimulation of the preoptic area of the hypothalamus two to four times a day for more than two weeks produces *ulcers* (French, Porter, Cavanaugh, and Longmire, 1954). Although probably the result of many factors, one is likely to be the increase in gastric secretion that occurs as a result of the stimulation of the PNS. In addition, those monkeys that eventually developed ulcers showed clear signs of emotional irritation—restlessness, pacing, and assumption of aggressive and escape postures—when they were electrically stimulated. Similar results were obtained from stimulating parts of the posterior portion of the hypothalamus, and these findings suggest that a neural system may be situated along the midline of the hypothalamus, extending from the preoptic area back into the upper spinal cord.

Other animal studies highlight the association between the workings of defense systems and the activities of the anterior portion of the hypothalamus. There are a number of reports that destruction of the anterior part of the hypothalamus protects guinea pigs from *lethal anaphylactic shock*. (Lethal anaphylactic shock is an extreme allergic reaction where the antigen-antibody reaction in the blood and its vessels is so severe that it causes damage to the vessels. Specifically, the increase in vascular permeability and vascular dilation is so widespread that the return of blood to the heart is inadequate and death usually occurs within a few minutes.) The mechanisms whereby anterior hypothalamic lesions prevent lethal anaphylactic shock in some animals are not known, but they appear to involve a decrease in antibody production and some protection against the effects of excessive levels of histamine that result from the allergic reaction (see Stein, Keller, and Schleifer, 1981, for a comprehensive review of these and other effects).

The Posterior Portion. The posterior portion of the hypothalamus is illustrated in Figure 7-11. In general, stimulation of the posterior portion of the hypothalamus activates the sympathetic branch of the autonomic nervous system. Electrical stimulation frequently produces increased blood pressure, increased heart rate, pupillary dilation, sweating, piloerection, cessation of movement of the gastrointestinal tract, and increased secretion by the adrenal glands (cortex and medulla). These are all SNS responses, except for stimulation of the adrenal cortex, which occurs because of an increase in the release of ACTH by the pituitary gland.

These responses are usually accompanied by increased arousal, which includes increased mental activity, increased muscle tension, and increased respiration—responses that are discussed in some detail in Chapter 8. In addition, electrical stimulation elicits many defensive behaviors, including sham rage, rage, attack, flight, and fear. When the lateral regions of the **lateral hypothalamus** are electrically stimulated, quiet aggression (predatory attack) can be evoked without significantly activating the SNS, as mentioned in our earlier description of this behavior.

We already noted that electrical stimulation of parts of the posterior portion of the hypothalamus two to four times a day for more than two weeks can produce *ulcers* in monkeys. Again, those monkeys that eventually developed ulcers showed clear signs of irritation and aggression when they were electrically stimulated—in fact, moreso than those monkeys whose preoptic area was stimulated (French, Porter, Cavanaugh, and Longmire, 1954). Also, electrical stimulation of the **posterior hypothalamus** causes *eosinopenia*, which is a reduced number of eosinophils in the blood. (You will recall that epinephrine and glucocorticoids from the adrenal glands inhibit the proliferation of white blood cells and that eosinophils are such cells.) In addition, electrical stimulation of the **mammillary region** increases the survival rate of guinea pigs subjected to *anaphylactic* or *histamine shock*, presumably by reducing one or more responses of the immune system (see Szentivanyi and Szekely, 1956).

Although much more research has to be done before we can determine the exact mechanisms at work here, it is apparent that the hypothalamus contains many areas whose stimulation alters the activity of the parasympathetic and/or sympathetic branches of the autonomic nervous system; that in many cases this activation appears to be integrated with defensive emotional reactions as reflected in altered defensive behaviors; and that these responses appear to be associated with alterations in the response of the immune system. As we have indicated in previous chapters, such findings are not, in themselves, absolute proof that these functions are all organized in the brain in some coexisting, inseparably related way. Nevertheless, they do suggest the existence of well-integrated mechanisms that are probably extremely refined in their workings.

The Upper Spinal Cord. In order to exert their effects on the autonomic nervous system and on defensive behaviors, the neural systems that are activated within the hypothalamus and other parts of the brain must contain pathways within the upper spinal cord. Within the upper spinal cord, an area called the **periaqueductal gray** appears to contain neurons that form a main pathway for neural impulses serving the autonomic nervous system. The periaqueductal gray is illustrated in Figure 7-11. As indicated, electrical stimulation produces many responses that can be attributed to activation of either parasympathetic or sympathetic nerves. In addition, electrical stimulation of this area elicits behaviors of sham rage, rage, and quiet attack. When this area is destroyed, the autonomic and behavioral responses evoked by stimulating the hypothalamus and other areas of the brain are largely abolished. We conclude, therefore, that this area is indeed transmitting neural information from the hypothalamus and other areas to structures below. However, the periaqueductal gray is probably not a region that simply transmits information from one area (like the hypothalamus) to another (like the lower areas in the spinal cord from which neurons going to organs or muscles originate). Rather, electrical stimulation of this area appears capable of eliciting defensive behaviors without neural input from higher areas, although the behaviors elicited are weak and fragmentary when compared to those of normal animals (see Molina and Hunsperger, 1962; Elison and Flynn, 1968; Clemente and Chase, 1973, for further comments).

The Limbic System. The limbic system is also very much involved in defensive responses. Electrical stimulation of the **amygdala** has been reported to affect many organs and functions of the body. Although varying with the location of the electrode and the intensity of the stimulation, the responses elicited indicate that this structure regulates both parasympathetic and sympathetic nerves. In almost all cases these autonomic responses—that is, responses

141

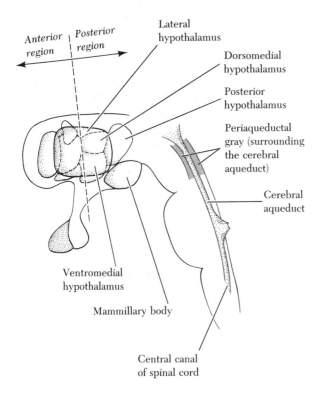

Figure 7–11. The posterior portion of the hypothalamus and the periaqueductal gray of the upper spinal cord, and their involvement in regulating the autonomic nervous system as well as defensive and other behaviors. Note the large number of effects that have been reported when portions of the posterior region are electrically stimulated or destroyed in test animals. Some of the organ responses listed above include the parasympathetic branch of the autonomic nervous system (see Table 7–1), but most of the organ responses are due to activation of the sympathetic branch (see Table 7–2).

Posterior hypothalamus and part of the mammillary body: *stimulation* increases blood pressure and heart rate, and elicits pupillary dilation, sweating, piloerection, hyperglycemia, cessation of movement of the gastrointestinal tract, and increased secretion of the adrenal medulla and cortex. *Stimulation* also leads to a state of arousal that includes increased muscle tension along with increased respiration. In addition, it causes eosinopenia (a reduction of the number of eosinophils in the blood), resistance to anaphylactic shock (see Figure 7-2), rage, sham rage, and alerting responses. *Stimulation* for more than two weeks (2–4 times per day) in this area also produces ulcers in monkeys. *Destruction* causes somnolence (sleepiness) and reduced rage reactions.

Dorsomedial hypothalamus: *stimulation* causes pupillary dilation, increased or decreased blood pressure, increased vasodilation of skeletal muscle, increased adrenal secretion (medulla), increased motility in the gastrointestinal tract, urination, defecation, flight, fear, and attack if the animal is prevented from escaping.

Ventromedial hypothalamus: *stimulation* causes pupillary dilation, salivation, piloerection, urination, defecation, increased blood pressure, increased vasodilation of skeletal muscle, alerting responses, sham rage, rage, attack, and flight. *Destruction* causes various behaviors ranging from docility and tameness to rage and attack.

Lateral hypothalamus: *stimulation* causes vasoconstriction, piloerection, urination, defecation, pupillary dilation, increased blood pressure, sham rage, and rage when the areas near the ventromedial hypothalamus are involved. *Stimulation* toward the lateral borders of the lateral hypothalamus causes quiet aggression (predatory attack). *Stimulation* also elicits eating and drinking behaviors, but these behaviors can be separated from each other and are not necessarily interdependent. These responses are not associated with strong activation of the autonomic nervous system. *Destruction* causes somnolence and apathy, but there is frequently aggression if the animal is provoked.

Periaqueductal gray: this part of the upper spinal cord contains many fibers coming from the medial areas of the hypothalamus, including the medial preoptic area, the dorsomedial hypothalamus, ventromedial hypothalamus, and the posterior hypothalamus. It seems to be a main pathway for impulses subserving the autonomic nervous system as well as impulses subserving defensive behaviors. *Stimulation* causes increased blood pressure, pupillary dilation, contraction of the bladder, increased respiration, changes in gastrointestinal motility and blood glucose levels, sham rage, rage, and quiet attack. These behaviors are still observed when the periaqueductal gray is completely separated from the hypothalamus, although in this case they are much reduced and often fragmentary. *Destruction* abolishes the defensive and autonomic responses evoked by stimulating the hypothalamus and limbic system.

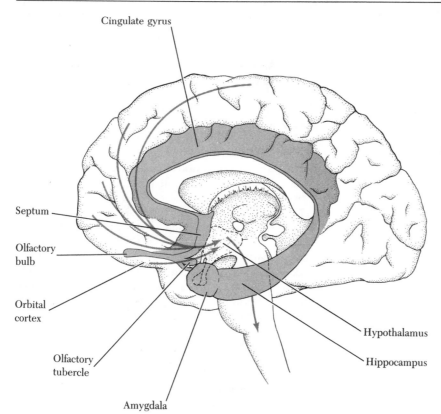

Cingulate gyrus

Septum

Olfactory bulb

Orbital cortex

Olfactory tubercle

Amygdala

Hypothalamus

Hippocampus

Figure 7–12. The limbic system and its involvement in regulating the autonomic nervous system as well as defensive and other behaviors. The arrows indicate the many connections existing between the frontal cortex and the hypothalamus and upper spinal cord (see Figure 7–13). Note the large number of effects that have been reported when portions of the limbic system (the amygdala, septum, olfactory area, hippocampus, and cingulate gyrus) are electrically stimulated or destroyed. Many of the organ responses are due to activation of the parasympathetic or sympathetic branches of the autonomic nervous system (see Tables 7–1 and 7–2).

Cingulate gyrus: electrical *stimulation* can cause rage, which can be suppressed by stimulating the hypothalamus; it also can evoke alerting responses, increases and decreases in blood pressure, piloerection, increased and decreased heart rate, cardiac arrest, increased salivation, and increased peristalsis in the gastrointestinal tract. *Destruction* has been reported to cause increased rage reactions, increased docility, and increased aggression and fear.

Amygdala: next to the hypothalamus and periaqueductal gray area of the upper spinal cord, the amygdala is the most involved in the autonomic and behavioral responses that accompany defense. *Stimulation* of the amygdala causes a variety of autonomic responses. Both increases and decreases have been observed in gastrointestinal secretion, gastrointestinal motility, blood sugar levels, heart rate, blood pressure, and respiration. *Stimulation* also causes increased salivation (both thick and thin—see Tables 7–1 and 7–2), pupillary dilation, pupillary constriction (rarely), increased secretion from lacrimal and nasal glands, defecation, urination, increased secretion from the adrenal glands, panting, and piloerection. In almost all cases these autonomic responses are well-integrated with behaviors such as docility, tameness, rage, fear, escape, attack, licking, swallowing, chewing, sneezing, coughing, alerting responses, gagging, retching, searching behavior, and drowsiness. *Destruction* of various areas of the amygdala in monkeys leads to docility, hypersexuality, placidity, increased oral behavior, and an increase in motor activity that includes

attending to and reacting to any visual stimulus (distractibility). In cats *destruction* leads to rage and aggressiveness. In both of these species *lesions* in the hypothalamus have been reported to abolish these effects, indicating that the signals from the amygdala affect these behaviors by influencing the activites of the hypothalamus. Other reported effects of lesions in the amygdala include apathy, depression, and vomiting.

Septum: electrical *stimulation* has been reported to inhibit the aggression induced by stimulating the hypothalamus. *Stimulation* sometimes evokes feelings of pleasure, happiness, euphoria, and grooming behavior. *Destruction* causes intense rage, usually lasting about 2–3 weeks, and increased excitability.

Olfactory area: *Stimulation* has been reported to increase gastric motility and secretion, increase salivation, and mostly decrease blood pressure. *Destruction* has been observed to sustain the duration of the alerting response with an accompanying increase in heart rate. This startle response seems to persist when it normally would have ceased due to habituation.

Hippocampus: *stimulation* has been reported to evoke rage, anger, anxiety, and growling, accompanied by increased respiration, increased salivation, and pupillary dilation. *Destruction* has been observed to increase the incidence of alerting responses, rage, aggression, fear, and pleasurable reactions.

in organs or tissues that are due to activation of para-sympathetic or sympathetic nerves—are well integrated with behaviors such as docility, fear, rage, attack, flight, chewing, coughing and gagging, alertness, and drowsiness. These effects and other general findings are listed in Figure 7-12.

Although the amygdala appears to be the region of the limbic system most involved in regulating defensive reactions, largely because autonomic and behavioral responses are consistently obtained from this region, it is by no means the only area of the limbic system that participates in regulating these responses. In many animals, destruction of the **septum** consistently evokes intense rage and increased excitability. Conversely, electrical stimulation appears to inhibit aggression and to elicit pleasurable responses. This inhibiting effect appears, in part, to be an action exerted via the hypothalamus because the rage elicited by electrical stimulation of the hypothalmus can be inhibited by stimulating the septum at the same time. In addition, rage, anger, fear, anxiety, and docility are all intensified by electrical stimulation or destruction of the **hippocampus** and **cingulate gyrus.**

Because of the diversity and number of emotional behaviors that appear to be regulated by the limbic system, some investigators describe this structure as the "emotional brain." A glance at the behaviors listed in Figure 7-12 certainly affirms the involvement of the limbic system, although, again, it would be incorrect to conclude that it is a "center" uniquely involved in emotions. For example, we have already seen that the hypothalamus and upper spinal cord are also very much involved, and we will soon discuss the additional involvement of the frontal areas of the cerebral cortex. It is probably more correct to look at the limbic system as a structure containing the parts of many *neural systems* that serve emotional responses as they course through the brain. You will recall that similar statements were made in Chapters 3 and 4 with respect to the involvement of the hypothalamus in eating and drinking behaviors.

With these qualifications, then, we can say that the limbic system appears to be especially (although not uniquely) involved in selecting behaviors that are *appropriate* to a given situation. In Chapter 3 we mentioned the **Kluver-Bucy syndrome**, a syndrome that appears to be unique to some individuals (monkeys and humans) suffering from damage to parts of the limbic system (see pages 26–27). This syndrome is characterized by:

a) psychic blindness, which involves impaired ability to recognize objects and sense their meaning

b) strong oral tendencies with a marked increase in

oral exploratory behavior

c) a strong tendency to react to and attend to visual stimuli, distracted by almost any object

d) a tameness and docility that includes the absence of aggression, anger, or fear

e) increased and aberrant sexual activity.

In part, these effects might be related to the role of the limbic system in memory and learning. Such functions as the recognition of objects certainly rely on prior experience and memory, as does one's ability to sense an object's meaning in order to respond to it appropriately. As noted above, these functions appear to be impaired when the limbic system is damaged. Similarly, when an animal with such damage continues to be startled or distracted in circumstances where it normally would have ceased responding, this impairment, as well as the increase in exploratory behavior, is likely to be related to the animal's inability to recognize objects and sense their meaning.

What is of special interest to us here is that when various parts of the limbic system are damaged, we see increased distractibility associated with behaviors indicating *increased excitement*, and an increase in *alerting responses* or *startle responses*. In the next section of this chapter we will see that these responses are part of the **alarm reaction**, a reaction that can strongly increase activity in the sympathetic nervous system.

It is important to realize that damage to the limbic system does not abolish the neural circuitry necessary to evoke responses involving the autonomic nervous system, the adrenal glands, or defensive behaviors. The limbic system appears to modulate lower areas of the brain, such as the hypothalamus and the periaqueductal gray of the upper spinal cord, where these responses are integrated. In fact, certain parts of the limbic system modulate each other as well. For example, the rage induced by stimulating the hypothalamus can be inhibited by simultaneously stimulating the anterior cingulate gyrus, certain parts of the amygdala, or the septum. Similarly, if an animal is made more docile by a lesion in the amygdala, a septal lesion will sometimes make it more aggressive. On the other hand, if an animal is made more aggressive by a septal lesion, a lesion in the amygdala will sometimes make it more docile.

The Frontal Cortex. The frontal cortex, illustrated in Figure 7-13, is more involved in defensive behaviors and responses involving the autonomic nervous system and adrenal glands than are other parts of the cerebral cortex. Within frontal cortex, **motor** and

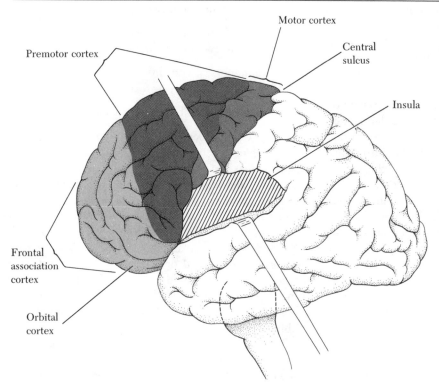

Figure 7–13. Frontal cortex and the insula, and their involvement in regulating the autonomic nervous system as well as defensive and other behaviors. Note the large number of effects that have been reported when the frontal cortex (containing motor, premotor, frontal association, and orbitofrontal areas) and the insula are electrically stimulated or destroyed. Many organ responses are due to activation of the parasympathetic or sympathetic branches of the autonomic nervous system (see Tables 7-1 and 7-2).

Insula: this "hidden" cortex, seen when the Sylvian fissure is spread apart, is continuous with frontal cortex in front, parietal cortex above, and temporal cortex below. *Stimulation* has been reported to increase and decrease gastric motility, increase gastric and abdominal sensations, increase taste and smell sensations, decrease blood pressure, decrease respiration, and increase salivation. It also evokes nausea, fear, a "sinking feeling" in the abdomen, a "bad taste" in the mouth, and feeling "sick to the stomach." Patients with seizures in this area experience feelings of fear, gastric and olfactory sensations, confusion leading to aggression, also rage, joy, depression, and sexual feelings.

Motor and premotor cortex: *stimulation* evokes pupillary constriction and pupillary dilation, and either increased or decreased blood pressure and heart rate; it also evokes sweating, and vasoconstriction or vasodilation of blood vessels in skeletal muscle. *Destruction* has been reported to increase the level of sweating, the incidence of piloerection, and the dilation of blood vessels.

Frontal association cortex: *stimulation* evokes the same autonomic responses as those listed above for premotor and motor cortex. One exception is SNS-induced vasodilation of skeletal blood vessels, which does not occur. *Destruction* has been observed to increase the level of sweating, the incidence of piloerection, and the dilation of blood vessels, increase heart rate, cause vasoconstriction of blood vessels, and increase epinephrine secretion. Behavioral responses include greater docility, apathy, depression, anxiety, and increase in the incidence of alerting responses (distractibility).

Orbitofrontal cortex: this area seems to be especially well-connected to the lateral hypothalamus. *Stimulation* evokes the same autonomic responses as those listed above. It also elicits increased or decreased respiration and salivation and has been reported to evoke alerting responses. *Destruction* has been observed to cause a temporary reduction in eating and drinking behaviors and an increase in oral behavior.

premotor areas are devoted to movement of skeletal muscles. (Skeletal muscle functions will be discussed in Chapter 9.) In addition, these areas of the cortex influence autonomic responses, as indicated in the text that accompanies this figure. In general, changes in blood flow in the skeletal muscles—caused by constriction or dilation of their vessels—result from stimulating well-localized regions of the motor and

premotor cortex. These regions are in fairly close relation to their corresponding somatic representations—that is, those regions that regulate the movement of skeletal muscles as they are distributed over the body (see Chapter 9).

The most frontal part of the cerebral cortex is called **frontal association cortex** and is also called **frontal lobes.** This area is called association cortex because it was formerly assumed to be especially associated with, or connected to, motor cortex, which serves movement. As noted in Chapter 6, this view is no longer prevalent. The frontal lobes have many connections with the limbic system, the hypothalamus and upper spinal cord, as indicated (by arrows) in Figure 7-12. In general, destruction of frontal association cortex has no pronounced effect on motor or sensory function; however, damage in this area seems to elicit "emotional" responses similar to those obtained from the limbic system and lower structures of the brain, such as apathy, depression, "silly" behavior, docility, anxiety, and distractibility. This finding corresponds well with the fact that frontal association areas have many connections with the limbic system. Electrical stimulation or destruction of the frontal lobes leads to a variety of autonomic responses, as listed in Figure 7-13.

Another area of the cerebral cortex, called the **insula**, seems to be especially involved in defensive behaviors. This "hidden" cortex, as it is called, also illustrated in Figure 7-13, is continuous with frontal cortex in front, parietal cortex above, and temporal cortex below; in other words, it is well located to receive and integrate information from many areas of the cortex—areas involved with auditory, visual, somatic sensory, and taste sensations as well as with many complex sensory functions such as those that serve language. Stimulation of this area evokes feelings, responses in the autonomic nervous system, and sensations that appear as if they are in the stomach, such as feeling sick or nauseous (see Penfield and Faulk, 1955).

IV. RELATION TO HEALTH

Nowhere is the relationship to health more obvious than in terms of our body's defense mechanisms, whose purpose is to keep us healthy and safe. We have just seen that precise brain mechanisms intensify or reduce defensive emotional and behavioral reactions as well as the activity of the parasympathetic and sympathetic branches of the autonomic nervous system. Furthermore, earlier in the chapter we discussed that the effects of parasympathetic and sympathetic stimulation, as well as adrenal stimulation (in the case of the adrenal medulla, through the SNS and with the adrenal cortex, ACTH) include augmentation or suppression of immune reactions. Because these various responses can be so closely interrelated, it is not surprising that there are many instances where psychological states are related to *organic* disease, the study and treatment of which is called **psychosomatic medicine**. To a certain extent we have

already confirmed the workings of these connections when we cited experimental evidence that brain stimulation can produce ulcers or protect animals from lethal anaphylactic shock. In most cases, however, experimentation has not been sufficient nor brain mechanisms understood well enough to cite specific evidence. Nevertheless, there is no doubt that under certain conditions when the defense mechanisms of the body are *intensified*, the increased intensity may be due to emotional states. For example, as noted earlier, it is fairly common for an emotional upset to trigger an attack in an asthmatic or to cause a person to suddenly break out with hives. Similarly, under certain conditions the defense mechanisms of the body are *suppressed* and this state can also be due to emotional upset. The onset of peptic ulcers following emotional upheaval is not an uncommon experience, nor is the well-documented observation that people undergoing intense or prolonged life crises are more likely to develop tuberculosis.

Potentially harmful agents are with us all the time. For example, all of us have a great deal of acid and other chemicals in our stomach that are capable of causing ulcers. Similarly, over a quarter of the population carries some *tubercle bacilli* in their bodies that can cause tuberculosis. In fact, all of us are exposed to all kinds of infectious agents every day. Most of the time a harmless agent is ignored by the immune system, or a harmful agent is quickly faced with an inflammatory barrier that walls off and/or destroys it. Given the proper environment, however, almost any agent can quickly harm the body. It sometimes takes only a few minutes for an asthmatic to develop an attack when he or she is emotionally upset. Peptic ulcers can sometimes appear within a few hours. Some people experience arthritic symptoms when exposed to a cold draft for only a short time.

Many of us temporarily experience a variety of symptoms which, in disease, are much more persistently experienced. When we are disturbed, for example, it is not uncommon to experience nausea and vomiting, excessive sweating, increased itching and scratching, increased blood pressure and heart rate, increased glandular secretions in the face (weeping, for example), decreased appetite, and a host of other responses. The difference between these "normal" reactions to upset and the same symptoms in disease is, of course, that in the former they are very short-lived, and in the latter they persist.

We will return to the topic of prolonged as opposed to short-lasting reactions, but first we will describe a particular physiological and emotional state that is highly defensive in its nature, occurring when we face—or believe we face—demanding or threatening situations. This state is called **stress**, and it is related to a specific set of responses called the **alarm reaction**. First we will discuss stress, then the alarm reaction.

Stress

"Stress" is not a distinct process that can be clearly separated from all other psychological and/or physiological processes. Therefore, even though its existence is commonly accepted, there is no concise definition of "stress." Instead, stress is defined in terms of the particular *responses* of an individual—whether to external situations or to one's own emotional or physiological states. For one person, for example, talking to 100 people from center stage, or going in a 747 across the country (or a Cessna to the next state) is extremely stressful, whereas to another it appears not only not to be so, but these events actually appear to be relaxing. Emotionally, the stressful state for one person can be one of excitement and tension, whereas to another these same states may not be stressful. Similarly, a sudden increase in blood pressure, a night without sleep, or a mild infection is stressful for one person, but apparently not so for another.

One important property of the stress response is that it is often associated with events perceived as *demanding* or *threatening*. As just mentioned, the emotions that accompany stress cannot be classified categorically as such; for one person the stressful state may be one of excitement and tension, for another, anxiety, for another, fear, resentment, depression, or being in a hurry. In all cases that involve stress, however, these states describe an emotional response to a situation perceived as demanding or threatening.

Properties of the stress reaction are more easily described in physiological terms where it is manifested by:

a) activation of the sympathetic nervous system

b) increased muscular ("nervous") tension (to be discussed in Chapters 8 and 9)

c) the release of certain hormones into the blood, especially epinephrine from the adrenal medulla and steroids from the adrenal cortex

d) reduced or intensified responses of the immune system.

Another important property of the stress response is that it can be elicited by *any* stimulus, called the **stressor**. This means that it is impossible to give a complete list of stressors—almost anything could qualify. The following are among the most common:

a) agents or events that cause physical damage to the body

b) emergencies that demand our full attention

c) fatigue or exhaustion

d) the experience of captivity

e) divorce, death or other situations involving personal or professional relationships

f) chronic anxiety, frustration, or angry feelings

g) exposure to "man-made" stimuli for which the body has little or no natural defense. These man-made stimuli, sometimes referred to as "stressors of the twentieth century," include synthetic chemicals (as in cosmetics, cleaning agents, or plastics) that evoke allergic reactions, urban living conditions, processed and artificial foods, and excessive use of drugs.

In general, there are two ways to look at stress:

1) As a *graded* response that always goes up and down in intensity. Using this formulation, any situations, emotions, or physiological responses that are associated with stress, such as those listed above, are part of a stress response; it is simply a weak reaction in some, much stronger in others, depending on the number of stressors and their intensity.

2) As a *threshold* response that causes harm. Using this formulation, no stimulus in itself is "stressful" unless it produces an imbalance that is psychologically and/or physiologically damaging.

For our purposes, we will look at stress as an especially important graded response that has the *potential* to harm the body if the response becomes too severe for any given individual.

Before continuing further, it is important to note that as we have defined them, stress responses are not necessarily detrimental. At times when we must confront a demanding or emergency situation, the reactions evoked in our body may well enable us to be maximally efficient in dealing with it. The problem, of course, is that many times the body's stress response is *not* beneficial and it can (and does) cause harm. There appear to be two reasons for imbalances to occur: 1) the response may be more than the body requires, because it then prepares for far more physical reaction than the situation demands, and 2) depending on many individual factors, physiological and psychological, a given stressor might simply be too much, alone or cumulatively, for that person.

As noted, whatever the cause, the symptoms of stress usually include one or more of the symptoms elicited by activation of the SNS or the PNS. Furthermore, it is well known that stressors lead to the release of ACTH by the pituitary gland, which, in turn, leads to the secretion of steroids by the adrenal cortex (see Figure 7-7). The specific mechanisms whereby adrenal secretions and the effects of activation of the autonomic nervous system may promote disease will be discussed later in this section.

The Alarm Reaction

The alarm reaction, often included as part of the stress response, is so specific that we choose to discuss it separately. The alarm reaction is evoked when a strong, novel, and usually extraneous stimulus reaches us. It can be evoked by potentially *harmful* stimuli, such as the "surprise" of a car suddenly cutting in front of us while we are driving, or by *harmless* stimuli such as the unexpected noise of a popping balloon. The alarm reaction usually occurs within a fraction of a second after receiving the sensory stimulus. Some of the properties of the alarm reaction are:

1) An ALERTING RESPONSE, sometimes called the ORIENTING REFLEX, characterized by a sudden cessation of ongoing behavior and an orientation toward the source of stimulation.

2) A SUDDEN EXCITATION OF THE NERVES OF THE SYMPATHETIC NERVOUS SYSTEM, producing constriction of the blood vessels, piloerection, and dilation of the pupils. The constriction of the blood vessels in the skin causes a person to look "pale." There is also constriction of the blood vessels in skeletal muscle. This effect in skeletal muscles is short-lived, however, because the sharp rise in blood pressure associated with the sudden constriction of blood vessels is quickly followed by baroreceptor activity, which is initiated by pressure-sensitive receptors in the carotid arteries and in the arch of the aorta, as discussed below.

You will recall that we briefly discussed baroreceptors in Chapter 4 when we mentioned that a change in blood pressure affects special nerve endings that lie in the walls of the aorta and carotid arteries. There we also noted that when blood pressure changes, neural impulses are propagated into the brain and, by altering angiotensin, antidiuretic hormone, and thirst mechanisms, water levels in the body are affected (see pages 41–43). Although this mechanism is important for water regulation, the baroreceptors are also very important for another reason: they respond to changes in blood pressure by immediately initiating responses that return blood pressure to normal levels. This quick response is called the **baroreceptor reflex**.

Figure 7-14 shows that neural impulses initiated by the baroreceptors are propagated into the upper spinal cord where they affect the **medullary respiratory area**, the **motor nucleus of the vagus**, and the **vasomotor area**. All of these areas are embedded within the **reticular system**, a neural system that is intimately involved in mechanisms of arousal, which is discussed in the next chapter. The medullary respiratory area regulates breathing, as discussed in Chapter 5. The motor nucleus of the vagus contains neurons that then leave the spinal cord to become the vagus nerve, which is part of the parasympathetic nervous system. The vagus innervates many organs in the body: In the heart, for example, it slows the heart rate and, to a slight extent, decreases its force of contraction. The vasomotor area contains neurons that leave the spinal cord and go to the sympathetic chains that were discussed earlier. From there they go to the heart and blood vessels where they increase heart rate, increase the force of contraction of the heart, and constrict most blood vessels in the body.

When blood pressure suddenly rises, neural impulses sent by the baroreceptors into the upper spinal cord produce effects that *counteract* the rise in blood pressure: the vasomotor area is inhibited, which in turn decreases the number of impulses transmitted through sympathetic nerves to the heart and blood vessels. Simultaneously, the motor nucleus of the vagus is stimulated, which decreases heart rate. This diminished activity decreases the heart's activity and increases the flow of blood through blood vessels, lowering blood pressure back to normal. Conversely, when blood pressure falls, the activity of the vasomotor center increases and the motor nucleus of the vagus is inhibited, events which bring blood pressure back up to normal.

3). The third aspect of the alarm response comes into play when THE ALARM CONTINUES BEYOND A SECOND OR TWO. When an extraneous stimulus remains unrecognized, for example,

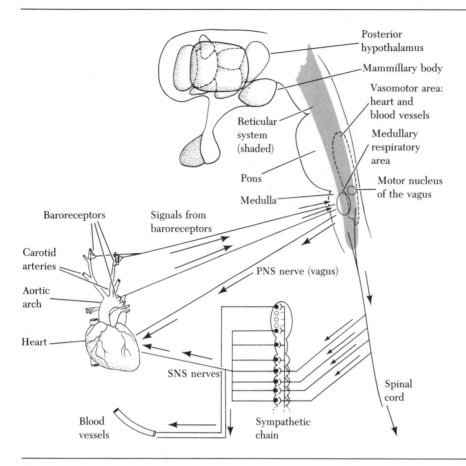

Figure 7–14. The baroreceptor reflex. When blood pressure rises, the baroreceptors send neural signals to the medulla, activating the vagus nerve (part of the parasympathetic nervous system—PNS) and inhibiting sympathetic nerves (part of the sympathetic nervous system—SNS). This process results in a compensatory decrease in blood pressure and heart rate. Conversely, when blood pressure falls, the vagus nerve is inhibited and the SNS is activated, leading to a compensatory rise in blood pressure and an increase in heart rate. The **vasomotor area** consists of those regions of the upper spinal cord that are most involved in regulating the activity of the heart and the blood vessels.

as when we watch a "scary" movie where something awful is about to happen but we do not know exactly what, or when we are alone at night and hear strange unidentifiable noises. In these cases, the responses are rather complicated. Not only is there a continued intense activation of the SNS, but the PNS is also activated, partly because of the baroreceptor reflex discussed above and partly as a result of direct activation within the brain. The continued SNS stimulation also leads to the release of epinephrine and norepinephrine from the ad-

renal medulla, and, as mentioned, ACTH release leads to the release of steroids from the adrenal cortex.

To recapitulate the sequence of events involved in an alarm reaction, first there is a quick "orienting" accompanied by stimulation of the SNS and followed almost immediately by the baroreceptor reflex that compensates for the increase in blood pressure by exerting an inhibiting influence on the SNS and activating the PNS. Most of the time this reaction doesn't go any farther. The stimulus is quickly recognized as extraneous and then we simply forget about it. Although we know the alarm reaction from our own experiences, it is especially vivid when we see it in animals. A grazing deer, for example, will be seen to suddenly orient itself to some stimulus, stand absolutely still for a few seconds, then simply continue grazing as if nothing had happened. If the alarm reaction persists, however, the continued SNS and PNS activation, as well as the release of adrenal hormones, produces a physiological state that is no different from that previously described for stress. Again, we note that a distinction must be made between long- and short-lasting defense reactions, which are discussed below in relation to their implications for health.

Prolonged vs. Short-Lasting Defense Reactions

Anything that activates the body's defense mechanisms for a short time is usually not harmful. When a person is startled or momentarily enraged or frightened, the reactions in the body come and go very quickly. This rapid on-off response is seen much more in animals and young children than in adults, who have a much greater tendency to "hang on" to the experience. As adults, we are more likely to think about a present situation in terms of our many prior experiences and/or we project a present experience into the future, imagining various outcomes involving our career, relationships, and so forth. For many, emotional states such as resentment, anxiety, and depression are long-lasting. These chronic states, which place our bodies in a state of continuous defense, are much more likely to harm us because alterations in the activity of the autonomic nervous system, coupled with changes in blood levels of epinephrine and adrenal steroids, can be sufficient to alter the responsiveness of the immune system.

Although a predatory state can sometimes last a long time, it is rarely harmful in this sense—quite likely because, as noted previously, the autonomic nervous system as a whole is not intensely involved in this type of aggression. It is interesting to note that predatory attack seems to be a positively reinforcing behavior. In the cat, for example, when the lateral hypothalamus is stimulated, the predatory attack state evoked appears to be the desired behavior if the animal is given a choice (see Roberts and Kiess, 1964). This finding is of interest given that this area, also connected with eating and drinking behavior, has been shown in self-stimulation experiments to be one of the most "rewarding." In other words, it suggests that the aggressive behaviors required to hunt and kill

for food are intimately connected to the survival behaviors of eating and drinking. In this context it is interesting that most of the areas of the hypothalamus that elicit rage and flight with accompanying responses from the autonomic nervous system are either strongly or mildly *aversive*. This response is obviously very important for survival and health, since it would indeed be unhealthy if we were "programmed" to enjoy or seek prolonged defensive reactions that would compromise our ability to be protected from harm.

This difference in the self-stimulatory "reward content" between regions of the brain whose stimulation evokes reactions programmed to serve survival needs, such as predatory attack, and those that do not may find its human counterpart in the unfortunate fact that cold, calculated aggression can be a positive experience whereas rage is usually a negative experience. Other animal studies corroborate this finding; electrical stimulation of the septum not only appears to inhibit rage reactions (see Figure 7-12), but an animal will usually self-administer stimulation repeatedly when an electrode is placed in this area of the limbic system.

Many of the sicknesses that develop from stress have to do with interactions among the autonomic nervous system, the adrenal glands, and the immune system. These interactions obviously involve the brain—most likely it is activities occurring within the brain itself that determine whether a defensive response occurs over a prolonged period. We have already mentioned that prolonged electrical stimulation of the hypothalamus of monkeys led to antagonistic, restless, and irritable behaviors and, eventually, to ulcers (French, Porter, Cavanaugh, and Longmire, 1954). The topic of disease in relation to stress is covered in more detail below.

Illness and Disease

There are many reports of a relation between disease and stress. Increased susceptibility to viruses, increased and decreased susceptibility to infection, growth or shrinkage of tumors, even heightened or diminished arthritic responses all have been reported to be caused by stress (see Rogers, Dubey, and Reich, 1979; and Rogers, Trentham, Reich, and Brigham, 1980). We have mentioned several times that many of the diseases we experience can be grouped into: a) those caused by an increased invasion of viruses, bacteria, or other harmful agents, b) those caused by a decreased responsiveness of the immune system (thus lowering our resistance to harmful agents), and c) those caused by excessive responsiveness of the immune system. The **hyposensitive reaction** (decreased responsiveness of the immune system) and the **hypersensitive reaction** (increased responsiveness) are both subject to the effects of secretions from the adrenal glands, sympathetic nerve endings, and parasympathetic nerve endings, although there are marked differences between these two reactions. In the hyposensitive reaction, for example, epinephrine and norepinephrine act on beta receptors, whereas in the hypersensitive reaction these adreno-medullary hormones act on alpha receptors (see Section II). Also, certain hormones that promote the hyposensitive reaction (especially epinephrine and adrenal glucocorticoids) increase intracellular levels of cyclic AMP, whereas those that promote the hypersensitive reaction (especially norepinephrine and acetylcholine) increase levels of cyclic GMP (see Figure 7-9). Furthermore, the hyposensitive reaction is mainly associated with sympathetic and adrenal activation, whereas the hypersensitive reaction *also* involves the activation of the parasympathetic nervous system. Some of the mechanisms contributing to these differences are further discussed later in this chapter.

The general components of the hypersensitive and hyposensitive reactions are summarized in Figure 7-15. As discussed earlier and illustrated here, the stress responses can clearly be beneficial to our body as well as harmful. The mobilization of physiological processes that prepare the body for "fight or flight" is appropriate and healthy if such a response is needed to meet a true emergency. Similarly, the proinflammatory response to stress is beneficial in facilitating a quick walling-off and destruction of agents that would otherwise be harmful. The anti-inflammatory response is beneficial in protecting the body as a whole from the inflammatory response; that is, when a specific part of the body is traumatized—either physically or through the actions of a toxic agent—the intense inflammatory response that ensues is localized principally to *that* area.

On the other hand, these responses can also be harmful to the body. The activation of the "fight or flight" pattern can lead to cardiac failure in a person with a weak heart. In some cases, the release of anti-inflammatory hormones can decrease the effectiveness of the body's protective mechanisms, leading to peptic ulcers, tuberculosis, and many other disorders. How does this occur? When infectious agents invade the body, the inflammatory response assures against their spreading. When anti-inflammatory hormones are released in high amounts for prolonged periods, as may occur when one is under stress, the resulting decrease in resistance—caused by the suppression of the immune system—can allow these agents to spread, causing a myriad of diseases, including appendicitis, typhus, and diphtheria. In the case of peptic ulcers, the "invasion" is not by an infectious agent but by the stomach's own secretions. In other words, the inflammatory defense reaction that normally acts as a barricade to protect the lining of the stomach against the stomach's own secretions is weakened by the release of anti-inflammatory hormones.

Conversely, when the proinflammatory response—or a reduced anti-inflammatory response—is combined with other PNS responses, such as increased salivary secretions, increased contraction of smooth muscle of the bronchioles, or increased secretion of mucus by the nose, throat or lungs, these responses can trigger asthma attacks, hives, and rhinitis (sneezing, swelling, and obstruction of the nasal passages). Increased inflammatory responses can also precipitate diseases such as arthritis (inflammation of a joint), gout (inflammation caused by the precipitation of uric acid in the joints), and nephritis (inflammation of the kidneys). Here the inflammatory response appears to cause the disorder rather than fight it. This paradoxical character of inflammation is also evident with allergies—hay fever, for example, where it is the inflammatory response itself that damages the nasal structures.

Those who suffer from chronic stress are frequently afflicted with peptic ulcers. Peptic ulcers can occur as the result of activation of either the hyposensitive or the hypersensitive reaction (see Figure 7-15). In the first case, ulcer production is mainly due to the combined effect of decreased resistance and increased gastric secretion promoted by adrenal glucocorticoids. In the second case, ulcer production is primarily due to PNS activation that causes the vagus nerve to increase gastric secretion through the release of acetylcholine.

We already mentioned the difficulty of trying to link specific emotions with specific physiological reactions. Nevertheless, this does not mean that emotions do not produce specific diseases. For example, in studying a variety of conditions—asthma, rhinitis, hives, ulcers—in 128 patients, Grace and Graham (1952) came to the conclusion that the symptoms expressed by each patient were in close conformity with a particular attitude the patient held toward an emotionally charged situation in their lives. Similarly, although the mechanisms of essential hypertension

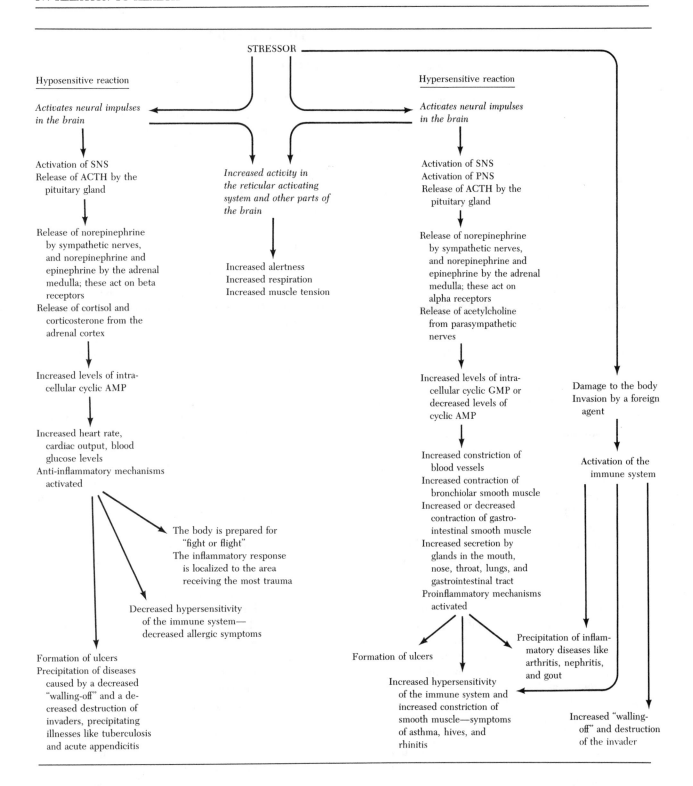

Figure 7–15. Comparison of hyposensitive and hypersensitive responses to stress. (The involvement of the brain is highlighted by italic type.)

(high blood pressure of unknown origin—the most common kind) and coronary heart disease are poorly understood, it is widely accepted that chronic stress contributes to these disorders, which appear to be related to particular attitudes a person has toward the achievement of personal, professional, and social goals. Some investigators believe that hypertension is more likely to develop in individuals with a high level of unexpressed anger, whereas coronary heart disease is more likely to occur in deadline-oriented persons who, striving to succeed, deny their feelings of fatigue and, should they fail, their depression (see Weiner, 1979; Henry and Meehan, 1981, for further comments). To date, however, it is not possible to draw any firm conclusions linking personality types with specific cardiovascular diseases, but the obvious assumption that psychological states influence cardiovascular function certainly is confirmed by the fact that blood pressure and heart rate are tightly regulated by the vasomotor area and the motor nucleus of the vagus, and that the activity of these areas of the upper spinal cord are not only regulated by baroreceptors, but also by many areas of the brain. The hypothalamus, for example, exerts powerful effects on blood pressure and heart rate, as do the limbic system and the frontal areas of the cerebral cortex, as is readily apparent from the results of electrical stimulation showing increases or decreases in blood pressure and heart rate to be a frequent response from these brain areas (see the autonomic responses listed in Figures 7-10 through 7-13). Moreover, in rats, cats, and dogs it has been shown that when specific regions of the upper spinal cord are damaged, this damage can result in hypertension which, interestingly, does not occur in these animals unless other regions of the brain—possibly parts of the frontal cortex and hypothalamus—remain intact (Reis, 1981).

Although the above statements concerning the relation between personality and organic disease may lack specificity, it is important to realize that the validity of this relationship is not diminished as a result. We can clearly and unequivocally state that *certain emotional states, especially of a defensive nature and of long duration, can help to produce organic disease.* On the other hand, we have seen that the specific systems that come into play—such as immunologic, autonomic, adrenal, or hypothalamic—are *extremely diverse in their nature; that is, these systems can respond in a variety of ways and produce different, sometimes opposite, effects in the body.* In our attempt to understand some of the fundamentals of psychosomatic medicine, it is essential that we explore this variability.

V. THE VARIABILITY OF IMMUNOLOGIC AND AUTONOMIC RESPONSES

Throughout this chapter we have seen how our defense mechanisms can be either intensified or reduced. This is true not only for the immune response, but also for the autonomic nervous system, defensive behaviors, and emotions. In other words, all of these mechanisms operate somewhere between "more" and "less." Although this might seem obvious, it is important enough to warrant further discussion.

Dynamic Equilibrium or Steady-State

Consider an airplane moving in the atmosphere at a steady speed of 300 miles per hour. Exactly because it is moving, the "steady" speed can be quickly changed to more (say, 400 mph) or to less (200 mph). In other words, if there is a change in conditions, the airplane is able to adjust by going either faster or slower. If the plane were stopped on the ground or if it were going as fast as it could in the air, there would only be one direction in which to adjust the speed—by going faster in the first case or by going slower in the second. The point is that by not being in between "more" or "less," the airplane is less able to respond to any condition that might come its way. The same is true for the direction of *our* plane. While it is "in the air" it can quickly move to the right or left, up or down, simply because its position is in between these possibilities.

Besides being able to adjust to conditions, our plane must also arrive at its destination on time; overall, it must maintain a certain speed and a certain direction. One particular condition that is constantly influencing our plane is the wind. As our plane moves, it is likely to meet head winds, tail winds, cross drafts, and strong currents that variously pull it down and push it up. To arrive at its destination on time, it must meet and respond to these conditions. For example, if there is a head wind, our airplane will have to work harder to maintain a "steady" speed. In this case the plane is actually going faster relative to the speed of the air than when there is no head wind. That our airplane is "steady" at 300 mph does not necessarily mean, therefore, that the plane itself is working at a steady intensity. As illustrated in Figure 7-16, if the plane is to maintain a "steady" speed, it must change its power whenever there is a head wind or tail wind. As our plane flies through the air, it is constantly making adjustments to forces that would otherwise change its movement; consequently, it is

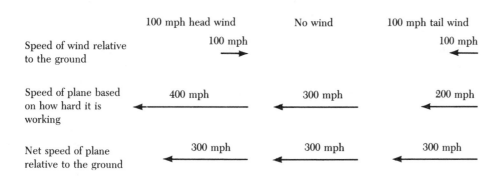

	100 mph head wind	No wind	100 mph tail wind
Speed of wind relative to the ground	100 mph →		100 mph ←
Speed of plane based on how hard it is working	400 mph ←	300 mph ←	200 mph ←
Net speed of plane relative to the ground	300 mph ←	300 mph ←	300 mph ←

Figure 7–16. An illustration demonstrating the workings of a dynamic equilibrium or steady-state. In this case a steady-state is being maintained by an airplane travelling at a net speed of 300 miles per hour (mph). The lengths of the arrows represent the speed of the wind (row 1) and of the airplane (rows 2 and 3). The arrows point in the direction that the airplane or the wind are moving. Note that the three different conditions (a 100-mph head wind, no wind, and a 100-mph tail wind—row 1) each requires a different response in terms of how hard the plane must work (row 2) in order to maintain a steady-state of 300 mph (row 3).

actually in **dynamic equilibrium** or in a **steady-state** with respect to all of these forces.

It is important to note that, precisely because our plane is in a steady-state, if for some reason an on-going influence were to stop suddenly, there is likely to be a very strong "reaction." For example, if the head wind illustrated in Figure 7-16 were to stop suddenly, the plane would find itself suddenly flying at 400 mph instead of 300 mph. In some circumstances, this "reaction" could be very dangerous—it could actually destroy the airplane. On the other hand, if for some reason the plane needed to suddenly slow down, the fact that there is a head wind would permit it to do so much more rapidly than if there were no head wind. Of course, a different set of reactions would occur with a tail wind. If a tail wind were to stop abruptly, the plane would "react" by going much slower.

The defense mechanisms discussed in this chapter all work together in tremendously intricate ways to produce a steady-state with respect to our health. A change in our emotional state, a change in the functioning of the autonomic nervous system, a change in the receptors sensitive to adrenal secretions, a change in the level of toxins or other foreign agents entering our body, a change in muscular activity, even a change in the weather can lead to rapid changes in our health and well-being (either abruptly speeding up or slowing down the "plane") and/or to rapid adjustments that serve to maintain health. It is important to realize that *all* of the changes listed are important. Depending upon other conditions, any one of them can precipitate disease. We will now look at some of the mechanisms involved in changing the balance between sympathetic and parasympathetic activities in the body.

Changes in SNS and PNS Balance

The PNS and SNS are both continuously active, even during the alarm reaction. Even though the alarm response usually includes an increase in heart rate and in blood pressure, and a host of other responses evoked by the SNS, it has been shown that the PNS is also activated—many of its effects are simply masked by the stronger responses from the SNS. These mixed effects are also seen when the autonomic nervous system is activated by stimulating structures within the brain. The pupils almost always dilate (SNS activation) but, in some cases, there is cardiac slowing and/or increased activity of the stomach or the intestines (PNS activation) whereas in other cases there is cardiac acceleration (SNS activation). We have already discussed the fact that some organs, like the bladder, stomach, and intestines, are dominated by the PNS and others—piloerector muscles, sweat glands, and blood vessels—are dominated by the SNS (see page 125).

Although the PNS and SNS are continuously active, *these two branches of the autonomic nervous system reciprocally inhibit each other;* that is, increased SNS activity initiates neural impulses that decrease PNS activity, and vice versa. This reciprocal inhibition is represented both in the upper spinal cord and in the hypothalamus. In the hypothalamus it exists between the anterior portion and the posterior portion. Reciprocal inhibition is especially apparent with respect to states of arousal or calmness. When we are aroused, there is both an increased activation of the SNS and an inhibition of the PNS. Because activation of the SNS causes even greater arousal, or at least will maintain an aroused state, arousal is a state that is likely to persist. Conversely, when we are calm, there is less SNS activity and greater PNS activity as well as a reduced state of arousal. Obviously, this state will also persist. These two responses are illustrated in Figure 7-17.

Figure 7–17. Relation between one's state of arousal and autonomic nervous system responses. Because of reciprocal inhibition between the SNS and PNS, when the SNS is activated the PNS is inhibited, and vice versa. Because SNS activity causes even greater arousal, or at least will maintain an aroused state, its arousal is likely to persist. Similarly, in a calm person, the reduced SNS activity will help maintain the calm state.

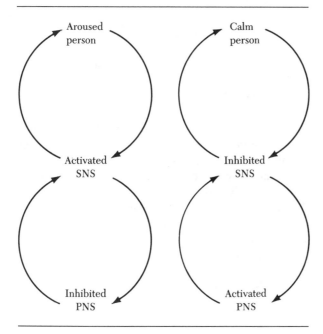

In addition, when muscles and joints are active, the input propagated into the brain from sensory receptors in the muscles, tendons, and joints is much greater (see Figure 6-7). These neural signals activate the reticular system and thereby maintain or increase arousal (see Chapter 8); they also increase SNS activity by their action in the upper spinal cord and posterior portion of the hypothalamus. Conversely, when the muscles and joints are inactive, there is decreased arousal and decreased SNS activity. The added contribution of muscular activity and muscular inactivity is shown in Figure 7-18. Once we are physically active, then, there are mechanisms that *maintain* our arousal and an activated SNS. This mechanism is very useful if our schedule demands that we be alert and "on our toes." If we wish to be less keyed up, however, we must first overcome the inertia of this system. Obviously, the best way to do this is to relax, for relaxation immediately begins to inhibit the SNS and allows us to enter the "calm cycle" illustrated in Figure 7-18.

When we are aroused, the resulting balance between SNS and PNS responses is strongly influenced by muscular activity—that is, whether our body is active or inactive. To a large extent this balance is due to the baroreceptor reflex. As you will recall, the baroreceptor reflex is activated only when there is a change in blood pressure. An increase in blood pressure occurs when we are in an aroused state and there is *little or no muscular activity* and no neural impulses propagated from the brain to initiate such activity. In this case, because of the vasoconstrictive effect resulting from the increased SNS activity that accompanies arousal (via norepinephrine's action on alpha receptors in blood vessels—see Table 7-2), there is an increase in blood pressure that is *immediately offset* by a baroreceptor response that reduces SNS activity and increases PNS activity, lowering blood pressure to normal values. The effects of the baroreceptor reflex are not restricted to the cardiovascular system. When this reflex is activated by increased blood pressure, the decrease in SNS activity and increase in PNS activity are accompanied by corresponding changes in the hypothalamus: the posterior portion becomes less responsive and the anterior portion becomes more responsive. In other words, an *aroused* person who is physically *inactive* is likely to have a complex balance of sympathetic and parasympathetic activities; that is, the SNS is stimulated but suppressed because of the baroreceptor reflex, which is also stimulating the PNS. At the hypothalamic level, the posterior portion is stimulated but suppressed by the baroreceptor reflex

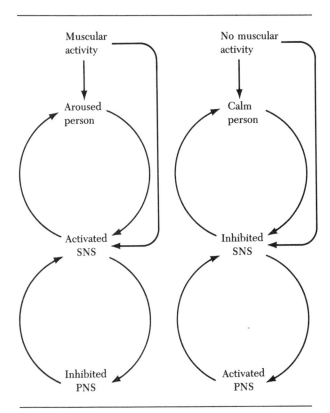

Figure 7–18. Relation between one's state of arousal, autonomic nervous system responses, and muscular activity. Increased muscular activity helps to maintain a state of arousal and increased SNS activity, whereas inactivity helps to maintain a calm state and reduced SNS activity.

which, because of reciprocal inhibition between the posterior and anterior portions, is also increasing the activity of the anterior portion of the hypothalamus.

Many times when we are in an aroused state *and physically active*, the SNS is activated with little or no increase in PNS activity because muscular activity is accompanied by *dilation* of the blood vessels in skeletal muscle. That is, a) when one moves skeletal muscle, impulses propagated from the brain activate SNS endings that release acetylcholine, causing vasodilation (see Table 7-2), and b) muscular activity produces metabolites in the muscles, such as carbon dioxide and lactic acid, and lowers oxygen levels, all of which are strong vasodilators themselves. Because of the vasodilation, *there is little or no increase in blood pressure,* and therefore the baroreceptor response is minimal. In other words, when a person is aroused and active, the balance between SNS and

PNS activities that occurs—SNS stimulation but no SNS suppression and no PNS activation—is likely to be quite different from that in an inactive person. At the hypothalamic level, there is a corresponding difference—in an active person the posterior portion is stimulated but not suppressed, and the anterior portion is not stimulated. These different mechanisms are illustrated in Figure 7-19 with respect to the intensity of SNS and PNS activity.

The fact that different emotional and behavioral reactions evoke different responses in the blood vessels of skeletal muscle has been shown experimentally in cats (Zanchetti, Baccelli, Mancia, and Ellison, 1972). When cats were forced to be immobile, but anticipated a confrontation with another cat, the blood vessels in their skeletal muscle were constricted. When fighting movements were allowed, these blood vessels dilated. Of interest was the additional observation that in immobilized cats anticipating a confrontation with a dog, mouse, or fire, the responses were *variable*—that is, in some cats their blood vessels underwent the expected vasoconstriction, but in others they underwent vasodilation, although the vasodilation was less pronounced than when there was movement. Perhaps some cats perceived the dog as a threatening object which set off a conditioned vasodilation in anticipation of flight, while the mouse was perceived as a very appealing object, again setting off a conditioned vasodilation, but in this case in anticipation of predatory attack. Whatever the case may be, these data confirm that blood flow in skeletal muscle can either increase (vasodilation) or decrease (vasoconstriction) in response to different emotional reactions as they relate to movement.

Thus, depending upon whether a state of arousal is accompanied by inactivity or activity, the autonomic nervous system shows two different patterns. With muscular activity, one sees an increase in SNS activity, enhanced muscle tone, increased heart rate, increased cardiac output, and increased respiration. In the case of muscular inactivity, the increase in all of these functions is not as great, but there is greater PNS activity.

In order to understand how these mechanisms tie in with emotional states, a few examples are listed in Table 7-4 according to their degree of muscular involvement. As indicated, someone suffering from prolonged and intense depression—typified by slow speech, slow body movements, feelings of helplessness, worthlessness, and withdrawn and apathetic behavior—is likely to experience quite different patterns of muscular activity (accompanied by differ-

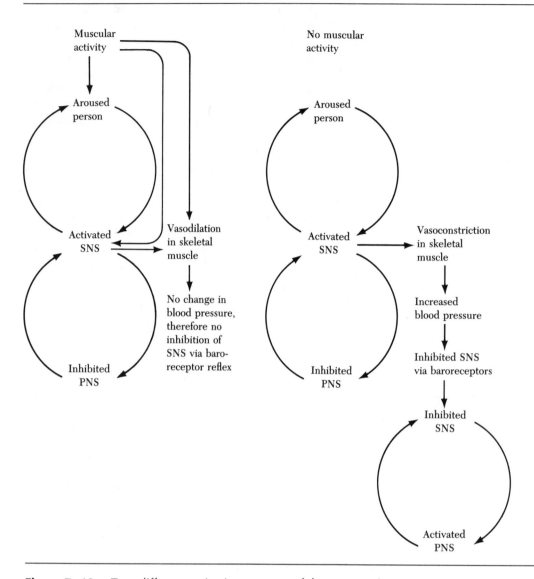

Figure 7–19. Two different activation patterns of the autonomic nervous system, both involving arousal. One pattern (left) involves muscular activity, the other (right) inactivity. With muscular activity the SNS is activated whereas with inactivity this SNS response is somewhat reduced and PNS activity increases.

ent patterns of autonomic nervous system activation) than someone suffering from prolonged and intense excitement—typified by nervousness, frantic, restless, often conflict-ridden movements, tenseness, states of seething with anger and resentment, sometimes mania, and, often, feelings of not having enough time.

Of course, changes in autonomic balance are taking place all the time. Each time we rest after having eaten a meal, PNS activity increases, or, when we are hungry and busily looking for something to eat, SNS activity increases. If, however, the state of hunger lasts a long time, or if we are constantly "fighting" to get food in our mouths, the stress is severe and can produce illness.

The interactions between the autonomic nervous system and emotional states are so complex, and individual differences so great, that it is not too worthwhile to attempt to relate particular emotional states with specific diseases unless a great deal is known

Table 7–4. Categorization of some defensive behaviors with respect to muscular activity and duration of response time.

Responses involving muscular activity	Responses involving little or no muscular activity	Duration of response
Prolonged rage (with anger or fighting) or escape (flight)	Fright (cringing, crouching, hiding)	Usually no more than a few hours
Resentment, anxiety, desperation, involving various types of behavioral arousal (anger, restlessness, etc.)	Resentment, anxiety, prolonged fear, desperation, depression, involving various types of withdrawal (giving up, apathy, etc.)	Sometimes many days or weeks

about the patient. This topic is further discussed at the end of the chapter; at this point, it is sufficient to emphasize that different emotions and behavioral patterns clearly produce different patterns of autonomic activity, and that these patterns differentially affect the immune system (see Figure 7-15).

Changes in the Activity of Harmful Agents

Infections can be caused by the different viruses and bacteria to which we are constantly exposed, or which we pick up at a relatively young age and carry around in our bodies for many years. Most of the time these viruses or bacteria are met with an inflammatory response that walls them off or otherwise delimits them. Under certain circumstances, however, they can suddenly proliferate and precipitate disease. Examples of such infectious agents are the *herpes simplex* virus (producing cold sores, canker sores, or fever blisters in the mouth, lips, nose, or genital regions; whether the symptoms above and those below "the belt" are caused by the same virus or two different viruses is an unsettled issue), the *herpes zoster* virus (producing the symptoms of shingles: chicken-pox-like blisters and pain in the chest and lower abdomen, sometimes severe pain from inflamed nerves, visual impairment when the eyes are affected, and painful sensations in the skin when the skin is touched), the *tubercle bacillus* (tuberculosis), and bacteria that cause Vincent's Disease (trench mouth, producing sores and inflammation of the gums and/or tonsils). The disorders elicited by these agents can be precipitated by anything that strongly suppresses the immune system, especially the release of adrenal steroids and epinephrine. Of course, emotional upset or any other physical or psychological stressor has the potential of

releasing these chemicals.

Many diseases are not caused by the "flaring-up" of bacteria or viruses that lie within us or that we are constantly in contact with. Rather, they are caused by the flaring-up of physiological conditions that are always present within us simply because they are part of our own working body. Responses like those of asthma and hives, some inflammatory reactions in muscles and tendons that produce symptoms of "aching" or "stiffness," disturbances in secretions of the stomach that can produce ulcers, metabolic disturbances that can lead to gout, and some forms of acne (caused by the plugging up of channels from sebaceous glands by skin cells) are all examples of disorders that can be caused by activation of our own bodily processes. Although the reasons why these processes are activated to the extent that they cause disorders are largely unknown, inflammatory and allergic reactions clearly involve an increased immune response, and ulcers are associated with persistently increased gastric secretions.

The disorders listed above are examples of conditions that are particularly sensitive to our general state of health. When a person is well-rested and healthy, conditions such as local infections, exhaustion and fatigue, or "stressful" emotional states (depression, anxiety, fear and resentment), capable of promoting asthma attacks, gout, "stiff" muscles, bleeding gums and many other symptoms, are much less likely to do so.

Before we end our discussion concerning the variability of defensive responses, we must comment on how this variability appears to be expressed at a cellular level, for these findings have direct relevance to how psychological states might produce organic disease.

Changes in the Functioning of Cells

There is an increasing body of evidence that alpha and beta receptors in cells, the receptors that appear to be responsible for many of the proinflammatory, anti-inflammatory, and other effects we have discussed in this chapter, are themselves changeable in their response. Alpha and beta receptors can alter their function in a number of ways. For example, it has been shown that persons who have hypersensitive immune systems, such as asthmatics, often have lymphocytes that are not as responsive to chemicals that activate beta receptors. This decreased beta-receptor response means that intracellular cyclic AMP levels do not rise as they normally would in response to epinephrine or norepinephrine, and, as a result, anti-inflammatory responses are suppressed. The overall effect of this decreased sensitivity of beta receptors is an activation of proinflammatory reactions. These workings may explain why stress or other conditions that activate the SNS and the adrenal glands often influence alpha receptors and thereby intensify inflammatory reactions in allergic people, whereas in others both beta receptors and alpha receptors—but especially beta receptors—are activated and no hypersensitive reaction develops.

Another mechanism, perhaps related to the one just discussed, is called *interconversion* of alpha and beta receptors. Under certain conditions it appears that beta receptors are actually converted into alpha receptors, and vice versa (see Szentivanyi and Williams, 1980, and below). Conditions associated with low metabolic activity, such as cold, seem to "switch" beta receptors into alpha receptors. This phenomenon may be one reason why cold is often found to be a stimulus for inflammatory reactions like asthma and arthritis in people sensitive to these diseases. Of interest is the finding that low rates of muscular contraction also seem to convert beta receptors to alpha receptors. That is, the fact that a person is lethargic or quiet not only will affect the balance between SNS and PNS activities, but, if there is a release of norepinephrine and epinephrine in response to stress or emotional upset, these chemicals might also directly stimulate proinflammatory reactions by their effects on an increased population of alpha receptors, thereby increasing intracellular levels of cyclic GMP. This interconversion of receptors might partly explain the strong correlation between depression and arthritis, at least to the extent that the stress of depression is frequently accompanied by little desire for physical exertion, especially in older people, the population most at risk for this disease.

A third mechanism involves the relation between norepinephrine, epinephrine, glucocorticoids, and "T" or "B" lymphocytes. It is known that some "T" lymphocytes suppress the response of "B" lymphocytes (these "T" lymphocytes are called *suppressor T cells*) and that some "T" lymphocytes increase the response of "B" lymphocytes (these are called *helper T cells*). Because "B" lymphocytes produce the plasma cells that release antibodies, anything that regulates their responsiveness can determine whether the response from the immune system will be strong or weak. It has been shown that glucocorticoids can decrease the number of helper T cells (see Katz and Fauci, 1979). This reduction, of course, is an anti-inflammatory response that is in keeping with the anti-inflammatory effects of glucocorticoids. On the other hand, it has been shown that cyclic AMP (which is increased by glucocorticoids) can also decrease the activity of suppressor T cells, leading to an increase in "B" lymphocytes and antibodies (see Katz and Fauci, 1978). This proinflammatory response seems to be dose-dependent; at least it is not observed when the concentration of cyclic AMP becomes too high. These findings indicate that the *amount* of glucocorticoid released as a result of stress or other stimuli could determine whether there is a proinflammatory or anti-inflammatory response; this assumption is consistent with certain observations that mild stress can sometimes worsen the symptoms of arthritis whereas strong stress can sometimes improve arthritic symptoms. It must be mentioned that the selective responses of "T" and "B" lymphocytes to adrenal hormones is currently under intense research, and we can expect our understanding of these mechanisms to change considerably in the near future.

As a concluding statement to this section on health, we must emphasize that although it is impossible to make any sweeping generalizations connecting any one emotion or set of emotions with a particular disease, it is quite likely that if one were to carefully investigate all of the symptoms unique to that individual, one could come up with a picture that would connect his/her psychological symptoms with his/her physical symptoms. Such a diagnosis would need to take into account the person's emotional state, general level of muscular activity, autonomic response stereotypy (the precise pattern whereby autonomic activation influences the organs—see page 135), degree of fatigue, current state of health (including the possibility of local infection and allergic reactions), and a host of other responses. Of course, if properly diagnosed, the possibility of a real "cure"—whether through psychotheraphy, change of jobs, change in living habits, change in exercise routine, prescription of antibiotics or other medications, or anything else—becomes much more accessible.

VI. CONCLUSIONS

In recent years, ideas about what aspects of an illness are psychological and what are physiological have broadened considerably. Although there are many reports of the spontaneous regression of tumors and remission of cancer in patients (see Everson and Cole, 1966), the scientific basis for the disappearance of untreated tumors remains unknown. Today, many agree that the mind and emotional states play crucial roles in the development and regression of cancer (see Stoll, 1979, for comments). There is also some evidence that the same kinds of emotions that can lower immunological resistance—hostile feelings, anxiety, feelings of helplessness—might also contribute to cancer formation; on the other hand, evidence exists to show that these emotions have no influence on the development of cancer and, according to some reports, they help to resist its formation (see Klopfer, 1957; Miller and Spratt, 1979, for data on humans; Peters and Mason, 1979, for data obtained from experimentally induced cancer in animals). There are also a number of reports that strengthening the patient's *belief* in a treatment—whether the treatment be surgery, taking a pill, exercising one's ability to mentally control a physical process (the aim of visualization therapy), hypnosis therapy, or strengthening the patient's will to live—can lead to the spontaneous regression of cancerous tissue (Klopfer, 1957; Stoll, 1979; Panagis, 1979). In the light of what we have discussed in this chapter, this variability of responses should no longer be surprising. Yet even though the idea that psychological states can influence the development and treatment of cancer is gaining increasing support, many observations remain anecdotal. It is best, we believe, to wait until more research is done before discussing these processes or drawing conclusions from them.

Beyond admitting that our behavior, emotions, immune system, autonomic nervous system, adrenal glands, and brain exert powerful influences on our body's protective mechanisms, evaluation of the processes outlined in this chapter is very difficult. We can state with certainty that we have presented the fundamentals of psychosomatic medicine, that we have indicated how broad the area is, and that many exciting things are going on. Even so, many remain skeptical toward any claim that a definite relation exists between mental and emotional processes and organic disease. A common statement about the role of psychology in the incidence of disease is that it is probably important "as long as there is some substantial physical event that happens first," or that "as a single causative factor it is not important." These statements are often followed by a detailed presentation of the physiology, pathology, anatomy, and pharmacology of the disease being considered. The bias of these assertions is exemplified by the fact that exactly the same statements can be made about viruses and bacteria. After all, we are exposed to harmful microorganisms all the time, yet each and every one of us does not get sick; couldn't we then assume that as a single causative factor these microorganisms are not important? Similarly, we could state that these microorganisms only become important once something else happens "first." Of course, this would be equally biased.

Again, we must not lose sight of the fact that emotions, behavior, the autonomic nervous system, the adrenal glands and their secretions, and the immune system clearly comprise a coexisting, inseparable set of processes serving our defense and health. In so doing, however, the concerted actions of these processes can promote illness as well—a contradictory action that is evident not only in psychosomatic disorders, but also in "pure" medical disorders and mental disease.

Everyone would agree, for example, that a person with a cold is "not well" or "sick." However, the symptoms—runny nose, stuffed sinuses, mucus-filled lungs—that often accompany a cold are also part of a defense system in the body geared to protect us from invasion by foreign particles. One might then ask whether this "disease" is protective or not. Similarly, everyone would agree that someone who constantly lives in a world of delusions is "not well." Often, however, these delusions are an adaptation to conditions that are perceived by the "sick" person to be real. In an address delivered before the Second International Psychoanalytical Congress in 1910, Freud stated:

> Let us remember, however, that it is not for us to advance upon life as fanatical hygienists or therapeutists. We must admit that this ideal prevention of all neurotic illness (by barring a person's flight into illness by exposing his symptoms) would not be advantageous to every individual. A good number of those who now take flight into illness would not support the conflict under the conditions we have assumed, but would rapidly succumb or would commit some outrage which would be worse than if they themselves fell ill of a neurosis. The neuroses have in fact their biological function as defensive

measures and their social justification; the "advantage through illness" that they provide is not always a purely subjective one. Is there one of you who has not at some time caught a glimpse behind the scenes in the causation of a neurosis and had to allow that it was the least of the evils possible in the circumstances? And should one really require such sacrifices in order to exterminate the neuroses, while the world is all the same full of other inextinguishable miseries?

On an everyday level, the concept that our psychological and physiological states have, as their primary intent, the maintenance of our health has, of course, been discussed with examples throughout this book. Thus, the fact that we are hungry when our blood nutrient levels are low, or thirsty when our blood volume decreases, or that we breathe more quickly when we are excited, or that we move our heads in order to maximize sensory input into our ears and eyes, or that we avoid many potentially harmful agents simply confirms that, in a general way, psychology and physiology work together continuously to maintain our health.

Recommended Reading

BIERMAN, C. and PEARLMAN, D. (editors). *Allergic Diseases of Infancy, Childhood and Adolescence.* Philadelphia: W. B. Saunders, 1980. *This book is recommended for advanced students. It is very well written and contains useful information about all areas of immunology and allergy.*

HERRERA, H. and FIALKOV, J. "Psychologic considerations in the evolution and natural history of bronchial asthma." In: *Bronchial Asthma*, edited by Gershwin, M. New York: Grune and Stratton, 1981, pp 405-426. *This article offers a clear, concise discussion of the place of psychological factors in asthma. The authors' discussion of social, family, behavioral, emotional, cognitive, and physiological factors is very useful in considering other disorders as well.*

KNAPP, P., MATHE, A., and VACHON, L. "Psychosomatic aspects of bronchial asthma." In: *Bronchial Asthma: Mechanisms and Therapeutics*, edited by Weiss, E., and Segal, M. Boston: Little, Brown and Co., 1976, pp 1055-1080. *A concise presentation of psychological factors contributing to asthma. Their possible connection to physiological responses, especially those originating in the brain, is also discussed. Recommended for readers with advanced knowledge.*

NORBACK, C. and THE ASTHMA AND ALLERGY FOUNDATION OF AMERICA (editors). *The Allergy Encyclopedia.* New York: The New American Library, 1981, 256 pages. *This paperback is recommended for anyone who wishes to know more about allergies and the immune system. It is written in nontechnical language for the general reader and contains an excellent glossary of terms.*

PORTER, R. and KNIGHT, J. (editors). *Physiology, Emotion and Psychosomatic Illness.* CIBA Foundation Symposium 8. New York: Associated Scientific Publishers, 1972. *This book contains seventeen articles written by different scientists. Each article is followed by a discussion among symposium participants. Recommended for advanced reading.*

SELYE, H. *The Stress of Life.* New York: McGraw-Hill, 1976 (paperback edition, 1978), 515 pages. *This paperback is recommended to anyone who wishes more information about stress. It is written in nontechnical language for the general reader. Although in some respects it is over-simplified, it contains a great deal of information about inflammatory reactions, the adrenal glands, disease, and stress.*

Arousal, Attention, Sleep, and Dreams: The Clinical Reality

Medical Disorder: Insomnia

Read this overture carefully before you read Chapter 8. The connections between the medical reality of insomnia and the basic underlying physiological and psychological processes that regulate normal arousal and sleep are developed in this chapter. (For more information on insomnia, see Hobson, 1982; Adams, 1980; Beutler, Thornby, and Karacan, 1978.)

Insomnia is a condition characterized by an inability to sleep. Insomniacs frequently go to bed and try to surrender themselves to sleep, but are plagued by bodily sensations such as pain in the limbs, they are worried or anxious and therefore nervously excited, they are engaged in vigorous mental activity, or they experience muscular tension and cannot relax. All of these conditions promote arousal and counteract drowsiness and sleep. Most chronic insomniacs suffer from some degree of depression. A depressed person typically has no trouble falling asleep but will experience light sleep or will wake up a few hours later and be unable to return to sleep. A very large percentage of psychiatric patients suffer from insomnia. Here, as with nonpsychiatric insomniacs, it is largely due to excessive arousal, often associated with depression.

Because we do not yet understand what constitutes "natural" or "normal" sleep, it is not possible to specify precisely what is "unnatural" or "abnormal" sleep. Some people sleep less than three hours a night and do not complain of being insomniac. Others dream that they are awake and believe they are insomniac even when an EEG shows that they undergo normal sleep cycles. (An EEG, an electroencephalogram, is a recording of the electrical activity of the brain as obtained from the scalp.)

In the general population, it is estimated that up to 10 percent use nonprescription sleeping medications, minor tranquilizers, alcohol, and other drugs to promote sleep. In most cases, these drugs are not helpful beyond a few days because tolerance to these drugs soon occurs and demands increasingly higher doses for sedation. At moderate to high levels, almost every type of sleeping pill disrupts sleep cycles, usually decreasing REM sleep, and often decreasing slow-wave sleep as well. (REM sleep and slow-wave sleep will be discussed at some length in this chapter. Briefly, REM sleep is sleep associated with rapid eye movements—abbreviated, REM—and an EEG having many components characteristic of an awake person. Slow-wave sleep is sleep associated with the appearance in the EEG of delta waves, which are slow waves with a frequency of less than 3-1/2 per second.) The disruption of sleep cycles by medications can in itself promote insomnia, or it can lead to increased insomnia once the medication is withdrawn. It is therefore best to avoid medication whenever possible.

In general, any method that reduces the intensity of arousal is helpful in treating insomnia. Reducing the intake of stimulating drugs like caffeine, engaging in some form of physical exercise during the day or relaxation exercise prior to bedtime, giving up daytime naps, and eliminating or otherwise dealing with situations causing anxiety, depression, worry, or pain are among the nonpharmacologic treatments the insomniac can use.

8

Arousal, Attention, Sleep, and Dreams

In this book we have frequently referred to a state called **arousal**. We will now look at it in more detail. Generally, arousal is associated with one or more of the following:

a) awakening from sleep,

b) increased alertness,

c) increased attention,

d) increased emotional responses,

e) increased activity of the sympathetic nervous system,

f) increased muscle tone and increased muscular activity.

Arousal is clearly a graded process; that is, all of the above qualities can be either more or less intense, and their intensity can change—sometimes rapidly, sometimes slowly.

We consciously experience many aspects of arousal, and these experiences help us to understand not only that various arousal mechanisms exist, but also that their workings are a part of many of our states. Sleep and arousal are obviously interrelated; the more we are aroused, the less we are able to sleep, and vice versa. Yet, because we have very little conscious experience while we are asleep, it is difficult to gain comparable clarity concerning sleep mechanisms. In general terms, just as a person is more or less aroused while awake, we know that a person is more or less asleep during sleep. Such phenomena as sleepwalking (somnambulism), sleep-talking, and dreaming have been observed throughout history, and clearly indicate that sleep is not a single state. On the basis of our own experience, we all know the difference between "light" sleep and "heavy" sleep, but it is difficult to define this difference in exact terms.

It was not until the late 19th and early 20th century, when we developed instruments to measure and record the electrical activity of the brain, that we began to study the mechanisms of sleep in more detail. This technique of recording the electrical activity of the brain was a major advance not only for studying sleep but also for studying the brain mechanisms responsible for arousal. We will therefore begin this chapter by briefly describing the various **brain waves** that have been recorded. After discussing brain waves, we will discuss the **reticular system**. We have already noted the importance of this system in Chapter 5 when we discussed arousal as it relates to breathing (see page 65), and in Chapter 7 when we discussed arousal in relation to stress and activation of the autonomic nervous system (page 147). Now we will take a detailed look at the functioning of this system and attempt to understand how it contributes to increased and decreased arousal. This will be followed by a discussion of the mechanisms of **attention** and **inattention**, **relaxation** and **sleep**, suppressive mechanisms like **satiety** and **boredom** that decrease our level of arousal, **dreaming**, and, finally, the relation of these mechanisms to our health.

I. BRAIN WAVES, AROUSAL, AND STAGES OF SLEEP

When electrodes are placed at different points on the scalp, they can be used to monitor the electrical activities of various regions of the brain. The electrical signals sensed by the electrodes result from the natural activity of large groups of cortical cells that generate electrical current simultaneously. (The activity of a few nerve cells or fibers would not generate enough current to be picked up through the skull.) The electrical recordings obtained from the scalp are called an **electroencephalogram** (abbreviated **EEG**). Certain distinct patterns are discernible in the EEG when a person is asleep or awake. These patterns, called **alpha**, **beta**, **delta**, and **theta waves**, are illustrated in Figure 8-1 (except for beta waves, which are discussed below).

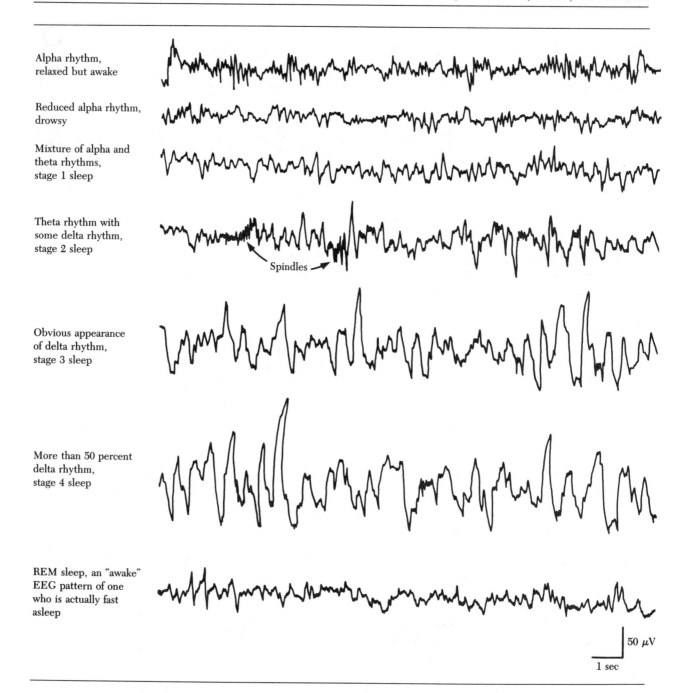

Alpha rhythm,
relaxed but awake

Reduced alpha rhythm,
drowsy

Mixture of alpha and
theta rhythms,
stage 1 sleep

Theta rhythm with
some delta rhythm,
stage 2 sleep

Spindles →

Obvious appearance
of delta rhythm,
stage 3 sleep

More than 50 percent
delta rhythm,
stage 4 sleep

REM sleep, an "awake"
EEG pattern of one
who is actually fast
asleep

50 μV

1 sec

Figure 8–1.   EEG descriptions of various stages of sleep. Note the
progressive increase in high-voltage, slow **delta waves** as a person
goes from an awake, quiet state to a state of deep sleep. Stages 1
through 4 are referred to as **slow–wave sleep.** Approximately 40 to 50
percent of a typical adult's seven to eight hours of sleep is spent in
stage 2 sleep (characterized by the occurrence of spindles in the EEG
pattern), and another 25 percent in stages 3 and 4. The remaining 25
percent is spent in **REM sleep,** often called **paradoxical sleep** because
of its awake pattern in the EEG.

Source: A. Rechtschaffen and A. Kales. *A MANUAL OF STANDARDIZED
TERMINOLOGY, TECHNIQUES AND SCORING SYSTEM FOR SLEEP STAGES OF
HUMAN SUBJECTS.* National Institutes of Health, Publication No. 204, 1968.

Alpha waves occur at a frequency between 8 and 13 per second and are present in the EEG when a person is quiet and resting, but awake. This EEG pattern is often accompanied by feelings of calmness and serenity; anything that produces tension—even a mental effort to solve a problem—will disrupt this rhythm. There are many reports that during meditation alpha activity is dominant in the EEG, not surprising given that meditation involves being quiet and relaxed, but awake. Just as meditation can be learned through practice, it has been shown that a person can both identify and intensify the occurrence of alpha activity by his/her own effort. Some people, in fact, consider meditation and the "alpha state" to be the same, but it is more correct to consider the alpha rhythm as simply reflecting a quiet but awake state—a condition that will produce an increase in alpha activity whether one meditates or not.

If a quietly resting, awake person is aroused by noise, or asked to open his/her eyes if they are closed, or becomes engaged in mental activity such as solving a problem, the alpha waves are replaced with lower voltage, faster **beta waves**. This arousal pattern in the EEG is also called "desynchronization," "alpha blocking," or the "arousal reaction" because there is often an alerting response or orienting reflex (see Chapter 7). These beta waves are usually between 13 and 25 per second but, with intense arousal, they can be as frequent as 50 per second. The lower voltage does *not* mean the brain is less active. Rather, it reflects the fact that the electrical currents generated by the neurons being recorded are not oscillating together (synchronized), but are busily doing different things (desynchronized). As a concrete example, consider a situation where everyone in a large classroom is asked to count "one, two, three" out loud together, but very softly. The effect of the simultaneity will be a clear, audible sound. On the other hand, if everyone is asked to talk to each other about anything they wish, but still softly, the combined effect will be a much more dispersed pattern of sound, none clearly audible. This difference would be especially apparent if listened to from a tape recording without the benefit of watching individual faces or focusing your attention on someone in the room. In a similar way, when alpha rhythm is "blocked" by beta rhythm, the cells switch from a synchronized activity, where many cells are being activated simultaneously, to a desynchronized activity, where the voltage of the recording falls considerably although there is increased cortical activity.

When we are resting quietly and then begin to fall asleep, we usually enter a state of "drowsiness." At this point the alpha waves become smaller, decreasing in amplitude. As the person falls asleep, the alpha

waves of the EEG are replaced by *slower*, more irregular waves—a mixture of **theta** (4 to 7 per second) and **alpha** (8 to 13 per second) rhythms. These waves average about 6 per second. Respiration and heart rate have become slower, the eyes are apt to roll slowly (not rapidly, as will be discussed later in the chapter), and the person becomes unresponsive to mild stimuli. One might also experience floating sensations and idle images during this period, which usually lasts only a few minutes. (These mental images are mental representations of objects or events that seem to "float by," relatively disconnected to directed thought processes.) This state is called **stage 1 sleep**. If awakened at this point, the person will probably claim not to have been asleep, even though mild stimulation had evoked no response.

This state is followed by **stage 2 sleep**, which is characterized mainly by theta waves, but also by brief bursts of alpha rhythm, in the EEG. These bursts are called "sleep spindles." In stage 2 sleep the person is less responsive to external stimuli than in stage 1 sleep. Although they do not predominate, slow **delta waves** (less than 3 per second) appear in the EEG in stage 2 sleep.

Stage 3 sleep is characterized by the obvious appearance of delta waves and the absence of sleep spindles. Stage 3 sleep generally occurs within fifteen minutes after a person has entered stage 2 sleep. **Stage 4 sleep** is characterized by a predominance of delta waves (more than 50 percent of the EEG). In these stages the person is deeply asleep and quite unresponsive to external stimuli. These stages are all depicted in Figure 8-1. Notice that the amplitude (height) of the EEG is larger in stage 4 than in the other stages of sleep, indicating greater synchrony, not more activity of the cells.

Summarizing the events described above, as a person goes from an aroused state to one of deep sleep, there is a progressive decrease in the activity of cortical cells and a progressive increase of delta waves in the EEG. Associated with these EEG changes is a gradual decrease in responsiveness to external stimuli and an increase in the time it takes for a person to feel fully focused and alert when awakened. In addition, a number of physiological changes occur—a decrease in muscle tone, blood pressure, heart rate, body temperature, breathing rate, oxygen consumption, thyroid hormone secretion, and urine production by the kidneys, a slight decrease in cardiac output, a dilation of blood vessels, and an increase in the secretion of other hormones (growth hormone, prolactin, and aldosterone). All of these effects are most pronounced during sleep stages 3 and 4.

It is important to realize that the EEG is essentially

a measure of *cortical* activity. Electrodes inserted into the deeper structures of the brain pick up electrical currents indicative of cellular activity in these structures and they, too, show changes reflecting a person's level of arousal; in many instances, however, the pattern of the recording is different from what is observed in the cortex. Therefore, the various brain waves we have just described are not electrical patterns characteristic of the brain as a whole, but specifically of the cortex when its activity is recorded from the scalp.

II. THE RETICULAR SYSTEM AND ITS EFFECTS ON AROUSAL, SLEEP, MUSCULAR ACTIVITY, SENSORY INPUT, AND ACTIVITIES OF THE AUTONOMIC NERVOUS SYSTEM

As announced at the beginning of the chapter, one particular neural system in the brain, the **reticular system**, is involved in arousal and seems to be especially responsible for the EEG patterns classically observed. This system begins in the medulla and pons of the upper spinal cord, and its activity influences the activity of almost every part of the brain. It is made up of many small, interconnecting nerve cells. In fact, "reticulum" means a fine network of fibers or cells. This system is illustrated in Figure 8-2. As shown in the figure, its main projections go from the pons to the thalamus, and from there to all areas of the cortex. "Projection," as discussed in Chapter 6, page 94, refers to the fact that neurons from one region—in this case, the reticular system of the upper spinal cord and thalamus—form a connection with another region (in this case, most regions of the brain). Other projections of the reticular system go to the hypothalamus and to the limbic system, but they go either directly or indirectly (that is, via some other structure like the thalamus) to the basal ganglia and the cerebellum as well. (The basal ganglia and the cerebellum are structures devoted to the control of skeletal muscle; see Chapter 9.) The reticular system also influences the lower portions of the spinal cord. In short, the activity of the reticular system affects the activity of virtually every area of the brain.

Effects on Arousal and Sleep

When the reticular system is electrically stimulated in the upper spinal cord (in the medulla, pons, and between the pons and the hypothalamus) of a sleeping animal, it will awaken instantly, and the EEG will immediately change from *slow waves* (mostly delta) to

a desynchronized, alert pattern (beta). This response corresponds to the neurological and behavioral effects observed when a resting animal is presented with a novel stimulus: it will orient itself toward the source of stimulation, its sympathetic nervous system will be activated, muscle tone will increase, and the electrical activity recorded in the EEG will switch from a predominantly resting pattern to a fast, low-voltage pattern. This **arousal** or **alerting response**, reflected in the EEG by the shift from alpha waves to beta waves, is not sensory-specific; that is, *any* novel stimulus activating *any* sense organ of the animal will affect the activity of all areas of the cortex.

On the other hand, if the spinal cord is cut right above the pons, isolating the medulla and the pons from the rest of the brain above, the animal goes into a coma and the EEG shows only slow waves. Furthermore, neither the EEG nor the animal will show any sign of arousal to normal awakening stimuli when such a cut is made, even when the main sensory pathways are left intact. Also, when barbiturates like nembutal (a general anesthetic) are administered, not only does the EEG show slow waves that remain unaffected by awakening stimuli, but these stimuli also fail to evoke behavioral or emotional arousal. Electrical stimulation of the reticular system also fails to arouse an anesthetized animal or change its EEG pattern. Thus, barbiturates act primarily on the reticular system within the upper spinal cord. It is interesting to note that barbiturates do not exert this action by blocking the transmission of information from specific sense organs. That is, in an animal anesthetized with barbiturates, a pinch of the skin or an auditory click will still create neural impulses that are propagated through the brain and received in corresponding areas of the cerebral cortex, even though the animal does not appear to perceive these stimuli and is not aroused by them.

It is also possible to elicit both behavioral and EEG arousal or sleep by stimulating areas into which the reticular system projects. For example, electrical stimulation at high frequencies of the posterior portion of the hypothalamus (which also exerts a strong influence on the sympathetic nervous system—see Chapter 7) and portions of the thalamus (called the "cephalic" portion of the reticular system) will arouse an animal from sleep. Conversely, when the thalamic portions of the reticular system and the anterior portions of the hypothalamus are stimulated electrically at low frequencies (8 to 10 cycles per second), the animal will get drowsy and go to sleep and the EEG will change from a desynchronized pattern to synchronized, slow-wave activity.

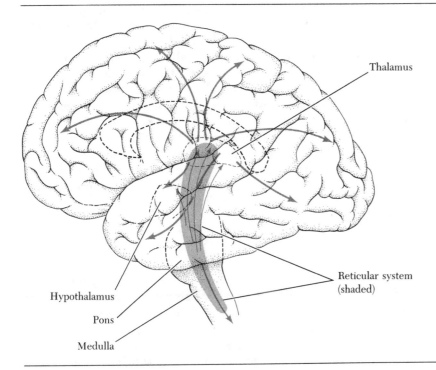

Thalamus

Reticular system
(shaded)

Hypothalamus

Pons

Medulla

Figure 8–2. The reticular system and its projections from the medulla
and the pons to the lower portions of the spinal cord, the
hypothalamus, the limbic system, the thalamus, and thence to the
cerebral cortex. Note that the reticular system sends projections
throughout the entire brain, including areas that control the activity of
skeletal muscle. The part of the reticular system that is within the
thalamus is sometimes called the "cephalic" portion of the reticular
system.

The information presented above is just a fraction
of the evidence suggesting that the reticular system is
involved in "waking up" the brain. Furthermore, its
stimulatory effects are not limited to the higher structures of the brain. In fact, the lower end of the reticular system is continuous with small nerve cells
that are found at all levels of the spinal cord. When
activated, these cells modify the activity of **motor
neurons**, special nerve cells that control the movement and tone of skeletal muscle. The influence of the
reticular system on muscle is discussed next.

Effects on Muscular Activity

When the reticular system is stimulated in the upper
spinal cord, the activity of motor neurons and the
muscles they innervate usually increases. Motor neurons originate at all levels of the brain and spinal cord.

When stimulated, they transmit neural impulses that
result in contraction of muscle fibers that make up
muscle. Thus motor neurons cause *movement* or *motion;* hence the term "motor." The activation of motor
neurons does not always result in movement, however; if there is little or no movement, there will be
an increase in *muscle tension.* It is for this reason that
stimulation of the reticular system in the upper spinal
cord is associated with both increased movement and
increased muscle tone. (The manner in which motor
neurons control the tone of muscles is discussed in
some detail in Chapter 9.)

When the lower three-fourths of the reticular system in the medulla is electrically stimulated, a decrease in the activity of motor neurons and a
corresponding decrease in muscular activity is usually
observed. Again, the fact that electrical stimulation of
the reticular system can either increase or decrease

muscular activity does not mean that this system is nonspecific. In fact, as discussed in the previous chapter with respect to the autonomic nervous system, it is a reflection of the existence of highly refined systems.

Effects on Sensory Systems

Electrical stimulation of the reticular system in the upper spinal cord also has a powerful influence on sensory receptors and sensory transmission systems, often leading to *reduced* sensory input. This reduction in response to stimulation of the reticular system has been observed in a variety of sensory systems. For example, the activity of nerve cells in the retina of the eye is inhibited; the transmission of sensory information from touch and pressure receptors in the skin is reduced in the spinal cord, thalamus, and even in the cerebral cortex; and neural impulses evoked by auditory clicks are reduced in the auditory nerve.

On the other hand, it has also been shown that electrical stimulation of the reticular system can *increase* sensory transmission. This response is especially evident for sensory receptors contained in special units called "muscle spindles," which are units sensitive to the activity of muscles, as will be discussed in the next chapter. Electrical stimulation of the reticular system can increase the activity of nerve cells in the retina of the eye as well (remember that it can also decrease the activity of these cells) and, when the thalamus is electrically stimulated or when appropriate sensory stimuli—such as a flash of light or an auditory click—are presented, the resulting responses evoked in the visual, auditory, or somatic sensory areas of the cortex can be increased by simultaneously stimulating the reticular system. In addition, the motor cortex, which is directly involved in the movement of skeletal muscle (see Chapter 9), usually becomes more excitable when the reticular system is stimulated.

The fact that sensory input can sometimes be inhibited and sometimes facilitated by stimulating the reticular system is undoubtedly related to the existence of very refined systems involved with *attention*. This topic will be discussed later in the chapter. For now it is enough to note that visual discrimination and discrimination in other sensory modalities can be improved through electrical stimulation of the reticular system.

Effects on the Autonomic Nervous System

In addition to its effects on behavioral and EEG arousal, sleep, sensory input, and the activity of skeletal muscles, the reticular system exerts powerful effects on the autonomic nervous system. The main areas of the upper spinal cord that regulate the heart and the sympathetic activity exerted on blood vessels, and the areas that regulate the activity of the vagus nerve of the parasympathetic nervous system, are all closely associated with the reticular system. This close association also holds for those areas of the spinal cord that regulate respiration (see Figure 5-6, Chapter 5), vomiting, and salivation. In addition, electrical stimulation of the reticular system activates the posterior portion of the hypothalamus, a region that also responds to electrical stimulation by increasing sympathetic activity and secretions from the adrenal glands (see Chapter 7).

The Multiple Effects of Reticular Activity

It is therefore clear that the reticular system is well equipped to integrate responses that serve different levels of arousal. Accordingly, if a person is drowsy or asleep, there will be slow-wave patterns in the EEG, depressed behavioral activity, decreased muscle tone, decreased activity of the sympathetic nervous system (and increased parasympathetic activity), decreased alertness, decreased respiration, decreased attention, and decreased responsiveness to sensory stimuli. Conversely, if a person is stimulated or excited, there will be fast, desynchronized patterns in the EEG, increased behavioral activity, increased muscle tone, increased activity of the sympathetic nervous system, increased alertness, increased respiration, increased attention, and increased responsiveness to sensory stimuli. From the foregoing description, it is obvious that the reticular system participates in all of these responses.

III. FACTORS THAT INFLUENCE THE RETICULAR SYSTEM AND AROUSAL

There are many factors that influence the reticular system. By now, this fact should not be surprising since our experience tells us that such diverse phenomena as sudden noise, emotional upset or excitement, mental activity, cold temperatures, emergency situations, increased movement of the joints, drinking coffee, hunger, sexual stimulation, and pain all increase our level of arousal. Conversely, such actions as closing our eyes, relaxing, turning off the lights, thinking of pleasant things, going to a quiet place, or being engaged in repetitive activities like counting sheep or rocking oneself all decrease our level of arousal or put us to sleep. Although a detailed discussion of the mechanisms involved in the above processes is beyond the scope of this book, we will briefly discuss some of them.

Sensory Input

It is obvious that the reticular system responds to sensory stimuli; that is, light, sound, touch or any other sensory stimulus will arouse us. In arousing us, however, the reticular system uses sensory stimuli quite differently from the way those structures of the brain discussed in Chapter 6 use them. Instead of being organized to inform us of specific external events, or to receive specific information from the sense organs, the reticular system is organized in a much more diffuse, nonspecific manner. In Chapter 6 we mentioned that sensory pathways generally serve separate sensory modalities. For example, a nerve cell that is part of the visual system will be activated by visual stimuli but not by auditory stimuli. In the reticular system this separation of sensory modalities is not usually apparent. Rather, neural impulses originating from one or another sensory receptor may all converge on the *same cell* regardless of the sensory modality involved. Sensory signals evoked by pinching the skin, flashing a light, and buzzing a tone can all activate the same cell in the reticular system. Although this organization would clearly be ill-suited for the major sensory systems, it is superb for eliciting a general response like arousal. Also, after electrical stimulation, the reticular system shows a slow return to pre-stimulation levels of activity. This slow return is quite different from what is observed when specific sensory pathways are stimulated, where there is usually a rapid return to pre-stimulation levels. Again, a rapid return to pre-stimulation levels is an important property, enabling us to discriminate specific sensory stimuli, especially as they quickly change in their quality and intensity, but, for generalized arousal, it is relatively unimportant.

Sensory impulses originating from receptors in the organs of the body also converge in the reticular system. Many of these impulses travel through nerves of the autonomic nervous system, both parasympathetic and sympathetic. They come from the baroreceptors and chemoreceptors, organs that respond to blood oxygen levels and blood pressure (see Chapters 5 and 7), and also from the stomach, intestines, lungs, mouth, and other organs. Sensory impulses travelling within neural pathways that originate from sense organs in the joints and muscles also converge in the reticular system. In other words, the reticular system receives sensory input that reflects not only what is happening in the external world, but also what is happening within many of the organs of our internal world.

Input from Other Areas of the Brain

Besides receiving input from all of the sense organs, the reticular system receives signals from all areas of the brain, many from the sensory and frontal areas of the cortex, the hippocampus, amygdala, septum, and hypothalamus. Thus, as discussed in Chapter 7, it should not be surprising that emotional reactions are strongly connected to our level of arousal. The convergence of impulses from many sources is illustrated schematically in Figure 8-3. In the next chapter we will see that the parts of our brain in direct control of the movement of our muscles—the motor cortex, the basal ganglia, and the cerebellum—also have many connections with the reticular system.

The Effects of Epinephrine and Acetylcholine

Various chemicals are known to directly affect the reticular system. Epinephrine and acetylcholine both make the reticular system more responsive to the various impulses that converge on it from all areas of the brain. As a hormone, acetylcholine is probably not as important as epinephrine. Released by various parasympathetic nerve endings, acetylcholine functions as a local transmitter that is usually quickly inactivated by enzymes and does not remain circulating long enough in the blood to affect the brain. We have already discussed the many effects of epinephrine, especially when it is released by the adrenal medulla during stress (see Chapter 7). Not only does epinephrine directly increase the responsiveness of the reticular system in the upper spinal cord, but it also increases the responsiveness of the posterior portion of the hypothalamus. In turn, the increased activity in the posterior hypothalamus stimulates both the reticular system and the sympathetic branch of the autonomic nervous system (see Figure 7-11, Chapter 7). Given these interconnections, we can readily see why emergency situations, strong defensive emotions, and other stressors have such a powerful effect on arousal and autonomic responses.

The Effects of Blood Oxygen and Carbon Dioxide Levels

Low levels of oxygen and high levels of carbon dioxide in the blood have a strong influence on arousal mechanisms. Low oxygen levels stimulate the reticular system mainly via the chemoreceptors in the carotid

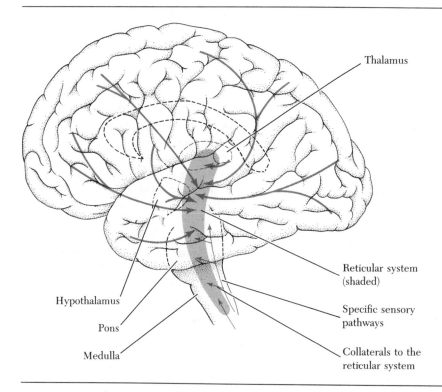

Figure 8–3. The convergence of neural pathways from the cerebral cortex, limbic system, hypothalamus, and sensory systems on the reticular system. Note that pathways converge on the reticular system from all areas of the brain, including those that regulate the movement and tone of skeletal muscle. Nerves serving the autonomic nervous system also send input to the reticular system from sensory receptors in the organs (mostly the heart, lungs, stomach, and intestines). Although specific sensory pathways bypass the reticular system on their way to the thalamus, collaterals are sent to the reticular system; that is, some sensory neurons converge on the reticular system even though many do not.

bodies (see pages 61–62), but high carbon dioxide levels stimulate the reticular system directly, including those areas that regulate breathing. As discussed in some detail in Chapter 5, the high carbon dioxide levels are quickly lowered by the increased rate of breathing, and this mechanism is a very important way in which body pH is controlled. As discussed also in Chapter 5, however, there are many factors—especially emotional—capable of arousing a person and increasing his/her rate of breathing even though blood carbon dioxide levels are not raised. The increased pH can then increase both neural and muscular excitability. The reticular system, then, is also responsible in large measure for the strong relation between our state of arousal and our rate of breathing.

The Effects of Other Chemicals

The reticular system is made up of many small, interconnecting nerve cells. Accordingly, there are many synapses or junctions between nerve cells in this system. Because each synapse serves as a point where chemicals are released by one neuron (called the "presynaptic" neuron) which then influences the excitability of another neuron (called the "postsynaptic" neuron), it is not surprising that the reticular system —which has many synapses—would be so easily influenced by chemicals. Other systems of the brain that have long neurons and few junctions, like the direct sensory pathways, are much less susceptible. Barbiturates and many other anesthetics block arousal and decrease muscle tone mainly through their effect on cells in the reticular system. Also, hormones such as estrogen and progesterone, which are released cyclically in the female in conjunction with other changes occurring in the reproductive cycle (see Chapter 10), can make the reticular system more responsive to electrical stimulation. This finding correlates well with the fact that female animals are generally more active and more easily aroused when they are in heat. Similarly, the stimulating effects of coffee are due to the fact that caffeine (the active ingredient in coffee) affects many organs, including the brain.

Multiple, Simultaneously Exerted Processes Influence Reticular Activity

The key role played by the reticular system in integrating processes that increase one's level of arousal

is illustrated in Figure 8-4. As illustrated, sensory stimuli and sensory experiences, many emotional states, increased epinephrine released by the adrenal glands, muscular activity, increased blood carbon dioxide levels—these and other factors can activate the reticular system which, in turn, can further increase behavioral, emotional, and mental activities. When one process is activated, it can lead to the activation of other processes. Note that all of the factors that arouse us reinforce each other because of the convergence of input into the reticular system. This is one of the main reasons why arousal is maintained for very long periods, as discussed in some detail in the previous chapter, and why it is such an influential mechanism in our body.

Processes related to decreased arousal are summarized in Figure 8-5. Note that in many cases decreased arousal is simply the result of a reduction in

Figure 8–4. Integration of processes related to arousal, illustrating the central role of the reticular system. Note that activation of one process leads to the activation of other processes. These activities are all associated with a desynchronized pattern and fast waves in the EEG. The involvement of many types of arousal—including behavioral, emotional, and sensory—is emphasized by the use of boldface type. The involvement of the reticular system is emphasized by the use of italic type.

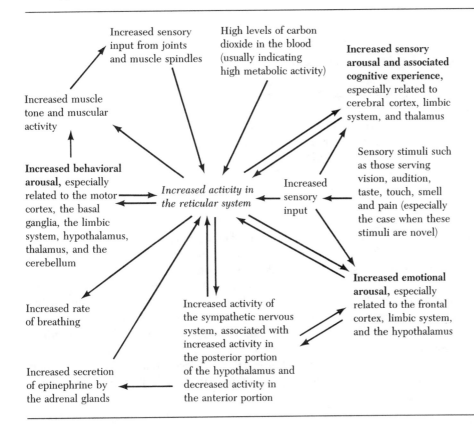

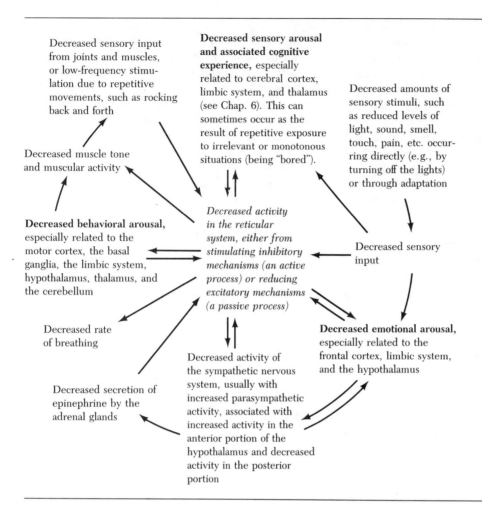

Decreased sensory input from joints and muscles, or low-frequency stimulation due to repetitive movements, such as rocking back and forth

Decreased muscle tone and muscular activity

Decreased behavioral arousal, especially related to the motor cortex, the basal ganglia, the limbic system, hypothalamus, thalamus, and the cerebellum

Decreased rate of breathing

Decreased secretion of epinephrine by the adrenal glands

Decreased sensory arousal and associated cognitive experience, especially related to cerebral cortex, limbic system, and thalamus (see Chap. 6). This can sometimes occur as the result of repetitive exposure to irrelevant or monotonous situations (being "bored").

Decreased activity in the reticular system, either from stimulating inhibitory mechanisms (an active process) or reducing excitatory mechanisms (a passive process)

Decreased activity of the sympathetic nervous system, usually with increased parasympathetic activity, associated with increased activity in the anterior portion of the hypothalamus and decreased activity in the posterior portion

Decreased amounts of sensory stimuli, such as reduced levels of light, sound, smell, touch, pain, etc. occurring directly (e.g., by turning off the lights) or through adaptation

Decreased sensory input

Decreased emotional arousal, especially related to the frontal cortex, limbic system, and the hypothalamus

Figure 8–5.   Integration of processes related to decreased arousal, illustrating the central role of the reticular system. Note that all of these processes are related to and reinforce each other. These activities are all associated with the development of a synchronized pattern and slow waves in the EEG, drowsiness, and sleep. The reduction of many types of arousal—behavioral, emotional, and sensory—is emphasized by the use of boldface type. The involvement of the reticular system is emphasized by the use of italic type.

the activities included in the previous diagram, or a result of decreased activity in the reticular system. In this context, decreased arousal is a *passive* process; that is, it is simply a passive consequence of a reduction of processes that would otherwise arouse us. Decreased arousal, however, is an *active* process as well; that is, it can also result from inhibitory mechanisms which, when *activated*, decrease arousal and induce drowsiness and sleep. This active process will be discussed later in the chapter. For now it is sufficient to note that, because of the workings of the reticular

system, many factors not only increase or decrease our level of arousal but, in exerting such actions, they also reinforce each other.

The importance of the reticular system in arousal mechanisms has been the primary topic up to this point. Other functions that depend on the workings of the reticular system are *attention* and *inattention, suppression,* and *sleep.* These functions have such special properties, however, that we have saved them for separate discussion. Let's first consider mechanisms of attention.

IV. ATTENTION AND INATTENTION

In general, attention involves two basic mechanisms: a) those involving our ability to *direct* our attention, and b) those involving our ability to *suppress* our attention. We will first discuss mechanisms that direct our attention.

Directing One's Attention

Directed attention involves an *increased responsiveness* in the sensory receptors and in the neural pathways serving the stimulus, and a *reduced responsiveness* in the sensory receptors and neural pathways that do not serve the stimulus. Although the mechanisms responsible for these effects are not well understood, the workings of the reticular system in the upper spinal cord, the thalamic portion of the reticular system, the sensory areas of the thalamus, sensory areas of the cortex, and frontal cortex all contribute to attentiveness.

One process that probably contributes to directing attention involves the effect observed when the thalamic portion of the reticular system is electrically stimulated with a weak current; that is, only a *specific* area of sensory cortex—that corresponding to the site stimulated in the thalamus—is thereby activated. The other areas of the cortex will remain unaffected. If a strong current is used, this selective response is likely to be replaced by widespread activation, as occurs with the generalized arousal characteristic of the alerting response. (This occurrence corresponds to our experience that the ability to selectively attend to something will always "lose out" to distraction if the distraction is strong enough.)

Another process involves neural impulses that are propagated from the sensory cortex down to the thalamus and also to the neurons that innervate the sense organs. It has been shown that each sensory area of the cortex can inhibit or facilitate signals coming from the sense organs with which this area of the cortex is affiliated. Thus, the visual cortex can send signals that either increase or decrease input from the retina, the somatic sensory cortex can control the strength of signals coming from somatic receptors, and the auditory cortex can control the intensity of the signal from the cochlea. Many of these responses can also be observed when the reticular system is stimulated, as discussed earlier. This capacity of the sensory cortex to modify our sensory input clearly corresponds to our ability to modify the intensity of our sensory experience, and is undoubtedly related to our ability to

"switch" our attention from one sensory modality to another.

The more we understand the mechanisms underlying attention, the more obvious it is that these mechanisms involve an integration of very refined neural circuits. For example, the **reticular nucleus of the thalamus**, which is a thin sheet of cells surrounding the thalamus, receives input from, and transmits signals to, all areas that seem to be most necessary for attention. It receives a great deal of input from the frontal cortex, the caudate nucleus (one of the basal ganglia that regulate muscular activity, as discussed in the next chapter), the reticular system, and also the thalamus. Although many details are not yet known, most of these structures are *topographically organized*; that is, certain regions within these structures are specialized for one or another sensory modality or they are more devoted to sensory input from one area of the body—like the hands—than another area, or they serve muscles of one or another part of the body. It has been shown that neurons from the reticular nucleus of the thalamus can either increase or decrease the neural activity in pathways serving such senses as vision or audition—an obvious requirement for being able to increase or decrease sensory input when one is attentive. This nucleus is *not* one of the specific sensory nuclei of the thalamus that serve as relay stations for sensory impulses going from the spinal cord to sensory cortex (see Chapter 6). Rather, it seems to be especially involved in modifying the activity of *other* thalamic nuclei, including those just mentioned, which are specific for various sensory modalitites.

Observations of humans or animals with brain damage also reveals that refined systems are involved in attention. For example, people suffering from damage to the frontal cortex often have a great deal of difficulty inhibiting strong response tendencies. That is, they find it difficult to maintain directed attentiveness when confronted with distracting stimuli. Destruction of the pathway that conveys signals from the frontal cortex to the reticular nucleus of the thalamus produces these same symptoms in animals. It appears that the interaction of the frontal cortex with the thalamic mechanisms described in the previous paragraph is important for maintaining directed attention, and is obviously related to our ability to *concentrate*.

One's *behavior* is also important in determining the strength of the sensory stimulus, as discussed in Chapter 6. The fact that we will stop what we are doing when we hear a strange sound and then listen very carefully, perhaps cupping our ears, perhaps closing our eyes or looking down at the floor or up at the ceiling—all of these behaviors increase specific sensory input that corresponds to the stimulus (in this case auditory) and reduce other sensory input.

We will now consider those mechanisms that make us *stop* paying attention to something when it is *not* considered to be relevant. Later in the chapter we will see that this behavior involves mechanisms that are also used when we wish to relax or go to sleep.

Suppressing One's Attention

When a stimulus that initially evoked arousal and then attentiveness continues to be given, an animal or person will cease paying attention to it after a while. This reduced attentiveness is called **habituation**. Habituation occurs not only as the result of *repetitive stimulation*, but also when the stimulus is perceived as being *irrelevant*. In general, habituation occurs in an ordered sequence. The first part to become habituated—that is, the first part to no longer respond to presentation of the stimulus—is the arousal or alerting response described in Section II. The animal or person no longer turns toward the stimulus, nor is there an increase in muscle tone, increased respiration, general desynchronization in the EEG, or anything else that is associated with the alerting response. What does still remain, however, is a clear signal localized in the area of the cerebral cortex that is specialized to receive input from the particular sensory modality involved. For example, even though a flash of light will no longer evoke generalized arousal, the visual cortex still responds. This discrete cortical potential that is localized to a specific area of sensory cortex is called the **evoked potential**. Evoked potentials are the result of signals that follow specific sensory pathways up the spinal cord, from there to specific areas of the thalamus, and thence to the sensory cortex. These pathways are separate from the reticular system, although they send collaterals to it (see Figure 8-3). At this point, even though the reticular system is no longer responding with generalized arousal, specific sensory pathways remain unaffected by habituation.

With repeated stimulation, cortical responses are reduced, followed by reduced responses in the specific thalamic nuclei that serve the sensory modality involved (for example, the lateral geniculate body for vision—see Chapter 6), and, finally, the sensory receptors themselves become quite unresponsive, partly because of **adaptation** (see pages 85–86, Chapter 6).

Adaptation is mainly due to fatigue and other processes occurring within the receptors themselves. That is, no active suppression of sensory input by the brain is involved. In other words, adaptation is a *passive* phenomenon, unlike habituation, which is an *active* process having nothing to do with interactions between the sensory stimulus and the sensory receptors. In habituation, the brain *inhibits* the mechanisms responsible for the arousal response, *inhibits* the evoked potentials in the cortex, and even *inhibits* the response of nerve cells that receive signals directly from the sense organs.

Habituation of the alerting response appears to be initiated from those structures in the brain that send impulses to the reticular system in the upper spinal cord. Within the reticular system, the alerting response is suppressed in two ways: a) by *reducing* the activity of neurons that would otherwise cause arousal, and b) by *increasing* the activity of neurons that, when stimulated, directly decrease arousal and even induce sleep. Both of these responses are common; for example, certain anesthetics—drugs that reduce or abolish sensation and are often associated with a loss of consciousness—can cause reduced arousal by inhibiting cells in the reticular system (response "a," above), and low-frequency electrical stimulation in certain areas of the reticular system will reduce arousal and cause slow waves to appear in the EEG, even causing the animal to fall asleep (response "b").

Habituation of selective attention—as opposed to the generalized arousal characteristic of the alerting response—is also initiated from structures in the brain that send signals to the reticular system, but in this case the impulses seem to converge on the reticular nucleus of the *thalamus* rather than on the reticular system of the upper spinal cord. The structures of the brain responsible for suppressing selective attention and the generalized arousal characteristic of the alerting response are discussed in the next section, which covers suppressive mechanisms. Many aspects of our functioning involve suppression, including *sleep, relaxation, boredom, lethargy,* and *satiety.*

V. SUPPRESSIVE MECHANISMS

The mechanisms of suppression are extremely necessary to our functioning. It is through these mechanisms that we are able to ignore literally thousands of stimuli all at once while still retaining the capacity to shift our attention in an instant to any one of these stimuli. If we were unable to suppress arousal responses every time we needed to pay attention to something, or if we were to wake up from sleep every time that something stimulated our sense organs, we would indeed be quite incapacitated. Needless to say, mechanisms of attention and mechanisms of suppression are closely related to each other. This association is exemplified in those suffering from damage to the frontal cortex who are unable to attend to a stimulus because of constant distraction by "novel" stimuli. This inability to suppress orienting reactions clearly impairs one's ability to maintain directed attention.

Just as we have seen with other mechanisms, suppression, too, involves many areas of the brain. In various experiments involving a number of species (rats, cats, dogs, and monkeys), it has been shown that destruction of either the frontal cortex, the preoptic areas of the hypothalamus, parts of the limbic system (septum, hippocampus, and amygdala), or the caudate nucleus interferes with the animal's ability to suppress a response. Damage in these areas can evoke responses of *hyperactivity*, *distractability*, and *hyperemotionality*. Conversely, electrical stimulation in these areas—especially at low frequencies—inhibits the animal's behavior and causes *drowsiness* and *sleep*. These structures of the brain, all strongly connected to each other and to the reticular system, make up part of the **forebrain suppressor system** illustrated in Figure 8-6.

Relaxation and "Letting Go"

When we wish to relax, we generally suppress the activity of the motor neurons that innervate the skeletal muscles, and this results in decreased muscle tone. Many areas of the brain, including the reticular system, the cerebellum, motor cortex, and the basal ganglia (which includes the caudate nucleus mentioned above), participate in regulating muscle tone, as will be discussed in some detail in the next chapter. However, when a person relaxes there is not only suppression of muscle tone and muscular activity, but also a "letting go" of many thoughts and feelings.

We do not understand what occurs in the brain when a person "lets go," yet it is obvious that suppressive mechanisms are involved in this process. For example, when a person goes to sleep, increased slow-wave patterns in the EEG, muscular relaxation, decreased arousal, and a reduced intensity of thoughts and feelings all occur at the same time.

"Letting go" also often involves switching from one set of *memories* to another set that is less arousing, preferably even pleasant. Many of the areas of the brain involved in suppressive mechanisms are, in fact, also involved in learning and memory. For example, when either the orbital region of the frontal cortex (see Figure 8-6), the olfactory bulbs, the septum, or the caudate nucleus are damaged, an animal will continue doing what it has *previously learned* rather than adapt by changing its response. In other words, the animal is unable to change its behavior as the task requirements change (see Mishkin, 1964; Butters and Rosvold, 1968; Schwartzbaum and Donovick, 1968). This learning deficit is probably related to the animal's inability to "let go" of what it has previously learned. A similar impairment observed in animals with damage to these areas of the brain is their apparent inability to stop performing a learned response that is no longer rewarded. This deficit is another indication that the forebrain suppressor system is involved in "letting go." Clearly, the areas of the brain involved in suppressing arousal responses are associated with the areas that allow a person to switch from one memory to another, and both of these occur when a person "lets go" and relaxes.

Sleep

As mentioned earlier, the reticular system is not the only part of the brain that reduces arousal and causes sleep when it is electrically stimulated at low frequencies. Low-frequency stimulation of the septal area of the limbic system, the caudate nucleus, some portions of the cephalic portion of the reticular system in the thalamus, and the orbital region of the frontal cortex will also reduce arousal and cause drowsiness and sleep. Both low- and high-frequency stimulation of the preoptic areas of the hypothalamus also produces these responses. Furthermore, when the preoptic area or the septum are destroyed in animals, severe insomnia is frequently the result. Again, these findings point to the fact that decreased arousal and sleep are *active* processes; that is, they are not merely the result of decreased activity of neurons that would otherwise cause arousal. Of course, when we turn off the lights, lie down, or relax and close our eyes, we are minimizing sensory input—stimuli that would otherwise arouse us. Nevertheless, sleep also involves the active participation of the forebrain suppressor system. We will say more about sleep later in the chapter.

Other Suppressive Phenomena

Besides their involvement in attention, relaxation, "letting go," and sleep, suppressive mechanisms play a role in other phenomena:

1) BEING GENTLY ROCKED BACK AND FORTH DECREASES AROUSAL AND INDUCES SLEEP. This probably has to do with the activation of vestibular receptors. The neural pathways serving the vestibular apparatus (see Figure 6-3) send a great deal of input into the reticular system of the upper spinal cord (see Figure 8-6).

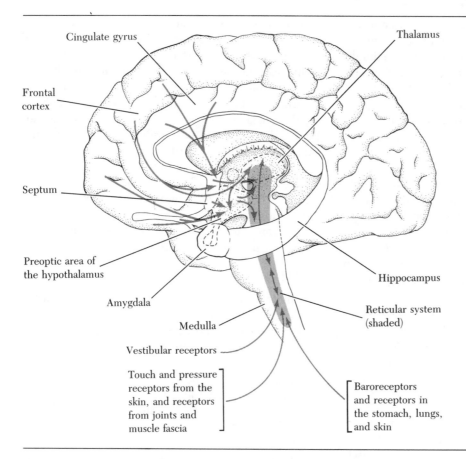

Figure 8–6. Schematic illustration of pathways that decrease arousal and evoke slow waves in the EEG. Many parts of this system have been found to induce sleep when they are electrically stimulated. This system is composed of two parts: a **forebrain suppressor system** and a **medullary system.**

The **forebrain suppressor system** consists of neurons from the frontal cortex, amygdala, hippocampus, and caudate nucleus (not shown—see Figure 9–4, Chapter 9). These neurons converge in the thalamus, septum, and preoptic area of the hypothalamus. From there they converge on the reticular system where they suppress arousal mechanisms, or they send projections to the cortex where they initiate neural mechanisms responsible for slow waves and synchronized patterns in the EEG.

The **medullary system** consists of neurons in the medulla. Coming from the vestibular apparatus, the baroreceptors, and receptors in other organs (the lungs, stomach and intestines), as well as touch and pressure receptors in the skin, joints and muscle fascia, neural impulses travel along pathways that converge in the medulla where they affect the reticular system and other structures to reduce arousal and evoke slow waves in the EEG.

Thus, neural impulses that reduce arousal originate from structures higher in the brain as well as from sense organs that send their signals up the spinal cord.

2) ACTIVATING THE BARORECEPTORS BY STIMULATING THE CAROTID SINUS (see Figure 7-14) REDUCES CORTICAL ACTIVITY AND PRODUCES SLOW WAVES IN THE EEG. Under normal conditions this activation is probably part of a mechanism designed to assure that conditions which might increase blood pressure, including arousal, are quickly suppressed in order to bring blood pressure back down again. However, this mechanism might also be partly responsible for some of the suppressive effects observed in people who are intensely involved in emotional reactions (see pages 154–156, Chapter 7).

3) A PERSON WITH A FEVER IS LIKELY TO BE DROWSY AND SLEEP A GOOD DEAL. It has been shown that when the temperature of the preoptic area of the hypothalamus is raised, neural activity in this area is increased. This is not surprising since the preoptic area has much to do with temperature regulation (see page 48, Chapter 4), and electrical stimulation of this area, even at high frequencies, produces drowsiness, sleep, and slow waves in the EEG.

4) MANY OF US HAVE SPECIFIC "SLEEPING HABITS" AND, WHEN CIRCUMSTANCES CHANGE, WE LEARN NEW SLEEPING HABITS. This phenomenon is related to the fact that sleep can be induced as a **conditioned response** —that is, made conditional upon certain circumstances. The involvement of suppressive mechanisms in this process is suggested by experiments in animals where, for example, a tone is presented shortly before inducing sleep by electrical stimulation of the preoptic area of the hypothalamus (a part of the forebrain suppressor system). When this procedure of "pairing" the tone with the electrical stimulation is repeated many times and the tone is finally presented *without* electrical stimulation, the tone alone will induce sleep; that is, the effect of the electrical stimulation (i.e., sleep) has been conditioned to the tone.

5) When animals are presented with a stimulus they have learned to associate with food, they will respond to the stimulus (say, a tone) by salivating. However, if the stimulus is continued in subsequent trials but *without* the reward, the animal will stop salivating. In performing experiments such as these on dogs, Pavlov observed that WHEN THE STIMULUS CONTINUED TO BE PRESENTED WITHOUT REWARD, HIS DOGS BECAME DROWSY AND EVEN FELL ASLEEP. He called this response **internal inhibition**, which seemed to be part of a process concerned with learning *not* to respond to stimuli. This response is just the opposite of what was described earlier, when we discussed the effects of damage in the forebrain suppressor system (see page 175). As you will recall, when these areas are damaged, the animal ceases to be able to unlearn a previous response when the reward is no longer presented. The similarity between Pavlov's "internal inhibition" and the suppressive responses that we all experience when we are *bored* deserve comment. It is well known that if some type of meaningful reward is introduced into an otherwise monotonous routine, a person will usually perform the task much more efficiently. This behavioral change probably occurs because the reward has the effect of releasing the person from the process of internal inhibition.

6) STATES OF SATIETY ARE OFTEN ASSOCIATED WITH DROWSINESS AND SLEEP. Not only will an animal become relaxed or sleepy after eating, drinking, and performing sexual activity, but there is also slow-wave activity in the EEG. It is interesting to note that electrical stimulation of the orbital part of the frontal cortex will induce sleep and slow-wave activity in the EEG, and that when an electrode is placed in this area and an animal self-administers stimulation, it will stimulate itself less frequently after having eaten. Thus this area not only participates in regulating arousal, but it is also one of the areas that participates in regulating eating (see Chapter 3). Some areas of the amygdala, one of the structures of the limbic system (see Figure 8-6), also evoke drowsiness, sleep, and slow-wave activity when they are stimulated. The amygdala also participates in regulating eating, drinking, and sexual behaviors, and it also contains areas that are rewarding. The amygdala has many connections with the preoptic area of the hypothalamus, the septum, and the frontal cortex (see Figure 8-6). From these clear functional and structural relationships, we can assume a powerful integration of reward mechanisms, satiety mechanisms, and the suppression of arousal. It is also worthwhile to note that when the small intestines are distended by inserting an inflatable balloon into the jejunem, sleep is induced; this same procedure has been found to produce slow waves in the EEG of animals (see Orr and Stahl, 1980). This mechanism probably contributes to the reduced arousal that occurs

after eating. Glucose injected directly into the hypothalamus will also lead to drowsiness and sleep (Booth, 1968).

This list of various events associated with the suppression of arousal makes it amply clear that suppression is important to our functioning. Given that the forebrain suppressor system responds to such functions as memory, learning, and conditioning, and that its workings are associated with states of reward, satiety, boredom, sleep, and attention, it is not surprising that we occasionally experience periods of drowsiness and lethargy even when we are *not* tired. Taking this one step further, it is also not surprising that intense *depression*, to the point of *withdrawal* and *apathy*, also occurs at times. The possible effects of these states on the activities of various organs has been discussed in Chapter 7.

VI. DREAMING AND OTHER PROPERTIES OF SLEEP

Although sleep has been studied a great deal by psychologists and physiologists, the only thing we are really sure of is that if a person is deprived of sleep he/she will get sleepy. There is also no doubt that a sleep-deprived person will show signs of malfunctioning of the mind when the deprivation exceeds two or three days. Abnormalities in memory, increased hallucinations and illusions, and increased difficulty in performing long, uninteresting tasks are commonly observed. On the other hand, none of these symptoms survive tests of careful scrutiny and controlled experimentation aimed at proving a unique relationship between these abnormalities and sleep deprivation. Individual differences are great, and one can demonstrate sleep-deprived persons who remain quite capable of performing concentrated, detailed tasks when asked to do so. Visceral functions and their control by the autonomic nervous system seem to be especially resistant to sleep deprivation; that is, even seven days without sleep has no negative effect on the functioning of the internal organs.

On a simple experiential level, we all know how much better we feel after a good night's sleep as opposed to when we have stayed up all night; however, even in this case, we don't know to what extent our "feeling lousy" after getting no sleep might be due to the arousal, stress, and excitement we undergo rather than to any direct restorative mechanism we might have missed because we didn't sleep.

Sleep deprivation is, in fact, a stressor which causes increased sympathetic activity and increased secretion of adrenal hormones—both epinephrine and glucocorticoids (see Chapter 7). In addition to the increased incidence of hallucination, symptoms such as fatigue, blurred vision, burning eyes, a distorted sense of time, a withdrawal from the external world, a tendency to avoid intellectual effort, and inattention are all commonly observed with sleep deprivation. When resting quietly, the EEG shows small alpha waves indicating drowsiness (see page 165), but it also shows intermittent slow waves, lasting two to three seconds, which resemble those seen in sleep. This brief occurrence of slow-wave activity is called "microsleep" because it is so short-lasting.

Sleep Cycles

When a person falls asleep, the EEG progresses from a pattern of alpha rhythms to the pattern of stage 1 sleep to that of stage 2 sleep and so on until stage 4 sleep is achieved—a state of deep sleep with prominent, high-voltage delta waves (see page 165). Even when we sleep, however, we do not simply spend the night in deep sleep. Rather, sleep stages appear in a cyclical fashion during the night. After spending a half hour to an hour in stage 4 sleep, we move through progressively lighter stages of sleep, followed by a return to deeper stages of sleep, then lighter stages, and so forth. Each cycle is about 90 minutes long, and there are about four cycles during an eight-hour sleep period.

In addition to the progressive changes from lighter to deeper to lighter stages of sleep, another pattern of EEG activity has been observed in studies of sleep cycles in animals and in human volunteers. This EEG pattern is completely different from the progressive changes in slow waves that are seen as one goes from stage 1 to stage 4 sleep. Just at the point where one would expect the EEG to look like that of stage 1 sleep—that is, one would expect the subject to be entering stage 1 sleep as sleep becomes progressively lighter in the cycle—the EEG suddenly becomes desynchronized with fast waves. The subject is far from awake (in fact, difficult to awaken), yet the EEG looks very much like it does during alert wakefulness. While this is happening, the person generally undergoes a distinct set of reactions: rapid eye movements (the eyes can be observed to move rapidly back and forth beneath closed eyelids), a profound loss of muscle tone, irregularities in heart rate and respiration, intense pupillary constriction, increased oxygen consumption and blood flow in the brain, penile erection in males, and vasocongestion of vaginal tissue in females. (The penile erection and vaginal vasocongestion that occur are not necessarily associated with dreams having sexual content.) Periodic bursts of physiological activity also occur during this type of sleep: blood vessels constrict and blood pressure, heart rate, and respiration all suddenly increase for short periods of time, then fall again. During an average cycle, this peculiar type of sleep, called rapid eye movement sleep (REM sleep) or paradoxical sleep (see below), usually lasts for 15 to 40 minutes and then the subject returns to the slow-wave sleep characteristic of stages 2, 3 and 4. A typical pattern of sleep cycles is shown in Figure 8-7. The heavy horizontal bars in this figure represent the highly unusual sleep described above, which, as shown, occurs four or five times in a typical eight hours of sleep.

Figure 8–7. Eye movements and EEG patterns typical of a night's sleep in a young adult. (The diagram represents a mean derived from many all-night recordings.) The "x's" mark the occurrence of rapid eye movements during REM sleep (indicated by heavy horizontal lines), and the EEG stages note the different EEG patterns observed during progressively deeper stages of sleep (see Figure 8–1). This figure displays one typical sleep cycle; in an actual night, the sleeper may enter stage 1 sleep many times, depending on how often he/she wakes up. Note that most stage 3 and stage 4 slow-wave sleep occurs within the first few hours after the onset of sleep, whereas most REM sleep occurs in the last few hours before awakening.

Source: Hartmann, E. THE BIOLOGY OF DREAMING, Charles C. Thomas, Publisher, Springfield, Illinois, 1967.

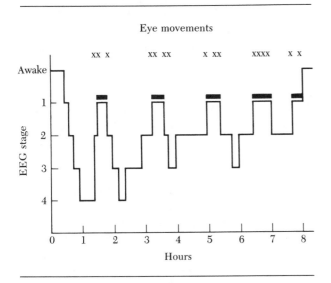

REM Sleep and the Occurrence of Dreams

The unusual sleep pattern described above has been given many names. As noted, it is usually referred to as **REM sleep**, because of the rapid eye movements; however, many call it **paradoxical sleep** because of the EEG pattern, which simulates that of an awake person. Others call it **D sleep** because of the desynchronized pattern of the EEG. We will call it REM sleep, simply because this is the term most often used.

A person awakened during REM sleep will narrate a dream about 80% of the time. Awakenings during periods of slow-wave sleep (stage 1 through 4) evoke reports of dreams much less frequently. It is for this reason that many people equate REM sleep with dreaming. Although this may turn out to be correct, it is premature to unequivocally assert that REM sleep and dreaming reflect one and the same state. Some reasons for restraint are listed below, along with some of the counter-arguments given to defend the unique role of REM sleep in dreaming:

1) As stated earlier, even though 80% report dreaming in association with REM sleep, 10-20% of sleep-study subjects when awakened from slow-wave sleep also report that they have been dreaming. It would seem, then, that dreaming is not restricted to REM sleep. In defense of the REM-dream hypothesis, some investigators make a distinction between mental activity and the story-like quality of dreams, and state that the "dreaming" which occurs during slow-wave sleep is not really dreaming at all, but rather mental activity concerning situations and events that are conceived during sleep. There is no agreement on this point because subjects awakened from slow-wave sleep also report vivid imagery and coherent themes in their dreams. Nevertheless, the reported incidence of dreaming is clearly much higher in subjects awakened from REM sleep.

2) Perhaps the main reason why few dreams are reported from subjects awakened from slow-wave sleep is because such people are generally confused and incoherent under these circumstances and, it is argued, they simply don't remember them fast enough. In contrast, someone awakened from REM sleep is immediately alert and coherent. This alertness is related to the fact that the cerebral cortex is much more active during REM sleep, which is why the EEG is desynchronized. The brain being already partially aroused allows the

sleeper to "wake up" more rapidly than someone awakened from slow-wave sleep. The fact that people awakened from REM sleep usually remember later that they were awakened, while people awakened from slow-wave sleep usually do not, tends to support the theory that dreaming during REM sleep is related to one's ability to remember rather than to dreaming itself.

The main counter-argument here is that increased alertness would not help a person to remember, because in many cases increased arousal tends to make a person forget rather than remember dreams. All of us have had the experience of remembering a dream while still "half asleep" only to have it slip away as we become more alert.

3) Birds and *almost* all mammals experience REM sleep. Reptiles sleep, but they don't appear to exhibit REM sleep. Can we conclude, then, that birds and *most* mammals dream, but reptiles do not? Some argue that this conclusion is incorrect: based solely on the (faulty) assumption that REM and dream sleep are the same, they claim there is no additional evidence supporting these distinctions with respect to dreaming in animals. A counter-argument is that dreaming is a recent development and is therefore seen only in higher animals such as mammals and birds.

4) Certain experiences—sleep-talking, sleepwalking (somnambulism), and certain "night terrors," especially strong nightmares and anxiety attacks—usually occur during slow-wave sleep or, in the case of sleepwalking, when a person is suddenly aroused from slow-wave sleep, especially stages 3 and 4. Therefore any special emphasis given to REM sleep is arbitrary with respect to mental phenomena.

Those who walk in their sleep generally will respond to external stimuli and will answer questions, yet it is difficult to fully awaken them and they will rarely have any recollection of the experience. Sleep-talking and night terrors are also not recalled, although persons having night terrors *do* know that they were frightened prior to having been awakened. In contrast, persons who experience a nightmare during REM sleep usually can recall the story and its imagery. From these studies, we have no doubt that mental activity is occurring during slow-wave sleep and that these experiences are generally not recalled—a characteristic of slow-wave sleep that was discussed above. However, as mentioned, some investigators believe that these phenomena are not the result of dreaming, but rather the result of mental activity that appears to be void of imagery and story-like themes.

5) Newborn infants engage in much more REM sleep than do adults. For the first two weeks of its life, an infant will spend 50 to 80 percent of its 16 to 18 hours of sleep each day engaged in REM sleep. In contrast, an adult will spend approximately 20 to 30 percent of eight hours' sleep in REM sleep. Does this mean that newborn infants dream more? Moreover, would it be reasonable to expect that their dreams would be "story-like?" There is a great deal of information indicating that the REM sleep of a newborn infant reflects neither being "awake" nor "asleep," but something else. For example, the newborn can be engaged in "awake" activities like crying, sucking, being drowsy, and be engaged in REM activity at the same time. By approximately one to three months of age, this pattern changes and these behaviors occur only when the baby is showing an awake EEG. REM activity now occurs only when the infant is asleep. Also, in contrast with children and adults, the newborn does not begin REM sleep by going into slow-wave sleep first; it enters REM activity directly from the "awake" state. In fact, it does not even have slow-wave patterns in the EEG. Only by one to three months of age do slow waves begin to develop, as well as sleep spindles (see Figure 8-1); at this age, the onset of sleep begins to be marked by the occurrence of slow-wave EEG patterns as in the adult.

The development of slow-wave sleep and sleep spindles in the EEG is believed to reflect a gradual maturation of neural pathways in the brain, especially the forebrain. This assumption correlates well with the fact that by one to three months a baby begins to show obvious attentive behaviors that were not apparent before this time. (You will recall that attention involves interactions between the forebrain, the reticular system, and sensory pathways—see page 173). The development of slow waves in the EEG takes a long time; although they make their appearance in the EEG of a three-month-old baby, they do not become adult-like until a child is about two years of age. Before two years of age, a child is spending 25 to 40 percent of its 12 to 16 hours of sleep in REM sleep, which is still more than in adults. For these and other reasons, many people believe that REM sleep reflects maturational or growth processes in the brain, perhaps related to memory processes. (This hypothesis will be discussed in more detail later in the chapter.) Those who believe that REM sleep and dreaming reflect the same state have not yet come up with satisfactory supporting data.

From these five observations, we think it likely that REM sleep is simply a different physiological and psychological state, characterized by many unusual activities including, in older children and adults, the occurrence of particularly vivid dreams.

In neurophysiological terms, there appears to be a definite separation between REM sleep and slow-wave sleep, in that REM sleep is strongly influenced by activity in the upper spinal cord whereas slow-wave sleep is strongly influenced by the forebrain mechanisms discussed earlier. REM sleep almost certainly represents a very particular activation of the upper spinal cord in the region of the pons. As indicated in Figure 8-8, the pons contains many structures that can produce the symptoms of REM sleep: eye movements, desynchronization of the cortical EEG and increased cortical excitability, twitching facial muscles, chewing movements, and even the massive suppression of muscle tone that is caused by activating the inhibitory portion of the reticular system. (The common "nightmarish" dream experience of not being able to run away from a frightening person or situation depends in part on the massive suppression of muscle tone characteristic of REM sleep.) In exerting their actions, *the mechanisms that cause REM sleep also inhibit the slow-wave response that would otherwise be seen.* This inhibiting effect probably occurs within the thalamus, the preoptic area of the hypothalamus, and perhaps in other regions of the forebrain suppressor system. In other words, the capacity of these brain regions to generate slow-wave sleep is inhibited during REM sleep. (Inhibition of the preoptic area may be one of the reasons why body temperature is not regulated during REM sleep to the extent that it is during slow-wave sleep or when a person is awake—see Chapter 4.)

We still are not sure of the physiological nature of dreams, but by now it should be apparent that we have learned a great deal about REM sleep. Although it seems quite possible that REM sleep provides the opportunity for dreams to be particularly vivid, picturesque, and story-like, we should not conclude, therefore, that REM sleep is uniquely responsible for or the result of dreams.

VII. RELATION TO HEALTH

Arousal and suppressive mechanisms have a profound and widespread influence on our health, both physiological and psychological. In this context, it is important to realize that mechanisms of arousal and mechanisms of decreased arousal are both *self-sustaining;* that is, once a person is aroused or depressed, these states are much more likely to be maintained—both physiologically and psychologically—than are many other processes. This self-sustaining quality relates not only to the convergence of behavioral, emotional, and mental factors, but also to their mutual reinforcement (see Figures 8-4 and 8-5). What does this mean? It means that someone who is "on the edge" because of emotional upheaval or feelings of boredom can be "pushed over" into abnormally intense states of arousal or depression by something that might otherwise be quite unimportant, such as a few cups of coffee or lack of exercise. Someone who is overly aroused or depressed can counteract the self-sustaining property of these mechanisms, but a certain amount of initiative, resolve, or effort is involved in doing so. (The overly aroused person may not wish to sit quietly and relax for a few minutes and the depressed person is usually not "gung-ho" enough to get out and exercise.)

For the most part, the activities we are engaged in on a daily basis reinforce arousal mechanisms; that is, people are often in a stimulated state that needs to be reduced. One way of doing this is to *avoid* situations that provoke intense arousal, not as a way of living, of course, but as a way of occasionally reducing the emotional, mental, and physical impact of arousal when there is no perceived advantage in (or need for) such stimulation. For people who work eight-hour days, morning and afternoon breaks and lunch serve as important periods of hiatus. During these periods we are given time to "let go" and, if we eat, not only is parasympathetic activity increased, (which automatically reduces sympathetic activity—see page 154, Chapter 7), but we are likely to calm down because we have learned that a full stomach plus intense sympathetic activity can make us feel sick. Furthermore, eating—by stimulating satiety mechanisms—activates the suppressive mechanisms discussed earlier in the chapter (see pages 177–178). Some people "automatically" eat more when they are overly aroused, knowing experientially that the ensuing satiety will be accompanied by a reduction of this restiveness.

We have already mentioned that, within the brain, reduction of arousal is both a passive and an active process. Avoiding stressful situations is one example of a passive way to reduce arousal. As noted earlier, there are many other ways to reduce levels of arousal through passive processes—lying down, closing one's eyes, turning off lights, shutting doors to reduce noise, and so forth.

As with passive processes, there are many ways to reduce (or, in this case, to suppress) levels of arousal

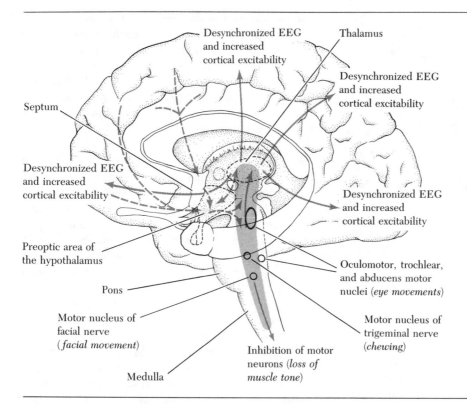

Figure 8–8. Expressions of REM sleep in relation to the activity of nuclei in various brain regions. (This activity is superimposed onto the mechanisms that cause slow wave-sleep, indicated by dashed arrows.) In the text below, responses characteristic of REM sleep are highlighted by boldface type.

In the PONS:

Neurons that control the **movement of the eyes** have many cell bodies that originate in the oculomotor, trochlear, and abducens motor nuclei illustrated above.

Neurons that control the **movement of facial muscles** and **chewing** have many cell bodies that originate within the motor nucleus of the trigeminal nerve and the motor nucleus of the facial nerve.

Many neurons that are part of the reticular system in the pons send their impulses to the thalamus, as indicated above by the heavy arrow between the pons and the thalamus. In the thalamus, this activity is projected to all areas of the cortex, causing **desynchronization of the EEG** and **increased cortical excitability,** as illustrated by the heavy arrows.

In the lower three-fourths of the MEDULLA:

The lower three-fourths of the medulla contains many neurons that suppress motor neuron activity in the spinal cord. This causes **decreased muscle tone.**

In the THALAMUS and HYPOTHALAMUS:

The mechanisms that cause REM sleep **inhibit the slow–wave response** that would otherwise be seen when parts of the thalamus and the hypothalamus are stimulated at a low frequency.

through active processes. Eating and sexual activity, for example, involve active processes because the associated satiety responses involve activation of suppressor mechanisms. Similarly, repetitive stimulation (perceived as irrelevant or monotonous), and gentle rocking of the body are also active means of suppressing arousal. Active suppression can also be *learned* although we do not, as yet, understand how this takes place. In this connection, you will recall that suppression of arousal can be a conditioned response involving the activities of the forebrain suppressor system (see page 177). (It is not known why some of us can relax easily whereas some of us can relax only with considerable effort; it is likely, however, that part of the answer lies in the degree to which each person can actively "let go" of states of arousal—a letting go that involves having learned to deal with emotional, mental, physical, even chemical states because, in their concerted actions, all of these factors produce our stimulated state.)

Prolonged states of arousal or depression can contribute to various illnesses, as was discussed at some length in the previous chapter. We considered the fact that stressors such as anxiety and fear affect the autonomic nervous system, the immune system, our state of arousal, and our muscular activity. We also explained that these processes are intimately connected to each other and that they form a powerful force in the body, especially in their concerted actions. It is important to realize that the relatively widespread responses resulting from excessive arousal or excessive suppression are much more influential with respect to our health than are the selective attention mechanisms. Although selective attention is extremely important in allowing us to differentiate among and concentrate on various things as we go through our day, the very fact that these mechanisms are so selective also means that they do not have widespread influence on many systems of the body. Of course, mechanisms of arousal and suppression are intimately involved in mechanisms of attention. Thus, the fact that we might have to suppress a great deal of activity in order to attend to reading a book in a noisy room filled with conversation, or that we might have to be quite aroused in order to push a button just at the right time in a video-game we are playing, will have much more influence on our health than the simple selective acts of reading or pressing a button.

We do not know to what extent dreaming is related to our health because it is impossible to stop a person from dreaming without also disrupting the person's sleep. However, we do know that if a person is deprived of either stage 4 slow-wave sleep or REM sleep, most of the loss will be made up as soon as the

person has the chance to sleep without interruption. This phenomenon is called **rebound** because the greater the amount of stage 4 or REM sleep deprivation, the greater the compensatory increase when the subject finally does sleep. It should be pointed out that if the deprivation involves REM sleep, the rebound will also involve REM sleep; similarly, if the deprivation involves stage 4 sleep, so will the compensatory sleep.

That we have such a rebound mechanism certainly indicates that we have some requirement for these types of sleep that needs to be made up. Although no consistent or marked impairment of psychological or physiological functioning has been reported following stage 4 sleep deprivation, REM sleep deprivation seems to interfere with one's ability to remember tasks learned prior to the deprivation (see, for example, Tilley and Empson, 1978). Thus REM sleep seems to be involved in increasing a person's ability to consolidate and retrieve prior learning. It is tempting to conclude that dreams, therefore, are involved in the formation of memory and the sorting out of prior experience. However, there is some interesting evidence that slow-wave sleep may actually impair the formation of memory, and that perhaps the observed effects are more a direct result of slow-wave sleep occurring *without* subsequent REM sleep than a result of REM sleep deprivation in itself. There are two reasons for this interpretation:

1) It has been shown that mice deprived of *all* sleep can learn to perform a task as quickly as non-deprived controls. However, REM-sleep-deprived mice learn less quickly. This learning impairment can be explained only as a result of slow-wave sleep, since both groups of mice—the group deprived of all sleep and the group deprived of REM sleep—were REM-sleep-deprived yet impaired learning was not observed in both groups. These data also suggest that the role of REM sleep is to *counteract* the harmful effects of slow-wave sleep on memory formation; animals that are not sleep-deprived at all show no impairment (see Rideout, 1979).

2) As discussed earlier in the chapter, people awakened from slow-wave sleep are much less likely to remember this awakening than are people aroused from REM sleep.

Although it is premature to draw any firm conclusions until we understand much more about sleep, it is likely, therefore, that if a person does not get a "complete" sleep—that is, a sleep that includes both slow-wave and REM sleep—learning disabilities may occur.

A number of investigators believe that the very mild effects of REM sleep-deprivation indicate that Freud's theory of dreams is incorrect. (Freud believed that the content of dreams reflects an interaction between a person's early experience—especially childhood—and events coming from the person's present life. He believed that dreams serve a *vital* function of permitting the expression of drives, unfulfilled wishes, conflicts, and so forth that would otherwise be repressed.) If, in fact, REM sleep actually is a state of dreaming, Freud's theory would indeed be in question—at least his assertion that dreams have a vital function—because the effects of REM-sleep-deprivation appear to be so mild. However, as discussed in the previous section of this chapter, there is plenty of reason to question the unique role of REM sleep as "dream sleep." Furthermore, the very fact that REM sleep has something to do with the consolidation and retrieval of recent experiences (at the least, seeming to counteract the damaging effects of slow-wave sleep) tends to support rather than deny Freud's ideas connecting dreams to recently experienced events.

The description of **insomnia** at the beginning of the chapter is an obvious example of the effect of psychological states on one's ability to sleep. Persons stimulated by intense emotional upset or worry simply cannot "let go" or relax because they are being bombarded by processes that maintain arousal (see Figure 8-4). Similarly, the fact that a depressed person frequently wakes up after just a few hours' sleep and is unable to fall asleep again is another indicator of the relationship between sleep disturbances and psychological disturbances. It has been estimated that perhaps 75 percent of all insomniacs are suffering from some degree of depression.

The fact that people can learn to modify their own EEG patterns has already begun to find an important place in the clinic and in health programs. The recognition of alpha rhythms is an important aspect of biofeedback therapies and meditation practices that one can be taught as a means of inducing complete relaxation. In clinical situations, some clinicians are having patients condition their EEG pattern to reduce or avoid the abnormal hyperexcitability of neurons that seems to provoke **epileptic seizures** (see Sterman and Shouse, 1980). It is well known that epileptic seizures are sometimes precipitated by "extraneous" stimuli such as emotions, music, noise, and flashing lights. The seizure usually occurs in those areas of the brain that are most predisposed to become hyperexcitable (such as the hippocampus, the motor cortex, the temporal lobe, and the amygdala).

As a final comment concerning their relation to health, we must again emphasize that arousal and suppression are profoundly connected to our psychological and physiological functions, and that prolonged excesses or deficiencies can produce a wide range of imbalances. Because there are so many different types of imbalances that may occur—ranging from inabilities to be attentive and concentrate to depression and lethargy, sleep disturbances, learning disabilities, abnormal breathing patterns, altered functioning of the autonomic nervous system and other processes that contribute to organic disease (Chapter 7), excessive muscle tension (Chapter 9), even epilepsy and excessive appetite—it is not possible to discuss them in detail. Those presented should give you a good idea of the many relations these mechanisms have to our health and well-being.

VIII. THE WORKINGS OF REFINED SYSTEMS: DIFFERENT TYPES OF "AROUSAL," "ATTENTION," "SLEEP," AND "DREAMS"

In Chapter 6 we considered the hypothesis that phenomena such as "consciousness" must be the result of one physiological process—a belief based on our perception that we experience consciousness as a single, unified thing. When we looked at it more carefully, we discovered that conscious experience involves many types of processes, and that different types of consciousness are at least partly defined by the sensory stimuli, sense organs, neural pathways, and structures of the brain that are involved. Among other things, we discussed that consciousness is not linked to one area of the brain; one area or another can be damaged without abolishing all conscious experience. Obviously, damage to an area can abolish *part* of our conscious experience, which part depending upon the structures involved and the functions they serve.

Perhaps the reticular system could be considered to be the most necessarily involved in the mechanisms of consciousness and arousal, inasmuch as severe damage in this area can make an animal or human permanently comatose. Even within the reticular system, however, many refined systems are at work. Small lesions within this system can selectively abolish arousal, slow-wave sleep, or REM sleep and can cause either coma or insomnia. Furthermore, in its normal functioning the type of arousal occurring at any given moment is clearly a result of the integration of many activities happening in very diverse structures of the brain. For example, the arousal characteristic of selective attention is localized to specific regions of the brain, whereas the arousal that occurs during the alerting response is widespread throughout the brain; in fact, the "takeover" by the alerting response severely restricts one's ability to remain conscious of, and attentive to, stimuli that are not a part of this response. Nevertheless, selective attention and the more diffuse alerting response are both arousal reactions involving activities within the reticular system. Moreover, both of these states of arousal or attentiveness also involve the thalamus, basal ganglia, and the cortex, as was discussed earlier in the chapter.

Our experience tells us that there are many different types of "arousal." We are all familiar with the states just mentioned; of being so distractible that we can't attend to just one thing, or being so attentive to one thing that we are oblivious to the rest of the world. We are also familiar with being engaged in a boring, repetitive task where we are quite active physically yet get sleepy and lethargic. Also, someone who gets up in the middle of the night to go to the bathroom is obviously more aroused than someone who is still asleep in bed, yet he/she is still apt to be not "fully awake" at the time and, by morning, probably won't remember having been up. Similarly, someone who is intensely disturbed is likely to be much more aroused than someone who has just awakened in the morning. Again, these different types of arousal all reflect different interactions occurring within the brain.

Similarly, we have seen that there are many different types of "attention," also served by different mechanisms. Mechanisms responsible for the alerting response and those responsible for directed attention to sensory input, for example, involve different neural pathways, as do suppressive responses like selective habituation to specific stimuli which we do *not* attend to, or general suppressive responses that can lead to sleep. Moreover, attentive processes occur whether we are asleep or awake. For example, a person from the country will often have a great deal of trouble sleeping in a big city because the din of city noises are constantly arousing; someone who has lived in the city, on the other hand, will not be aroused by these stimuli. The sensitive relation between suppressive mechanisms and attention is further exemplified by the sleeping mother or father who will sleep through loud, familiar noises but quickly awaken when their baby makes even the slightest noise.

"Sleep" is another example of an experience that appears to be singular when, in fact, it isn't. Not only are there different stages of slow-wave sleep, but there is an entirely different type of sleep called REM sleep. Aside from the differences between slow-wave sleep and REM sleep already discussed in this chapter, it is also clear that a person is more attentive during slow-wave sleep than during REM sleep. Animal studies have shown this to be especially true for discriminative tasks that involve *non-attendance* to a stimulus. For example, there is good discrimination between a tone that will lead to a shock (requires attendance) and a second tone that will not lead to a shock (requires non-attendance) during slow-wave sleep, a discriminative ability that is lost or greatly reduced during REM sleep (see Buendia, Sierra, Goode, and Segundo, 1963). These reactions probably involve forebrain suppressor mechanisms, not only in generating slow-wave sleep, but also in attentive mechanisms involving habituation (see pages 174–175, also Hernandez-Peon and Sterman, 1966, for data in humans and animals).

Is there any reason to assume that "dreaming" is different from the other processes discussed above? Dreams are certainly experienced in a general sense as being all "one thing," yet there is a difference between the vivid, story-like dreams reported during REM sleep and the more journalistic-like dreams reported during slow-wave sleep. This difference is likely to be a reflection of the fact that the body (including the brain) is functioning quite differently in these two types of sleep, as discussed earlier. Moreover, there is no clear reason to assume that dreaming occurs only while we are asleep. Someone who is "daydreaming" is obviously experiencing "internal thoughts," "wishes" or "stories" similar to those experienced in some dreams, although in this case the person is awake. Also, we have already mentioned that sensory isolation quickly places a person into a dream-like state where one is apt to experience many visual illusions although awake (see page 106, Chapter 6). It is interesting to note that after having left the isolation tank, a person is likely to quickly forget most of the experience. This is not unlike the case with "night" dreams. Furthermore, we all know how quickly the content of our daydreams slips away from us once we "snap out" of them.

On another level, we must mention the firm belief of many that there are distinctly different *types* of dreams. Although it is beyond the scope of this book to discuss the world of dreams, some examples of such dream categorization are: a) dreams that incorporate simultaneously occurring external events, such as an alarm clock going off, b) inner-knowledge dreams that portray some aspect of ourselves we are unable to see when we are awake, c) wish-fulfillment dreams, d) erotic dreams, which often, but not always, have a physiologic component, e) nightmares, f) out-of-body dreams, g) a category called prophetic dreams (which have to be distinguished from "statistical" dreams that seem to be prophetic but are actually the result of a person's selecting dreams that fit the occasion and ignoring those that don't) and h) daydreams, which can have any of the qualities listed above. This list is being offered simply to indicate that we experience different types of dreams. What actually distinguishes one type from another is likely to be related to the psychological and physiological processes occurring at the time—as we have seen throughout our discussion of body/self phenomena.

On close inspection, then, both our knowledge of the body and our own experience deny the singularity of such phenomena as dreams, consciousness, arousal, attention, and sleep. Instead, these phenomena must be regarded as expressions of the workings of highly refined mechanisms operating to produce one or another "state" at any given time. As such, we cannot exclude the possibility that we could develop *new* forms of attention, arousal, and dreams if we were to develop comparable new working mechanisms. In effect, this is exactly what happens when we reach puberty: with the development of reproductive functions, we clearly develop new forms of attention, arousal, and dreams.

IX. CONCLUSIONS

The information presented in this chapter certainly makes one appreciate the vast extent to which physiology and psychology are integrated with respect to the workings of arousal and suppressive mechanisms, and the extent to which these processes serve our health, contributing as they do to such necessary functions as wakefulness and sleep, attention and inattention, alertness, relaxation, and "letting go." Because arousal and suppressive mechanisms exert a very widespread influence, it is also not surprising, given that physical, mental, and emotional states all contribute to their workings, that imbalances occur for many different reasons. What may be more noteworthy, however, is that, in their concerted actions, a state of optimal functioning is generally maintained with respect to our ability, mentioned earlier, to ignore thousands of impressions at once while still re-

taining the ability to shift our attention to any one of these stimuli—for example, to go to sleep at night yet retain the ability to wake up in an instant, or to be very alert yet retain the ability to relax.

We will now look at skeletal muscles and their involvement in muscle tone and movement. Skeletal muscles make up about 40 to 50 percent of our body by weight—a very large part of ourselves to be involved in just one organ system. Correspondingly, we will see the enormous impact this system has on our general functioning.

Recommended Reading

BROUGHTON, R. "Sleep disorders: disorders of arousal?" *Science*, 159, 1070-1078, 1968. *A discussion of enuresis (bed wetting), somnambulism, and nightmares. Well written and easily understood.*

CLEMENTE, C. "Forebrain mechanisms related to internal inhibition and sleep." In: *Conditioned Reflex*, 3, 145-174, 1968. *This article describes and defines the forebrain inhibitory system within the brain. The suppression of behavior, sleep, EEG changes, and behavioral conditioning of the forebrain inhibitory system are some of the topics discussed.*

DAMASIO, A. "The frontal lobes." In: *Clinical Neuropsychology*, edited by Heilman, K., and Valenstein, E. New York: Oxford University Press, 1979, pp 360-412. *This review covers the structure and function of the frontal lobes. Included are several case histories of patients suffering from brain damage. Over 120 references are listed.*

DESMET, J. "Attention, voluntary contraction, and event-related cerebral potentials." *Progress in Clinical Neurophysiology*, Volume 1, edited by Desmet, J. Basel: S. Karger, 1977, 256 pages. *An excellent review of brain mechanisms responsible for attention and the initiation of movement. This book is quite technical and is recommended for advanced readers.*

FRENCH, J. "The reticular formation." *Scientific American*, 196,5, 54-60, 1957. *This article offers an excellent introduction to some of the functions and structures of the reticular system within the brain.*

LUCE, G. *Current Research on Sleep and Dreams.* Department of Health Education and Welfare (DHEW), Publication No. (ADM) 75-244, 1975, 125 pages. *An excellent discussion of the EEG and its relations to sleep, the effects of sleep deprivation, and sleep disorders. This monograph can be understood by the lay reader.*

OREM, J. and BARNES, C. *Physiology in Sleep*, edited by Orem, J. and Barnes, C.   New York: Academic Press,

1980, 347 pages. *This book is a thorough review of the physiology of sleep, covering changes in blood pressure, heart rate, blood flow, body temperature, secretions of hormones, as well as effects on various organs. Recommended for readers looking for advanced knowledge in this area.*

ROCKSTROH, B., ELBERT, T., BIRBAUMER, N., and LUTZENBERGER, W. *Slow Brain Potentials and Behavior.* Baltimore: Urban and Schwarzenberg, 1982. *This book covers the neurophysiology of slow potentials and discusses their relation to various drugs, emotions, cerebral tasks, and cognitive processes such as attention, expectancy, motor preparation, positive and negative reinforcement, and self-regulation of EEG activity. Recommended for readers with some background in neurophysiology.*

Skeletal Muscles, the Control of Movement, and Muscle Tone: The Clinical Reality

Medical Disorder: Tension Headache

Read this "overture" carefully before you read Chapter 9. The connections between the medical reality of tension headache and the underlying physiological and psychological processes that regulate normal muscle contractions are developed in this chapter. (For more information on tension headache, see Plum, 1982; Heyck and Dalal, 1981; Ryan and Ryan, 1978.)

There are many types of headache. In one classification, fifteen major categories are listed according to their causes (see Heyck and Dalal, 1981). A common cause of headache is pain due to contraction or spasm of the muscles of the head and neck. These headaches are called "muscle-contraction" headaches, as well as "tension" or "nervous" headaches. Tension headaches are characterized by steady pains, usually described as cramps in the back and/or sides of the head or neck. The pain may shift from one location to another or may remain localized in one region. The headache may last for weeks, months, or sometimes even years.

With prolonged contraction, the muscles of the head and neck—sometimes also the muscles of the shoulders and jaws—become sore and tender. The pain can be so constant and severe that it hurts to move the head, comb one's hair, or don a hat. This sustained muscle tension can be secondary to other (primary) conditions, such as constriction of the cranial arteries and diseases of the teeth, sinuses, or ears. In these cases there is often an accompanying sustained contraction of adjacent skeletal muscles of the head and neck which then (secondarily) become sore. Many tension headaches are not secondary to other disorders but are a direct result of increased muscle tension brought on by emotional states such as anxiety, worry, depression, frustration, and other reactions.

Medications can sometimes help to temporarily reduce symptoms in a person who would otherwise be incapacitated by the pain. These medications are usually analgesics (pain-reducers), muscle relaxants, tranquilizers, or mild sedatives. The best treatment for tension headaches due to stress-evoking circumstances, however, is to alleviate the excessive tension. As arousal mechanisms begin to relax there is usually a direct relaxation of muscles. Techniques that help a person to relax are often, therefore, all that is required. When such headaches are frequent and severe, prevention or alleviation of anxiety, worry, and other disturbing states of mind is sometimes best achieved with professional counselling, particularly when these reactions have become part of one's daily life, or seem to be constant.

9

Skeletal Muscles, the Control of Movement, and Muscle Tone

In this book we have repeatedly seen how psychological and physiological factors are inseparably interconnected as they influence the activity of our organs and serve our behavioral, emotional, and mental states. In all instances this integration is represented throughout the body, although the brain is obviously most centrally involved.

The processes we have discussed generally involve organs or systems whose activities are not easily changed by direct voluntary effort. With eating and hunger, we considered metabolic processes and the role of blood nutrients, the stomach, and the intestines. With drinking and thirst we mentioned the kidneys, blood volume, and osmotic pressure. With breathing we emphasized the involvement of blood gases and body pH. Finally, with emotional reactions we noted the involvement of the autonomic nervous system and its intricate and varied functions. Eating fills our stomach and initiates digestive processes that allow solid foods to be absorbed, and breathing allows oxygen to enter and carbon dioxide to leave the body; yet the actual secretion of gastric juices, the contraction of intestinal smooth muscle, the conversion of fats, proteins, and carbohydrates into blood nutrients, and the formation of hydrogen ions and bicarbonate ions is not under our voluntary control. We noted this fact in relation to the sense organs by explaining that even though we can modify the activity of the eyes by opening or closing our eyelids or by turning our head, or alter the activity of touch and pressure receptors as we grasp one object or another, once these sense organs are activated, neural processes occur without much voluntary control.

Although the above processes are not easily changed by direct effort, we have seen that they are very much subject to prior learning, prior conditioning, and, especially, our level of arousal. Thus, someone who is emotionally upset is not likely to be as hungry as someone who is calm, nor as likely to digest food well because sympathetic activity inhibits digestive processes. Similarly, we have seen that sensory receptors and neural pathways serving the senses are modified not only by our level of arousal and prior conditioning, but also by mechanisms that serve attention.

In considering **skeletal muscle**, which is defined as muscle attached to the bones of the skeleton, again we see that the contractile process itself is not directly under our control. Rather, it involves an interaction of calcium ions with proteins within the muscle that causes filaments, which are small threadlike fibers, to slide past each other. Each time a muscle contracts, it uses up enormous amounts of energy. The energy comes from adenosine triphosphate (ATP—see Chapter 3), which is "coupled" with the contractile apparatus in muscle. When the neurons that serve a skeletal muscle are activated, they produce changes in the muscle which, in turn, lead to its contraction. In their normal functioning, skeletal muscles contract only in response to neural activity. The contractile apparatus is illustrated in Figure 9-1.

Skeletal muscle has many special properties. Not only does it respond to different levels of arousal, learning, and prior conditioning, but *its activity is much more under our control than is the case with the other organs.* That is, even though we do not directly control the contractile process itself, in many instances we can easily control whether or not this contraction will take place. By an effort of "will" we can increase or decrease the neural activity responsible for the contraction of skeletal muscle. In addition, skeletal muscle and the bones (joints) they serve have many stretch-, pressure-, and pain-sensitive receptors that send a great deal of sensory input into the

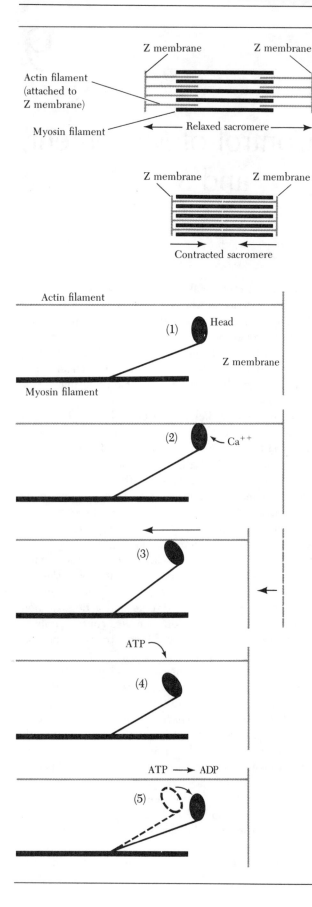

Each muscle is made up of thousands of muscle fibers. Each muscle fiber is a cell. Within each muscle fiber are hundreds to thousands of myofibrils. A single myofibril viewed under an electron microscope reveals thousands and thousands of sarcomeres. The sarcomere is the portion of a myofibril that lies between two successive Z membranes and forms the contractile unit of the muscle.

The actual contraction of muscle is brought about by the sliding of the actin filaments over the myosin filament. The myosin filament remains stationary. This process shortens the distance between the Z membranes, at the ends of the sarcomere. Although the manner in which ATP is used and the mechanism whereby the actin filament slides over the myosin filament are not completely understood, the following mechanisms are believed to be responsible for contraction:

(1) The cross-bridge is unattached to the actin filament.

(2) Calcium ions allow the head of the cross-bridge to attach to actin filament.

(3) As soon as the head is attached, there is a power stroke which causes the head to tilt. This tilting causes the actin filament to slide over the myosin filament, as indicated by the arrow.

(4) A reactive site exposed by the tilted head allows ATP to bind. The bound ATP detaches the head from the actin filament.
(5) The bound ATP is cleaved to form ADP. The released energy cocks the head back to its original position where it is ready to participate again in the reactions.

Figure 9–1.   The contractile apparatus of muscle. Note that as muscle contracts (step 3), ATP is used to "recock" the head (steps 4 and 5).
(Adapted from Guyton. A., HUMAN PHYSIOLOGY AND MECHANISMS OF DISEASE, W. B. Saunders, Philadelphia, pp. 92–93, 1982.)

brain. *This input keeps us well apprised of the state of activity of our muscles and their performance*—again, much more so than with other organs. Finally, skeletal muscle makes up a full 40 percent of our body and, therefore, *its activity exerts a great influence on our energy requirements.* Under normal resting conditions, for example, about one third of the energy of the body is used by muscle. During prolonged physical labor, this proportion can increase to two thirds or three quarters. Before discussing such topics as muscle tension, voluntary movement, the initiation of movement, the role of the brain in regulating muscle contraction, and the relations of muscle contraction to health, let's first discuss some of the fundamentals of muscle contraction.

I. MUSCLE CONTRACTION

The contraction of skeletal muscle serves two basic functions: the establishment of **movement** and **muscle tone**. Each time a muscle contracts, it either moves the bone to which it is attached, which then causes the muscle to *shorten*, or, if these bones do not move, it makes the connections between them firm and tense, in which case the muscle doesn't shorten but, instead, develops *tension*.

Phasic and Isometric Contraction

The first type of muscular contraction described above is called **phasic**, which refers to the fact that the muscle changes its length as it is being used—meaning that it shortens when it contracts and lengthens when it relaxes. The muscles of the face, larynx (speech), arms, legs, hands, feet, and neck are often involved in phasic contractions. The second type of contraction is called **isometric**, indicating a continuous (tonic) contraction that does not change the length of the muscle but, rather, increases its tension. The muscles of the back, the neck, and the legs (when standing) are often undergoing isometric contraction.

Phasic contraction is obviously the type of muscular activity used for voluntary and reflexive movement. Isometric contraction is the type of muscular activity responsible for maintaining our posture and keeping us from collapsing when we stand or sit; it is constantly adjusting the tension of the connections between and among our bones so that we don't lose our balance as we change our position relative to the force of gravity. Not only does isometric contraction serve to maintain our posture and equilibrium, it also provides a needed "tone" in all skeletal muscles, in-

cluding those that are phasic in nature. Thus, even when muscles are at rest there is a degree of tension in them.

Under normal resting conditions, about one-third of the energy of the body is used by muscle. A great deal of this activity involves isometric contraction. How much isometric contraction is occurring at any given time is dependent on many factors. These include:

1) POSTURE—When we are standing or sitting, more tension is required to maintain these postures than when we are lying down (energy consumption increases by about 33 percent when we are in upright postures).

2) DEGREE OF AROUSAL—An increase in our emotional, attentive, behavioral, or sympathetic activities affects the reticular system, and increases muscle tone (see Chapter 8).

3) STATE OF EQUILIBRIUM—When we are in a situation requiring constant adjustment to maintain our balance, as when walking on a thin curb along a street, muscle tension increases because of our increased attentiveness as well as because of increased activity of postural muscles.

4) PATTERN OF BEHAVIOR—The number and types of muscles involved in isometric as compared to phasic contraction depend on how the muscles are being used. When we are very active, as when shovelling dirt or snow, many muscles are involved in phasic contractions instead of isometric contraction. When we are less active, as when driving a car, more muscles are involved in isometric contraction, and when we are quite inactive, as when sitting or standing still, isometric contraction becomes the dominant form of contraction.

Motorneurons and Muscle Spindles

As previously mentioned, contraction of skeletal muscle occurs when neural impulses reach the muscle. These impulses travel along the axons of neurons that originate in the spinal cord. The neurons that innervate skeletal muscle are called **motorneurons**. There are two types of motorneurons which originate in the spinal cord: **alpha motorneurons** and **gamma motorneurons**.

Alpha motorneurons innervate most of the fibers of the muscle and cause the muscle to contract. Gamma motorneurons do not directly cause the muscle to contract; rather, they are smaller neurons that innervate special fibers within skeletal muscle called

intrafusal fibers. These intrafusal fibers make up a unit within the muscle, called the **muscle spindle**. There are many muscle spindles within a muscle. (Muscle spindles are surrounded by, and attached to **extrafusal fibers**, which are the main contractile units of the muscle, innervated by alpha motorneurons.) When the muscle contracts due to the activity of alpha motorneurons, the muscle spindle does *not* contract along with the rest of the muscle. Rather, the muscle spindle contracts only when gamma motorneurons are activated. The muscle spindle is illustrated in Figure 9-2, along with the skeletal muscle and joint it serves.

When the muscle spindle contracts because of increased activity of *gamma motorneurons*, this contraction sets off special sensory nerve endings within the spindle. These sensory neurons, which are sensitive to stretch, are called **annulospiral endings** (see Figure 9-2). The annulospiral endings in the muscle spindles send their input back into the spinal cord where they directly influence *alpha motorneurons*, causing these neurons to become more active. This, in turn, causes contraction of the same skeletal

muscle from which the muscle spindle originates. There are two ways, then, in which skeletal muscles are activated to contract: a) directly, by excitation of alpha motorneurons in the spinal cord, and b) indirectly, by excitation of gamma motorneurons in the spinal cord that causes sensory nerves from the muscle spindles to activate alpha motorneurons, also in the spinal cord.

II. MUSCLE TONE AND TENSION

Movement involves activation of *both* alpha and gamma motorneurons by structures in the brain and spinal cord. (This topic is discussed later in the chapter.) In comparison, increased (or decreased) muscle tone involves activation (or inhibition) primarily of gamma motorneurons. These mechanisms are illustrated in Figure 9-3.

The close association between arousal and muscle tension was emphasized a number of times in the previous chapter. Correspondingly, Figure 9-3 shows that gamma motorneuron activity (and therefore muscle tone) is primarily regulated by the reticular

Figure 9–2. The muscle spindle, showing its innervation by gamma motorneurons and its sensory nerves, called the "annulo-spiral ending." For clarity, only one large muscle spindle is shown but, in reality, each muscle has many muscle spindles, which are no larger than the extrafusal fibers that surround them. Also shown are alpha motorneurons that innervate the extrafusal fibers of the muscle (and cause the muscle to contract), and sensory nerves and receptors in the muscle and joints.

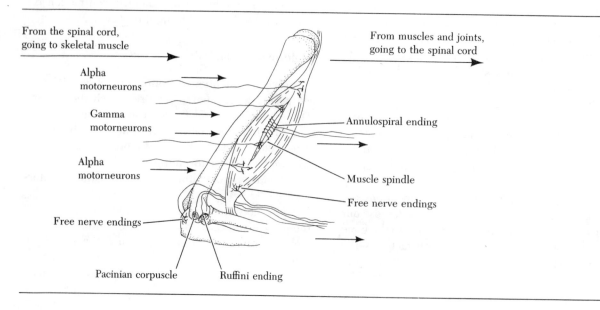

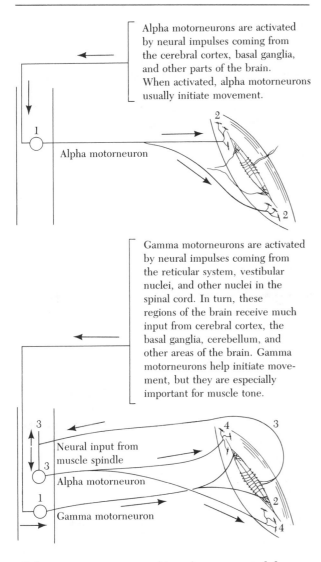

Alpha motorneurons are activated by neural impulses coming from the cerebral cortex, basal ganglia, and other parts of the brain. When activated, alpha motorneurons usually initiate movement.

1

Alpha motorneuron

2

2

Gamma motorneurons are activated by neural impulses coming from the reticular system, vestibular nuclei, and other nuclei in the spinal cord. In turn, these regions of the brain receive much input from cerebral cortex, the basal ganglia, cerebellum, and other areas of the brain. Gamma motorneurons help initiate movement, but they are especially important for muscle tone.

3   4   3

Neural input from muscle spindle

3

Alpha motorneuron

1   2

Gamma motorneuron

4

Alpha motorneurons: neural impulses propagated down the spinal cord from the brain activate or inhibit alpha motorneurons (1). Alpha motorneurons cause the muscle to contract or relax (2). If the muscle does not shorten, it will develop tension.

Gamma motorneurons: neural impulses propagated down the spinal cord from the brain activate or inhibit gamma motorneurons (1). Gamma motorneurons activate muscle spindles (2). Annulospiral endings in the muscle spindle send neural impulses back into the spinal cord, and both activate alpha motorneurons and send their input back into the brain (3). Alpha motorneurons cause the skeletal muscle to contract or relax; if the muscle does not shorten, it will produce tension (4).

Figure 9–3. Alpha motorneurons, gamma motorneurons, and the contraction of skeletal muscle.

system and nuclei dispersed in the upper spinal cord. As a secondary influence, all of the structures of the brain that are involved in the control of muscular activity exert their effects on gamma motorneurons (and therefore muscle tone) by transmitting impulses into the reticular system. It should be no surprise, therefore, that emotions, mental activity, and many other factors can influence muscle tone, as is summarized in Figures 8-4 and 8-5 of the last chapter and as illustrated in Figure 9-3.

What happens at a physiological level when we become emotionally aroused or otherwise excited is that activation of the reticular system increases the activity of gamma motorneurons, stretching the muscle spindles and thereby *reducing* the desired length of the muscles they serve—that is, there will be greater excitation of alpha motorneurons and an increase in the degree of contraction of the muscle which, then, will reduce the stretch of the muscle spindle. *In other words, the reticular system and other structures of the brain connected to it reset the tone of the muscle at a greater degree of contraction.* Conversely, if the reticular system decreases the activity of gamma motorneurons, the muscle spindles become relaxed and the desired length of the muscle they serve will be *longer* (less excitation of alpha motorneurons). Under normal conditions, the muscle spindles are always active. (Not only is there always some gamma motorneuron activity, but sensory input from the annulospiral endings in the muscle spindles is also constantly influencing the activity of alpha motorneurons.) The muscle spindles can therefore either be excited or inhibited, producing either increased or decreased contractions in the muscles from which they originate.

We are all familiar with the experience of having pain in the back and/or in the neck when we are "tense." This muscular response will be discussed in some detail later in the chapter; at this point, however, we should note that muscles which cannot move very much because of being attached to relatively immobile bones, such as those in the back or those in the neck and shoulders that are required to hold our head steady, are prime candidates for developing excessive muscle tension when motorneuron activity is increased. Because of their important postural functions, *these muscles cannot or will not shorten much when they are activated* and, consequently, there is no "relief" given to the muscle spindles and the increased muscle contractions continue. When these contractions go on for a prolonged period of time, the extra tension that develops in the tendons that attach these muscles to bones can cause inflammation and pain. This response often makes the contractions even more intense, not only because the neural impulses serving the pain sensations directly activate the motorneurons within the spinal cord that innervate these muscles and tendons, but also because pain usually increases the person's state of arousal, further activating the reticular system.

What occurs in the muscles mentioned above is very different from what occurs with the muscles that control the movement of our hands, for example. In this case the muscles are *free to shorten*, and so there is a let-up in the driving of alpha motorneurons due to the decreased stretch of the muscle spindles. That we do not get a sore arm from increased activity of the muscles serving our hands is *not* because these muscles are 'less active. We have all observed the constantly moving, "nervous" hands of a person who is overly aroused, and we know this does not cause sore muscles. If we are writing a great deal, however, the constant grip on the pen or pencil, and the tension that develops in the effort to move the hand carefully, *can* give us a sore arm. In this case, the contraction of muscles is much more steadily maintained than when we are nervously wringing our hands; in addition, our attentiveness is usually increased when we write, and this, too, increases muscle tone.

III. MOTOR SYSTEMS OF THE BRAIN AND THE REGULATION OF MOVEMENT

The control of motor functions is a very complex process that involves interactions with almost every structure of the brain—the **cerebral cortex**, the **thalamus**, the **basal ganglia**, the **cerebellum**, and, as already mentioned, the **reticular system**. These structures are illustrated in Figure 9-4.

The Primary Motor Cortex

One of the more important areas involved in the control of movement is called the **primary motor cortex**. This area of the cerebral cortex is a band which runs across the cerebral hemispheres just in front of the central sulcus. It is laid out in a topographic manner very similar to the organization we described in Chapter 6 for the somatic sensory cortex, except that electrical stimulation of the somatic sensory cortex is likely to evoke *sensations* in one or another part of the body whereas stimulation of the motor cortex is likely to produce *contraction of muscle* in specific areas of the body. The organization of the primary motor cortex is presented in Figure 9-4.

The primary motor cortex contains some long neurons that originate in this cortex and go directly to motorneurons in the spinal cord. Most cortical cells, however, do not go directly to the spinal cord. Rather, they go to the basal ganglia (especially the caudate nucleus and the putamen—see below), many

areas in the upper spinal cord (including the reticular system), and the cerebellum.

Just as we have seen with the somatic sensory cortex, the primary motor cortex also devotes disproportionately large areas to the hands, face, lips, jaws, tongue, and pharynx. In fact, wherever it has been possible to note a topographic organization of the motor system within the brain—as in the cerebellum and in the basal ganglia—we see large areas devoted to the head and hands. This is understandable when we think about the very precise movements that we make with our fingers, thumbs, and vocal apparatus. In fact, our ability to vocalize and our ability to perform skilled movements with our hands is one of the most distinguishing features of human beings. When parts of the primary motor cortex are damaged, the muscles regulated by these areas become flaccid and paralyzed; that is, the person will not be able to contract these muscles, which remain relaxed (flaccid). This effect is rarely permanent, however; presumably, other parts of the brain "take over" and assume, to some extent, those functions that were originally served by this part of the primary motor cortex before it was damaged.

When a movement is initiated, the cells in the primary motor cortex begin to fire approximately 50 to 60 milliseconds (.05 to .06 seconds) *before* the movement occurs. Furthermore, the more neurons that are activated, the stronger the contraction of muscle. These findings fit well with the idea that the motor cortex is involved in initiating movement. As we will see, however, this is not the only part of the brain that is involved in initiating movement.

The Premotor Cortex

In addition to the primary motor cortex, the **premotor cortex** or **motor association area** also contributes to the control of movement. Electrical stimulation in this area usually evokes responses in groups of muscles, producing postural changes, sometimes rhythmic movements of the body, sometimes chewing, swallowing, or vocalization. When this area is damaged, there is no sign of muscular weakness or change in muscle tone as occurs with damage in the primary motor cortex, but there is a loss of the detailed coordination of muscular movement such as is involved in speech, movement of the head, voluntary eye movements, and fine hand movements. All of these functions involve extensive integration of motor output with sensory input. Writing and talking, for example, are integrated with visual and auditory sensations, as discussed in Chapter 6. The rotation of the head is integrated with the movement and position of the eyes, the excitation of the vestibular apparatus, and sensory input from the joint receptors of the neck; these all contribute to our sense of balance and

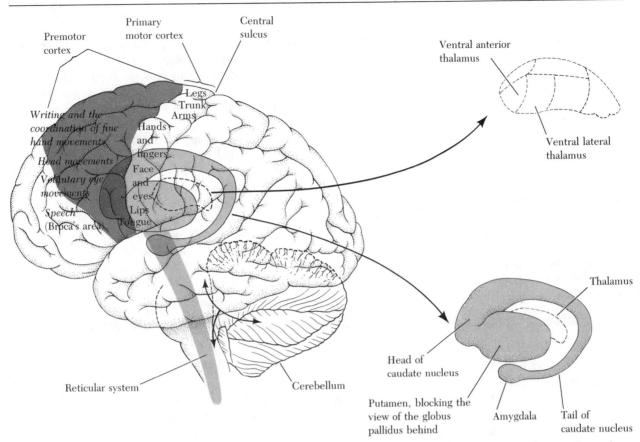

Premotor cortex (also called motor association area): this area regulates coordinated movements such as those used for speech (Broca's area), the movement of the head, the coordinated use of the hands, and the control of eye movements. Although electrical *stimulation* of this area causes muscle contraction, more current is needed than in the primary cortex. *Damage* does not produce obvious signs of muscle weakness or changes in muscle tone, although it does impair the coordinated use of muscles, as mentioned above. When damage in the premotor cortex is combined with damage in the primary motor cortex, however, the impairment is greater than when the primary motor cortex alone is damaged.

Basal ganglia: the basal ganglia include the caudate nucleus, putamen, and globus pallidus. (The amygdala and claustrum are not directly involved in motor functions, and are therefore not considered in this chapter.) These areas regulate the controlled execution of slow movements that initiate and accompany actions such as getting out of a chair, walking, speaking, and writing. All nuclei of the basal ganglia send signals to the reticular system and other nuclei in the spinal cord. Electrical *stimulation* of the caudate nucleus will cause an animal to cease its ongoing behavior (arrest reaction) and can cause sleep, whereas electrical stimulation of the globus pallidus evokes muscle movements. In general, *damage* in the caudate nucleus and putamen increases muscle tone and causes abnormally excessive activity, whereas damage in the globus pallidus leads to decreased muscle tone and decreased muscular activity.

Primary motor cortex: this area mainly regulates finely controlled movement (especially of the fingers, thumbs, vocal apparatus, face, and head). It is topographically organized; electrical *stimulation* of different regions of the cortex causes muscular contraction in different parts of the body. The legs and the feet are represented in the area that starts on top of the motor cortex and folds over into the medial surface behind (not shown). Large areas are devoted to the fingers, the lips, tongue, and vocal cords. *Damage* to this area causes flaccid paralysis of the muscles, although this effect is rarely permanent.

Cerebellum: this area regulates many aspects of movement, including the timing and strength of rapid movements and movements that maintain posture and balance. Sensory input into the cerebellum is topographically organized, with large areas devoted to the head, neck, and hands. The topographically organized motor cortex sends its input to corresponding points in the cerebellum and vice versa. Massive *destruction* causes clear disturbances in voluntary movements (especially fast movements), difficulty in maintaining one's equilibrium, tremor, deficiencies in exerting the proper strength of muscular contraction for a given movement, and deficiencies in exerting the proper sequence and timing of muscular contractions that make up the components of a complex motor act.

Figure 9–4. The major motor systems of the brain: the reticular system, the cerebellum, the basal ganglia, the thalamus, the premotor cortex, and the primary motor cortex. Note the space occupied by the basal ganglia in relation to the rest of the brain.

our ability to adjust the position of our body relative to the force of gravity. (Mechanisms involving posture and equilibrium are discussed later in the chapter.)

The cells in the premotor cortex become active as long as 800 milliseconds (0.8 seconds) *before* movement occurs. Thus this area is also involved in the initiation of movement.

The Basal Ganglia

The basal ganglia consist of the **caudate nucleus**, the **putamen**, the **globus pallidus**, the **amygdala**, and the **claustrum**. Because the amygdala and claustrum do not appear to be directly involved in motor functions, they will not be considered in this chapter. However, the caudate nucleus, putamen and globus pallidus, which lie between the cerebral cortex and the thalamus (see Figure 9-4), have a great deal to do with the movement of skeletal muscle. These nuclei have many connections with the motor cortex above and the reticular system below. In fact, as indicated in Figure 9-5, all of the areas of the brain that regulate the contraction of skeletal muscle are interconnected and modify each other's activities through a series of feedback loops.

Destruction or improper functioning of the basal ganglia is partially responsible for the muscular rigidity, tremor, and loss of voluntary movement (usually leading to immobility) seen in patients suffering from Parkinson's disease. Damage to these areas is also responsible for the constant, uncontrolled, frequently changing movements of the limbs and/or face that occurs in a disease called "chorea" (one type of which is known as St. Vitus Dance), as well as the slow, writhing movements of the hands or feet and unstable posture seen in patients suffering from a disease called "athetosis." In all of these diseases, voluntary movements are impaired, and strong emotion (such as

Figure 9–5. Motor feedback loops involving the motor cortex, the basal ganglia, the thalamus, the cerebellum, the reticular system, sensory pathways, and nuclei in the upper spinal cord. Only some of the major pathways are shown, but they are enough to indicate that all of the major brain structures regulating skeletal muscles are functionally and anatomically interconnected.

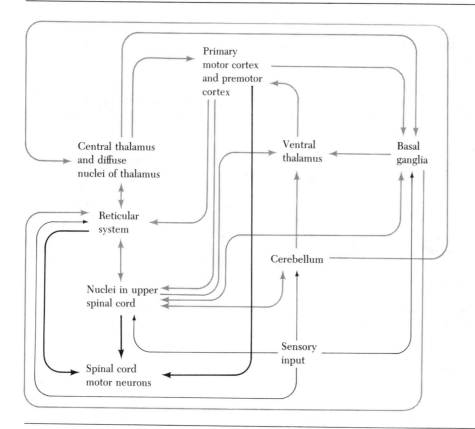

anxiety) or a voluntary effort to move usually makes the symptoms worse. These clinical findings make it clear that the basal ganglia are intimately involved in controlling the movement of our skeletal muscles. Also, the fact that they receive heavy input from and send much output to the reticular system indicates their interaction with arousal mechanisms.

Interestingly, although the motor cortex is necessary for humans and other animals that have fine use of their hands (like primates and raccoons), the workings of the basal ganglia are all that is needed for birds' movements and are sufficient for almost all movements made by cats (including those needed for walking, eating, fighting, and sexual behavior).

In humans, the basal ganglia are especially important in the control of slow movements—getting out of a chair, for example. Again, however, this control is exerted in conjunction with input to and from the motor cortex, as outlined in Figure 9-5. As we have seen with the motor cortex and premotor cortex, the basal ganglia are also activated *before* muscle movement is initiated. In fact, persons suffering from Parkinson's disease do not develop the same degree of activation of the premotor and motor cortex before movement as do those who are normal. Thus, the basal ganglia participate in the initiation as well as the regulation of movement.

The Cerebellum

The cerebellum is a prominent structure that lies behind the upper spinal cord where it is almost completely covered by the cerebral cortex (see Figure 9-4). The cerebellum receives input from the cerebral cortex, the basal ganglia, the reticular system, nuclei dispersed throughout the upper spinal cord that receive signals from the vestibular apparatus and as a result of eye movements, and from spinal pathways containing sensory input from muscle spindles, the tendons, and the joints. In other words, the cerebellum continually receives information about the activity of skeletal muscles as well as receiving information from all areas of the brain that regulate these muscles. Cerebellar output strongly affects alpha and gamma motorneurons of the spinal cord because of its influence on the reticular system and on nuclei dispersed throughout the upper spinal cord, and also because of its influence on the thalamus, motor cortex, and basal ganglia. These interconnections are illustrated in Figure 9-5.

The more we understand the workings of the cerebellum, the more we are appreciating its intricate involvement with muscle movement. A few findings are summarized in the notes to Figure 9-4, but we

should emphasize that this brain structure exerts an important influence over a) the reticular system and vestibular nuclei, thereby greatly modifying the activity of the motorneurons that control *postural muscles* and *muscle tone*, and b) the entire motor system which is involved in the execution of *rapid, skilled movements*. In general, the cerebellum seems to refine and adjust the activities exerted by the rest of the brain; that is, electrical stimulation of the cerebellum does not seem to affect sensation, nor does it directly cause movement of muscles as does stimulation of the motor cortex.

Damage to the cerebellum can cause a lack of coordination in carrying out movements, tremor, and, often, a loss of one's ability to make the fine postural adjustments needed to maintain equilibrium. The lack of coordination is characterized by poor timing of muscle contractions and poor control of the strength of these contractions. The loss of equilibrium is characterized by swaying from side to side when walking and difficulties maintaining a fixed posture when standing (balanced) on a narrow base. These deficiencies all involve disruption of fine control over the reticular system, over nuclei in the upper spinal cord, and over other structures of the brain that control skeletal muscle, especially through their effect on gamma motorneurons.

The way in which the cerebellum controls rapid, skilled movements is especially interesting. In part, the cerebellum appears to be organized to serve this function. Input into the cerebellum from various parts of the body is topographically organized, with disproportionately large areas devoted to the head, neck, and hands. The topographically organized motor cortex sends its input to corresponding points in the cerebellum and vice versa. When persons with cerebellar damage are asked to touch something placed in front of them through a rapid movement of the hand, they cannot predict ahead of time how far the movement of their hand will go and, as a result, often overshoot the mark. In persons with an intact cerebellum, the response is a very rapid movement that is suddenly "braked" just before reaching the object, and then a slow, controlled movement until the object is touched. It is generally believed that the fast then braked movement is controlled by the cerebellum whereas the slow approaching movement is controlled by the basal ganglia. (If you pay keen attention, you can experience both of these mechanisms in action by quickly touching your nose with your finger.) Often a person with cerebellar damage is able to carry out accurate movements slowly. When asked to perform the task rapidly, however, the movements lose their accuracy.

For example, when a person with extensive cerebellar damage is asked to perform a rapid, skilled task such as typing, the movements are jerky instead of smooth, the progression of movement is frequently lost (one "loses track" of where one's hands are in the sequence), and the strength of muscular contractions is often misjudged (either too much or too little). These movements occur so quickly in a normal person that there is actually not enough time for the movement to be controlled by sensory feedback. In this sense, the cerebellum "predicts" patterns of movement. That is, it is involved in monitoring the production of "preprogrammed" patterns of movement and their timing. Persons suffering severe cerebellar damage experience similar deficiencies with talking, writing, and playing musical instruments, all of which involve rapid, skilled movements. When a person with cerebellar damage is talking, their speech can be almost unintelligible because some syllables are held too long, others not long enough, and some are too loud. At the same time, there is an inability to keep track of, or coordinate, the rapid progression of movements required.

The cerebellum also modifies activities that are not directly related to motor functions. This control is partly exerted through the reticular system, which affects all areas of the brain. For example, electrical stimulation of the cerebellum of animals has been observed to inhibit sympathetic activity, increase sham rage and attack reactions along with increased sympathetic activity, and increase eating and grooming behaviors, whereas damage has been reported to reduce aggression and have a taming effect (see Riklan, Halgin, Shulman, Cullinan, and Cooper, 1978; Ball, Micco, and Berntson, 1974; Berman, Berman, and Prescott, 1974; Berntson, Potolicchio, and Miller, 1973; Reis, Doba, and Nathan, 1973). The cerebellum's mechanisms of action in regulating these effects has not been studied sufficiently, but it seems likely that it exerts its influence by modifying the activity of other structures of the brain.

It is interesting to note that electrical activity in the cerebellum also occurs *before* a movement is initiated, just as we have seen with all other structures of the brain involved in regulating skeletal muscle. These early neural activities will be discussed in some detail in the next section of the chapter.

Many Areas of the Brain at Once

There is an enormous amount of integration among the various structures of the brain that control the motor system. This fact is illustrated in Figure 9-5, which indicates that major pathways interconnect the motor cortex, the basal ganglia, the reticular system, the cerebellum, and nuclei in the upper spinal cord. For example, the caudate and the putamen of the basal ganglia receive input from the motor cortex and send neural signals to the ventral thalamus via the globus pallidus, which is also one of the basal ganglia. In turn, the ventral thalamus—which receives additional input from the cerebellum and other structures—sends its signals to the motor cortex, thereby completing a vital "loop" in the control of movement. Furthermore, all of these structures receive sensory input, especially from the muscles, joints, and skin.

Although we have discussed the cerebral cortex in a manner which implies that the area in front of the central sulcus serves only the motor system (Figure 9-4) and the area behind this sulcus serves only somatic sensation (see Figure 6-21), in fact there is considerable overlapping of these functions. There are cells in the somatic sensory cortex that serve motor functions and there are cells in the motor cortex that serve sensory functions—although electrical stimulation of these areas is far more likely to evoke a motor response in the motor cortex and a sensory response in the somatic sensory cortex. Furthermore, there is extensive communication between the somatic sensory and motor cortexes via "U" fibers that run beneath the central sulcus. In summary, all of the major areas of the brain that participate in regulating movement communicate with each other and also integrate sensory input.

IV. VOLUNTARY MOVEMENT AND THE INITIATION OF MOVEMENT

Voluntary movement is a process that has many different aspects. In general, when a movement is occurring without conscious participation it is considered to be "involuntary"—that is, it occurs "automatically." However, this does not mean that movements occurring with conscious participation are necessarily "voluntary." For example, people who have the "nervous" habit of wiggling their toes or jiggling their feet can be quite aware of these rhythmic movements although they are happening automatically.

Similarly, when a movement is *initiated* by "conscious" effort it is usually considered to be "voluntary." However, the initiation of movement in itself need not be voluntary, as exemplified by reactions such as the alerting (orienting) response or the many movements we make quite automatically when we are driving a car or performing any number of tasks that have become routine for us. In fact, the initiation of movement seems to span an entire range of "efforts" —from highly conscious effort (such as stepping from one loose stone to another in order to cross a stream) to activities requiring some conscious effort (such as stepping over railroad tracks) to activities that require almost no conscious effort (like going to the bathroom in the middle of the night).

Other factors that enter into any consideration of voluntary movement are learning, memory, and attention. Movements being learned for the first time require much more attention, much more voluntary effort, and much more sensory feedback than movements that have become habitual. Here again, however, we see that we are not looking at simple processes. For example, those functions that are most represented in the motor cortex—the ability to do fine movements with the hands and the ability to use the vocal apparatus for speech—definitely require sensory input in order to function normally. Most of us have had the experience of leaving the dentist's office with a numbed tongue and lips and discovered how difficult it is to enunciate clearly, or have had our ears plugged for one reason or another and discovered how difficult it is to speak coherently without hearing ourselves. Similarly, many of us have experienced the difficulty of unbuttoning our jackets or writing a note when our hands are numb from the cold. Moreover, this sensory input need not be perceived "consciously"; that is, persons whose hands are numb will have trouble unbuttoning their shirt whether the unbuttoning is performed "automatically" or "voluntarily."

The processes described above are only a sample of the many experiences we have that point to the conclusion that the initiation of movement, voluntary movement, and "will" are not singular experiences, but, instead, varied processes resulting from many ongoing interactions occurring within us. We have already seen this in previous chapters where we discussed "stress," "consciousness," "arousal," "sleep," and "dreams."

The Effects of Brain Damage

To further explore these mechanisms, we will extend the discussion begun in Chapter 6 where we mentioned that some people with damage in the pathway connecting the auditory association cortex (Wernicke's area—see Figure 6-22) to the speech area of the frontal cortex (Broca's area) have trouble copying words that sound alike. This motor defect is not due to an inability to write but, rather, to an inability to discriminate between certain words that have been learned through their sound. Persons who have damage in the auditory and parietal association areas of the cortex can sometimes suffer from a host of other writing disabilities, such as being unable to write

what is heard, being unable to write what is seen (copying), or being unable to write complete sentences despite their ability to write individual words. In many cases, the person becomes frustrated, knowing what is being asked for but simply unable to do it.

Another type of loss of voluntary behavior involves dysfunction due to damage of the premotor cortex. In this case, the necessary muscular coordination may be lacking; when writing, for example, the person is unable to direct the pen carefully with the muscles of the fingers and hand.

Cerebellar damage can also be manifested in disabilities of voluntary behavior. In this case, the person might be unable to write words quickly, in sequence, with coordinated movements—in other words, to write "automatically." When persons with cerebellar damage pay attention to the joint-by-joint progression involved in writing, they write quite well, albeit slowly.

When the basal ganglia are severely damaged, the most prominent symptom is difficulty in controlling the onset of writing. Other symptoms are the inability to control hand tremor and to prevent general rigidity of the muscles, a rigidity that prevents smooth, coordinated writing.

Again, many areas of the brain contribute in one way or another to the initiation of movement and its control. The specific defects in one's ability to voluntarily regulate these behaviors depend on the precise location and the extent of the brain damage.

Learning Skilled Movements

Another way to appreciate the interactions involved in voluntary movement is to look at the general pattern by which skilled motor activities are learned. As children, we learned to write as the result of persistent, fumbling attempts to make our hands "follow our eyes and ears." This early period involved an enormous amount of feedback from sensory receptors—not only our eyes and ears as the letters were voiced out loud, but also the sensory receptors in the skin and joints of the fingers and hand that gave us the "feel" of writing. As we copied letters and words from the blackboard, we had to write very slowly. This slow pace allowed time for the requisite feedback from these sensory receptors.

Not only were vast areas of the brain involved in our learning to write, but writing also involved a great deal of tension of the muscles all over the body. This diffused motor response was due to the activity of the reticular system—an activity associated with arousal and attention, and, at the same time, increased muscle tone.

As we became more able to write, visual input and auditory feedback slowly became less important, leaving only feedback from sense organs in the hands, arm, and fingers. At this point our writing was undoubtedly directed much more by the motor cortex, basal ganglia, and somatic sensory cortex than by auditory or visual cortex. There was also a decrease in muscle tension—we were able to "relax" more while writing—and our writing became more rapid. Interestingly, our writing became freer not only from sensory feedback, but also from the need for detailed voluntary effort.

As we became even more dextrous, no conscious feedback was necessary except for the vigilance required to alert us if we made a mistake. At this point the control was largely regulated in the cerebellum. Not only could we write "automatically," but also we could write so rapidly that any sensory feedback would actually be too slow. If we made a mistake we could correct it afterwards, but the mistake would be carried out before we "knew" it. Furthermore, we became much more relaxed as we wrote—our attention being directed much more to the content of what we were writing than to the mechanics of writing.

We have been implying that voluntary movement, sensory feedback, rapidity of movement, the degree of relaxation, and the amount of "automaticity" all vary according to the brain structures most involved. Although this is correct, it is important to realize that, normally, the entire motor system is involved at the same time, as illustrated in Figure 9-5.

Neural Activity Preceding Movement

Which structures of the brain are first activated (before movement occurs) depends on where the "impulse" comes from that initiates motor activity. As mentioned earlier, electrical activity can be recorded from many areas of the brain well before a movement occurs. Perhaps the most dramatic changes involve prolonged shifts of the electrical recordings either in a positive or negative direction. These shifts last a long time, being as short as 50 milliseconds (.05 seconds) in duration and as long as several seconds. As is also the case with the EEG, these shifts are the result of recording the combined activity of many nerve cells at one time.

Some of these shifts are well localized in the cortex and in subcortical structures, whereas others are recorded in widespread areas. The best-localized shift is called the **motor potential**, which usually begins 50 to 60 milliseconds before the movement occurs. This surface-negative potential occurs in the motor cortex in an area corresponding to the muscle about to be moved, and it represents the discharge of neurons that are directly involved in the movement. However, a similar shift is observed in the areas of the ventral thalamus that relay neural activity to the motor cortex. Furthermore, in patients with Parkinson's disease—where there is damage to the basal ganglia—the motor potential recorded in the motor cortex is severely reduced, indicating the involvement of these structures also. In other words, a number of areas—cortical and subcortical—contribute to this shift.

Another shift, called the **premotion positive potential**, occurs 80 to 90 milliseconds before movement. Again, many areas of the brain respond during this period, which some researchers believe to be the time when the actual command for movement takes place.

Other shifts occur much earlier, sometimes several seconds before, but usually starting no later than 800 milliseconds before movement occurs. There are a number of different shifts that occur during this period, and what these shifts look like when they are recorded depends on many factors. For example, if a person is asked to perform a slow movement, the shift occurs well before the shift that would be involved in performing the same movement as rapidly as possible. Also, when a motion is being learned, these shifts are more widespread in the cortex (and higher in amplitude) than after it has been learned. This fact has also been noted in the thalamus. Related to this finding is that the amplitude of the shift is greatest when there is a great deal of attention required preceding the movement. In addition, the shape of the recorded shift is different for those given a preparatory stimulus alerting them to be ready for a subsequent command to move than when instructed to move spontaneously. These early shifts have been recorded from the cortex, thalamus, caudate nucleus, reticular system, amygdala, preoptic area of the hypothalamus, cingulate gyrus, and the cerebellum.

Different circuits seem to be involved in these early shifts:

a) A circuit similar to the one for attention, discussed in the previous chapter, that involves frontal cortex, parts of the thalamus, the caudate nucleus, motor cortex, the preoptic area of the hypothalamus, and parts of the limbic system. (That the caudate nucleus makes connections with the septum of the limbic system, as well as with the orbital frontal cortex, supports the notion that this circuit includes the forebrain suppressor system; see Figure 8-6, Chapter 8.)

b) A circuit involved in slow movements that includes the basal ganglia, parts of the thalamus, and motor cortex;

c) A circuit involved in rapid movements that includes the cerebellum, parts of the thalamus, and motor cortex.

The reticular system is involved in all of the above circuits, although its reponses are not the same in each of them.

Although much more can be said about these early shifts, it is far better to wait until we understand them much better. Until further research elucidates their function, they are at least an indication that all areas of the brain which directly or indirectly control movement are "primed" well before a movement occurs.

V. RELATION TO HEALTH

It is obvious that movement is a necessary function and that without it we would not survive. The skeletal muscle system is a superbly organized system of hundreds of muscles; some extending, some flexing, some rotating, some simply supporting our bones, while others stretch and position our vocal cords, our mouths, and other parts of our face and body. Most of us take the running of this system for granted, yet, as all of us know who have pulled a muscle in our back or strained a muscle in a limb, if even one of these muscles is impaired in its functioning we can become quite disabled for an extended period of time.

There are many diseases of muscle. The muscular dystrophies, for example, are hereditary diseases characterized by a progressive deterioration of the cells of the muscle tissue. As the muscle fibers degenerate, they are replaced by fat cells and fibrous tissue. A number of muscle diseases involve inflammatory conditions. Sometimes many muscles are inflamed simultaneously, as in polymyositis, and other times the inflammation of muscle is part of a more general inflammation of connective tissue, such as in rheumatoid arthritis or rheumatic fever. Other muscle defects are indirectly caused. Muscular atrophy, which is shrinkage or wasting of muscles, occurs when a muscle is paralyzed because of damaged or cut nerves, when there is prolonged restraint (as when a limb is in a cast), or sometimes with multiple sclerosis, which is a disease of the brain and spinal cord that attacks the covering of nerve cells, usually resulting in paralysis. Abnormal activity in muscles is often associated with brain defects, as discussed earlier, or with abnormalities in the neuromuscular junction, which is the junction where neurons join

muscle. This is the case in *myasthenia gravis*, a disease characterized by a quick onset of fatigue and weakness of muscles, sometimes so extreme that they almost cease to function. Myasthenia gravis appears to be caused by abnormal and reduced functioning at the neuromuscular junction. All muscular diseases are crippling and, as such, are likely to have profound effects on a person's psychological well-being.

The very fact that muscles are so richly innervated by both motor and sensory nerves is one of the main reasons why their functioning is so much a part of our conscious experience and voluntary effort, and obviously one of the reasons why muscular disabilities are so devastating. In many cases, proper medication, physical therapy, and sometimes psychotherapy do much to improve a person's ability to deal with muscular disease. Most of us suffer from muscular ailments of one type or another, although not as serious as those mentioned above. These conditions are noted below as part of a discussion of the importance of conscious experience and voluntary control of muscle to our general health.

The Importance of Conscious Experience and Voluntary Control of Muscle

When we pull or strain a muscle, we usually recognize the problem and take care of it by either *resting* or *avoiding* excessive use of that muscle. Even with more chronic problems like backaches, the symptoms are vivid and we do what we can to alleviate the pain. There are many causes of back pain—damaged vertebrae, faulty discs, and either weak or cramped back muscles. Sometimes these defects can be corrected only through extensive medical treatment, but often a person will search for and find exercises and postures that relieve the condition. The fact that our skeletal muscles are so powerfully connected to conscious experience and voluntary effort makes it relatively easy for us to monitor the health of our muscles and take curative action when it is necessary.

Our ability to monitor the state of our muscles and alter their activity is not matched by a corresponding ability with respect to our internal organs. Stressful circumstances of one type or another might strongly affect the autonomic nervous system and/or the immune system (see Chapter 7), but we often are not aware of a dysfunction until we are quite sick. Even if we *are* aware of some imbalance, it is not easy to modify our internal activity by conscious effort.

In Chapter 7 we emphasized the strong connection between a person's level of arousal and effects on the autonomic nervous system and immune systems. In

Chapter 8 we pointed out that the entire brain, but especially the reticular system, modifies our level of arousal. We also indicated that arousal and suppressive mechanisms affect the functioning of our body much more than do selective attention mechanisms. Because all of these processes are connected to muscle tone, *the state of tension of our muscles is a very important and definite indication of events occurring inside ourselves as well.* For example, when our muscles are extremely tense we are likely to be concurrently affected by other arousal mechanisms, including increased activity of the sympathetic nervous system and its varied effects. Similarly, when we feel weak and heavy, we are likely to be concurrently affected by other suppressive mechanisms including complex imbalances such as those discussed on pages 154–156 of Chapter 7.

Because of these correspondences, we can use our ability to control the activity of our skeletal muscles in a biofeedback process which influences many aspects of our functioning besides muscle tension. When we attempt to reduce muscular tension by relaxation, for example, we begin by decreasing our levels of emotional and mental arousal. To put it another way, if we are aroused emotionally or if we are intensely involved in mental activity, we will not be able to relax physically unless we also reduce this emotional and/or mental activity. Conversely, if we are attempting to "snap out of" a lethargic state, we are much more likely to succeed if our efforts include increasing our emotional and/or mental arousal, such as by exposing ourselves to novel situations, looking at things in a "new" way, or promoting aggression sparked by a desire to win or succeed (see Figure 8-4, Chapter 8, and page 177).

These efforts to modify our state of arousal are, of course, not directed at a specific internal organ nor at any specific system that might be malfunctioning because of stress or some other factor. Rather, the effort is more likely to involve a general change in our autonomic balance and the responsiveness of our immune system—a shift that could, in turn, affect us in a very specific way depending upon our response stereotypy, our susceptibility to infection or allergies, and a host of other factors discussed in Chapter 7.

This indirect manner of "healing" ourselves is something we frequently make use of as we go through our day, and *it is one of the safest and wisest ways for us to influence the internal organs by our own effort.* We are simply not equipped to handle anything more direct. If for some reason we were given the necessary sensory feedback and motor control over one of the organs or systems operating within the body, we would almost certainly create an imbalance that could

be far worse than what we are already experiencing. This point was discussed at some length in Chapter 5 when we pointed out that, in most circumstances, when we try to voluntarily control our rate of breathing, it takes only a few minutes to produce a state of imbalance. One can well imagine the disastrous results that could occur if we were suddenly charged with directing our own heart rate and blood pressure. Thus, we should regard it as very fortunate that our body allows us to modify internal organs and systems mainly by monitoring and controlling the activity of skeletal muscle, where too much or too little activity is relatively harmless.

Muscle Tension and Pain

Although, as described above, we are relatively well equipped to modify the activity of skeletal muscles by conscious effort, nevertheless we often do not pay much attention to our muscle tone. Why? Because muscle tone is mostly controlled by gamma motorneurons (see pages 193–195) which are chiefly influenced by the reticular system, the cerebellum, the basal ganglia, and other subcortical areas of the brain that do not integrate sensory input to produce conscious experience to the same extent as does the cerebral cortex (see Chapter 6).

When we are excessively tense, however, we often *do* experience *pain* or *discomfort*—sensations "designed" to alert us—in the region of the neck and shoulders. As mentioned in Chapter 6, pain is a very special sensation. Not only is our ability to perceive it consciously represented throughout the brain, but, by its nature, it is an experience we wish to change because it is disagreeable. The reasons why the neck and shoulders are so susceptible to muscle tension are explained below.

When we are awake, a great deal of activity is involved in integrating muscle tone, movement, and the maintenance of our equilibrium and posture. These activities occur as the result of a complex integration of signals involving:

a) vision and the movement of the eyes,

b) the position of and movement of the head,

c) the position of our body in space, and

d) the contraction of muscles that maintain tension all over the body (mostly in the back, neck, and legs when standing).

Many parts of the body are involved in these mechanisms, as is illustrated in Figure 9-6.

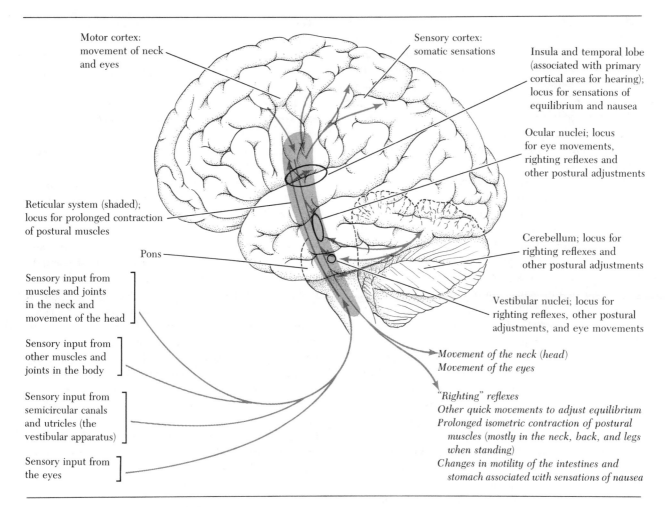

Motor cortex: movement of neck and eyes

Sensory cortex: somatic sensations

Insula and temporal lobe (associated with primary cortical area for hearing); locus for sensations of equilibrium and nausea

Ocular nuclei; locus for eye movements, righting reflexes and other postural adjustments

Reticular system (shaded); locus for prolonged contraction of postural muscles

Pons

Cerebellum; locus for righting reflexes and other postural adjustments

Vestibular nuclei; locus for righting reflexes, other postural adjustments, and eye movements

Sensory input from muscles and joints in the neck and movement of the head

Sensory input from other muscles and joints in the body

Sensory input from semicircular canals and utricles (the vestibular apparatus)

Sensory input from the eyes

Movement of the neck (head)
Movement of the eyes

"Righting" reflexes
Other quick movements to adjust equilibrium
Prolonged isometric contraction of postural muscles (mostly in the neck, back, and legs when standing)
Changes in motility of the intestines and stomach associated with sensations of nausea

Figure 9–6. Sensory input, brain regions, and motor output concerned with equilibrium and posture. The *head and neck* are especially involved, which is one of the reasons why the neck is often a focus for muscle tension when a person is aroused. Note that the vestibular apparatus, the eyes, and sensory receptors in the muscles and joints of the neck and other parts of the body all play a role. The activity of these organs is responsible for neural input that influences the reticular system and its associated nuclei (especially the vestibular nucleus and ocular nuclei), the cerebellum, the basal ganglia, the motor cortex, somatic sensory cortex, the insula, and parts of the temporal lobe. In turn, activity in these regions of the brain is what determines the sensations and muscular activity that gives us our sense of equilibrium and ability to make postural adjustments.

Figure 9-6 shows that the head plays a central role in maintaining our sense of balance and equilibrium, not only because it embodies our eyes but also because it contains the vestibular apparatus (see Figure 6-3). Furthermore, the position of the head is constantly monitored by sense organs in the muscles and joints of the neck, and its movement is carefully controlled by neural impulses originating in nuclei associated with the reticular system and the cerebellum.

These nuclei are dispersed mainly in the pons and in the area between the pons and the hypothalamus. Their actions are modified by sensory input from the eyes and the vestibular apparatus, as well as by structures higher in the brain.

The power of this system is exemplified by the **righting reflex**, a set of reflexive movements that tend to restore an animal's body to its normal, "right" position in space. For example, when a cat is held with its paws pointing up, and then it is dropped, its head immediately begins to turn to its normal upright position and its body then "follows" so that the cat lands on its feet. These quick adjustments that "right" the cat involve neural activity in the vestibular nucleus and other nuclei within the upper spinal cord, the reticular system, and the cerebellum—activity which is regulated largely by sensory input from the muscles and the joints in the neck, and from the vestibular apparatus.

The righting reflex, and other adjustments rapidly made to maintain our equilibrium, are often "predictive." That is, if we are suddenly knocked off balance for some reason, our limbs will extend instantly in order to prevent the anticipated fall. Although the cerebral cortex participates in such functions as moving the head and eyes, and sensing their position, a great deal of the sensory input that serves mechanisms such as the righting reflex does not appear to involve the higher structures of the brain. For example, input from the muscle spindles not only directly affects the activity of alpha motorneurons in the spinal cord (see Figures 9-2 and 9-3), but a great deal of it goes to the cerebellum and structures in the upper spinal cord where it is used to reflexively adjust our postures and modify muscular activity—especially muscle tone.

It is therefore clear that the muscles of the neck are an important part of our body's system for maintaining balance and equilibrium. As with the face, mouth, pharynx, thumbs and fingers, the brain devotes large areas to the neck.

As discussed earlier in the chapter, the muscles of the face, hands, and fingers are phasic in their nature. That is, they are relatively free to shorten and cause movement either of the bones to which they are attached or of the tissues which they comprise. When these muscles become active, for example, they need not develop excessive tension—they can simply move more. This movement can take place quite automatically; that is, we might be quite aroused and yet unaware that our "nervous" hands are "giving us away" to another person.

In general, we are also not likely to be aware of the increased muscular activity in the neck. In contrast to the type of "nervous" activity mentioned above, however, the expression of arousal in the muscles of the neck is quite different. These muscles, which must hold our head in a relatively steady position, are *not* that free to move. As explained earlier, it is in these muscles that tension often develops. Excessive tension in this area does produce *pain*, coming mostly from the tendons that attach these muscles to bones.

(The mechanisms responsible for exciting the nerve endings that mediate pain are not well understood; it is believed that pain results because excessive tension produces metabolites and/or inflammatory reactions that lower pain thresholds.)

The point here is that *we might not be aware of excessive arousal as it is expressed in the activity of muscles, but we cannot help noticing it as we experience pain.* Because of the special role played by the reticular system in regulating equilibrium and posture, and because of the related requirement that the head be held more or less stationary with respect to the rest of the body (because exaggerated movements of the head will activate vestibular receptors and visual receptors, leading to sensations of nausea and dizziness), it is not surprising that the most common sites of muscle tension brought on by arousal are the neck and shoulder regions, and that one of the most extreme symptoms is **tension headache**, as described at the beginning of the chapter. (Pain signals can also come from other regions, of course—commonly the back, especially when there is already something wrong with it.) Thus, the pain we feel in the neck and shoulders when we are anxious or tense is, in fact, a *healthy* way in which the body forces us to pay attention to perhaps excessive arousal. In this sense, although pain is a disagreeable sensation, it serves as an important biofeedback mechanism alerting us to reduce arousal levels.

Regulating Our Energy Use

Finally, it is important to realize that skeletal muscle makes up approximately 40 percent of our body and, because of this, it can use up enormous amounts of energy. We have no control over the expenditure of most of our body's usable energy, the energy needed to synthesize proteins and other chemical substances the body requires for maintenance and growth, for neural activity, for glandular secretions, for the creation of new cells, and for a host of other reactions essential to our existence. However, we *do* have some control over the activity of skeletal muscles. For example, by changing our activity from sitting at rest to walking slowly, the total amount of energy used by the body actually doubles (from 100 Calories/hour to 200 Calories/hour). It increases another five-fold when we are engaged in the very strenuous activity of walking up stairs. Thus, aside from its other functions, skeletal muscle allows us to greatly modify how much energy we are using.

Under normal conditions we have more than enough energy to meet all of our needs and activities.

In some instances, as when suffering from malnutrition, sickness, or starvation, a person is helped more by resting than by becoming too active. For most of us, however, the problem is the reverse: we have too much usable energy and much of it then gets stored —that is, we are overweight. In this case, increasing muscular activity is a direct way to lose extra weight because the increased energy demand will mobilize and use up stored fat in the body (provided, of course, that we don't compensate by eating more). (Although nutrition is not discussed in this book, we should mention that persons trying to lose weight by eating less must not compromise the body's need for essential nutrients, such as certain amino acids, vitamins, minerals, and fats. Proper dieting is generally accomplished by eating a variety of foods so that the body receives a full complement of these nutrients. Individual differences are great, and anyone trying to reduce body fat should be well informed before making drastic dietary changes.)

VI. THE WORKINGS OF REFINED SYSTEMS: PURPOSEFUL BEHAVIOR, VOLUNTARY BEHAVIOR, AND DIFFERENT TYPES OF "VOLITION" OR "WILL"

It is apparent that different structures and pathways within the brain serve different types of muscular activity—slow movements and rapid movements, phasic contractions, and contractions that mainly increase muscle tension. Moreover, these movements vary in the type of sensory feedback, learning, and memory they require. Arousal movements, such as the alerting or orienting response, involve the reticular system; postural reflexes are mainly represented in vestibular and cerebellar nuclei; and skilled movements serving speech are largely represented in primary motor, premotor, and temporal cortex. In each case these areas integrate different processes, ranging from arousal to equilibrium to functions that require a great deal of sensory input, attention, and prior learning.

There is little indication of any truly purposeful movement ever being evoked by electrical stimulation of just one motor area of the cerebral cortex. In fact, when the motor cortex is electrically stimulated the subject will report that there was no "wish" to move, only a feeling of having been "forced" to move. Similarly, stimulation of the motor cortex has never been reported to evoke purposeful or dextrous movements—only contractions of certain groups of muscles.

It *is* possible, however, to evoke *diffuse* "purposeful" responses, such as arousal, sleep, and orienting reactions, by electrical stimulation of the reticular system and the basal ganglia. These responses are very widespread in their effects and, unlike most of our movements, are not specifically directed. In addition, many *specific* "purposeful" behaviors such as scratching, rhythmic stepping movements of the limbs, and (in the medulla) respiratory and cardiovascular adjustments, are initiated by neural activity organized within the spinal cord.

There is no doubt that electrical stimulation of the hypothalamus and limbic system evoke more "purposeful" behaviors than are elicited from stimulation of the motor cortex, premotor cortex, or the basal ganglia—areas of the brain that directly control skeletal muscles. This is not surprising when we recall that the hypothalamus and limbic system are powerfully involved in regulating and affecting the autonomic nervous system, reward, hunger, thirst, satiety, sexual behavior (see Chapter 10), defensive responses, and many other related processes. All of these processes come into play to refine behavior beyond the capacity of the motor cortex alone.

From what has been said, it is clear that "purposeful movement" is a varied process, determined by the workings of many refined systems operating within our bodies. For example, electrical stimulation of the hypothalamus and limbic system—which evokes behaviors such as eating, drinking, rage, and flight reactions—obviously activates the motor system, but these responses are quite different from diffuse arousal responses or specific scratch behaviors.

Similarly, the initiation of movement, "will," and "voluntary" behavior also do not appear to be singular phenomena. Rather, as discussed in some detail in Section IV, they appear to result from the workings of many refined systems, all interconnected and varying at any one time, just as we have seen with consciousness, arousal, attention, sleep, and dreams. This being the case, we would expect that were one to develop the capacity to move "new" muscles—a situation analogous to our developing new sense organs in relation to consciousness (see pages 109–110, Chapter 6)—we would also experience new and/or different "volition." This, in fact, is exactly what happens with those who assiduously learn to wiggle the ears or who learn to move the little toe independently of the other toes. To take it one step further, we should remain open to the possibility that many other kinds of "will" could be developed provided we received the necessary experiential feedback and had the necessary perseverance.

Although in this chapter we have been discussing volition only as it applies to muscular activity, we do, of course also have the ability to direct our thoughts and feelings. Here, too, "will" is not a singular phenomenon. For one, a great deal of our "regulation" of thoughts and feelings involves suppressing their expression. For example, controlling a reaction like anger often involves stopping the movement of facial muscles, and, controlling an unwanted thought, stopping the muscles of speech. Another way we "regulate" thoughts and feelings is by shifting our attention, or by changing the circumstances to which we are reacting. Instead of feeling frustrated and angry as we talk to an "obnoxious" person at a party, for example, we may excuse ourselves and talk to someone else. Or, if we wish to stop thinking about the economy, we might turn to the sports section of the newspaper. These examples of regulating thoughts and feelings involve engaging ourselves in different activities, but we can also regulate them by becoming engaged in activities that serve the same purpose, such as "forcing" ourselves to express ongoing feelings of love or anger, or to write down thoughts so that they can become clearer. We could go on, but these examples are sufficient to indicate that as it relates to our ability to direct thoughts and feelings, "will" certainly appears to be as varied a process as it is with movement.

VII. CONCLUSIONS

The contraction of skeletal muscle—phasic and isometric—is regulated through the workings of several neural systems whose circuitry is a part of many structures of the brain. In their interplay, the activities of these systems produce movements ranging from slow to rapid and from reflexive to highly skilled, and they serve such varied functions as maintaining posture and equilibrium, initiating movement "at will," and performing general movements, such as walking, and very precise learned movements, such as writing and talking. The fact that much of our physical, emotional, and mental activity is strongly tied in with mechanisms that either suppress or increase arousal has been emphasized once again, this time in specific relation to muscular activity. We have seen that our ability to be conscious of the activity of our skeletal muscles and to regulate their activity is extremely important to our health. Not only do these abilities allow us to "control" our behavior, but they allow us to consciously perceive our level of arousal, thereby giving us an opportunity to modify arousal levels by reducing the discomfort and pain often associated with muscle tension.

Recommended Reading

DESMET, J. "Attention, voluntary contraction, and event-related cerebral potentials." *Progress in Clinical Neurophysiology, Volume 1*, edited by Desmet, J. Basel: S. Karger, 1977, 256 pages. *An excellent review of the brain mechanisms responsible for attention and the initiation of movement. This book is quite technical and is recommended for advanced readers.*

FRIEDMAN, A. "Characteristics of tension headache: a profile of 1420 cases." *Psychosomatics*, 20,7, 451-461, 1979. *This article defines and describes tension headaches and outlines several ways they can be distinguished from migraine headaches. There is also a brief discussion of the causes of tension headaches and their treatment.*

LASSEN, N., INGVAR, D., and SKINHOJ. E. "Brain function and blood flow." *Scientific American*, 239,4, 62-71, 1978. *A nicely written and well-illustrated article describing the functions of the cerebral cortex.*

ROCKSTROH, B., ELBERT, T., BIRBAUMER, N., and LUTZENBERGER, W. *Slow Brain Potentials and Behavior.* Baltimore: Urban and Schwarzenberg, 1982. *This book covers the neurophysiology of slow potentials and discusses their relation to various drugs, emotions, cerebral tasks, and cognitive processes such as attention, expectancy, motor preparation, positive and negative reinforcement, and self-regulation of EEG activity. Recommended only for readers with some background in neurophysiology.*

Reproduction, Sex Hormones, and Behavior: The Clinical Reality

Medical Disorder: Infertility

Read this "overture" carefully before you read Chapter 10. The connections between the medical reality of infertility and the basic underlying physiological and psychological processes that regulate normal reproductive functions and sexual behavior are developed in this chapter. (For more information on infertility, see Lief, 1982; Walker, 1982; Warren, 1982; Yen, 1982.)

Infertility can be defined as the inability of a couple to conceive after having made attempts for one year (Walker, 1982). Approximately 15 percent of married couples are unable to conceive. The causes of infertility are many: defective functioning of the reproductive organs, impaired functioning of the pituitary gland, abnormal functioning of the hypothalamus, inadequate sexual behavior, and emotional, mental, or physical stress.

The brain, the pituitary gland, and the reproductive organs must function properly and in concert in order to assure fertility. Activities of the brain and the autonomic nervous system contribute to emotional, physiological, and behavioral mechanisms responsible for sexual desire, sexual excitement, and sexual behavior. In addition, the hypothalamus produces and releases chemicals, called "releasing factors," that regulate many of the activities of the pituitary gland, including its production and release of gonadotropins. Gonadotropins, chemicals released from the pituitary gland into the blood, regulate the activity of the ovaries in females and the testes in males. (The ovaries produce eggs and the testes produce sperm.) In turn, the ovaries and the testes release chemicals, called "sex hormones," which maintain many reproductive organs and also influence the brain and other tissues.

Infertility can be caused by defects in spermatic function in males, or defects in ovarian or uterine function in females. In males, infertility results when the semen lacks sperm, or the number or quality of sperm is impaired. In females, failure of the egg to escape from its follicle, a process called "ovulation," or failure of the egg to fully mature within the ovary, causes infertility. Infertility also occurs when the uterus in the female is unable to properly maintain the newly conceived human being. The above disorders can be caused by excessive fibrous tissue, usually in response to infection, or by abnormal secretions of chemicals by the reproductive organs. In addition, they can be caused by starvation or undernourishment, both of which are usually associated with inadequate secretion of gonadotropins from the pituitary gland. Infertility can also result from physical obstruction of the fallopian tubes, or from excessive radiation of the testes or ovaries by X-rays.

When circulating gonadotropin levels are greatly diminished, absent, or otherwise abnormal, defects in the functioning of the pituitary gland are a likely cause. As just mentioned, these defects can be the result of starvation or undernourishment, but they can also be caused by tumors, infection, and other pathologies of the pituitary gland.

Defects in pituitary function can result from impaired hypothalamic function. The levels of releasing factors in the hypothalamus can be greatly diminished, absent, or otherwise abnormal as a result of tumors, infection, inadequate blood supply, trauma, and other pathologies of the hypothalamus, including effects induced by starvation or inadequate nutrition. Infertility associated with abnormal neural functioning can also be caused by abnormal levels of sex hormones, abnormal levels of pituitary gonadotropins, or inappropriate release of neural chemicals (see Chapter 11). Sometimes abnormally high levels of sex hormones are the result of liver disease, or are the result of the adrenogenital syndrome, a condition characterized by excessive liberation of sex hormones from the adrenal glands.

Emotional factors cause or contribute to about 25 percent of all infertility (Walker, 1982). These factors operate in many ways. Patients suffering from anorexia nervosa are almost always infertile and, as noted earlier, even less severe states of undernutrition can alter the activity of the pituitary gland—possibly the hypothalamus as well—thereby lowering the levels of gonadotropins and sex hormones (see Warren, 1982, and, for a description of anorexia nervosa, the beginning of Chapter 3). Sexual performance itself can be a cause of infertility. If, for example, sexual desire is so inhibited in one or both partners that copulation seldom occurs, conception is unlikely to occur. Often this situation reflects some incompatability between the partners, but sometimes depression, fatigue, sexual trauma (such as rape or incest), or chronic illness are involved. Even when sexual desire is adequate, there can be recurrent and persistent inhibition of sexual excitement. In males this is manifested by partial or complete failure to attain or maintain erection until completion of the sexual act. In females this is manifested by partial or complete failure to attain or maintain adequate lubrication or swelling (vasocongestion) of the vagina. Anxiety and depression are commonly responsible for this kind of inhibition, which often triggers a vicious cycle: inadequate sexual excitement leads to further anxiety caused by fear of failure, a perceived need to please the partner, or a sense of not meeting some fantasied standard of sexual performance. Some males experience premature ejaculation, which, in some chronic cases, is classified as a disorder. (Although the time lapse between erection and ejaculation is indeed a problem in relation to a man's desire to voluntarily control when ejaculation occurs, it is not usually a condition that prevents conception, unless ejaculation occurs before entry.) Premature ejaculation is usually a consequence of anxiety, sometimes associated with extreme sexual excitement.

In Chapter 7 we indicated that emotional factors such as anxiety or fear often underlie changes in physiological function, especially those occurring in organs and tissues affected by the secretions of the adrenal glands and the activity of the autonomic nervous system. We also indicated that certain regions of the brain, including the hypothalamus, limbic system, and frontal cortex, are especially involved. As a whole, the reproductive system is very sensitive to these changes. There are many reports that stress or depression can make a person temporarily infertile (see Walker, 1982; Jones, 1976; Altman, Sachar, Gruen, Halpern, and Eto, 1975; Loftus, 1962; Rakoff, 1962). Within the brain, any condition that alters the ability of the hypothalamus to produce and secrete releasing factors can cause infertility. How this occurs is still largely unknown, but a number of findings indicate that stress and depression can alter the activity of hypothalamic neurons that regulate the production and secretion of releasing factors (see Yen, 1982; Lachlin and Yen, 1978).

Sexual excitement is associated with activity in both the parasympathetic and the sympathetic branches of the autonomic nervous system. Activity in parasympathetic nerves is responsible for penile erection, vaginal lubrication, vasocongestion of the clitoris, erection of the nipples, and other erotic responses. Sympathetic nerves are involved in ejaculation and the orgasmic response in women and men. Because anxiety, fear, or other defensive reactions can activate the sympathetic nervous system, and because this activation is often associated with inhibition of the parasympathetic nervous system (see Chapter 7), these emotional states can block or cause a cessation of erotic reactions to sex. This response can lead to impotence and frigidity which, in turn, can affect fertility. This same mechanism is often involved in premature ejaculation since ejaculation is primarily a sympathetic response.

In treating infertility, one must first search for its causes. Of primary importance is a thorough examination of the couple for abnormal reproductive function. If conditions such as infection, inadequate nutrition, inadequate secretions of gonadotropins, and/or physical obstruction are present, these can sometimes be treated. Proper treatment must also include a thorough sexual history to determine any dysfunction in sexual performance between the partners. For a health professional to obtain a complete and accurate history, both individuals in the couple must be open and honest; to achieve this level of disclosure, the interviewing professional must be sensitive and caring, and assure confidentiality. If anxiety or stress appears to be a major cause, teaching the couple relaxation exercises, encouraging an open sexual dialogue between them, decreasing stressful life events such as occupational pressure, or, in some cases, psychotherapy or counselling, are often successful.

10

Reproduction, Sex Hormones, and Behavior

All of the physiological/psychological processes discussed so far in this book have been a part of our experience as far back as we can remember. Eating, drinking, breathing, sensory experiences like seeing and hearing, defensive reactions like anger or fear, and functions such as attention, sleeping and moving our body are all processes that have evolved and developed—both psychologically and physiologically— almost since the day we were born. Because of this familiarity, we tend to take for granted the coworkings of physiology and behavior that operate in all of these functions. Every once in a while, however, when we are particularly hungry or become sick with the flu, or go for a few days with very little sleep, we notice that our psychological state and our physiological state are inseparably connected.

Sexual functions are very different from those listed above. During the first eight to ten years of our lives, they remain functionally dormant. Then, as the result of a process called "puberty," there is a very rapid growth and development of our reproductive system. By the time we have reached the age of 15 years, most of us have changed from being relatively asexual boys and girls into men and women, reproductively fertile and filled with desires and emotions not experienced before. *What distinguishes this physiological/psychological process from the others is that it first occurs when we are relatively old.* In other words, there is no doubt in any of us at this time that a new physiological process has developed along with a new psychological process.

The information presented in this chapter is somewhat complicated because it includes many different topics. In no way can sexuality be understood as a single process. For example, what constitutes "female" or "male" is intimately connected with our **sexual development**, which starts with conception and culminates in **puberty** some 14 years later. We will look at this process in some detail, including those reproductive mechanisms that operate in a fertile female and those that operate in a fertile male. We will also look at the various chemicals, all of which are called **hormones**, that are secreted by the glands responsible for reproductive functions. (You will recall that a hormone is any chemical that is secreted into the blood and transported throughout the body to exert specific actions on one or another organ.) This information will help us to understand sexual processes as well as give us an idea of what is known about the influence of chemicals on behavior. By looking at the areas of the **brain** that are involved in reproductive functions, we will gain additional insight into the role of the nervous system. We will mostly look at **heterosexual behavior** (sexual behavior involving a partner of the opposite sex), but we will also discuss some aspects of **homosexuality**. We will take a brief look at **reward** mechanisms as they are related to sexual processes, as well as **aggression** and **maternal behavior**. In addition, we will consider the workings listed above as they influence one another, especially as they act in concert to promote fertility. Finally, we will consider how reproduction relates to **health**.

Because the easiest way to understand mechanisms of reproduction is to follow sexual development, starting with fertilization and the beginning of a new human being and ending with sexual maturation after the onset of puberty, we will discuss sexual development in some detail. In addition to helping the reader to understand reproductive physiology, this discussion provides information on what distinguishes female from male—a topic of interest to all of us, given the importance we place on our sexual identity. Although many of us are clear about sexual differences, the bivalent nature of sexual function is not widely appreciated.

I. EARLY DEVELOPMENT OF THE SEXUAL ORGANS AND GENERAL COMMENTS ON THEIR ADULT FUNCTIONS

When fertilization takes place, the male reproductive cell, or **sperm**, unites with the female reproductive cell, or **ovum** (the egg). When they unite, each cell contributes its genetic material to the new individual. This genetic material is contained in 23 structures called "chromosomes." One of the 23 chromosomes given by each reproductive cell is called a "sex chromosome" because it is important in determining the sex of the new individual. Sex chromosomes are designated by the letters X and Y. The ovum from the female always contains an X chromosome. The male sperm can contain either an X chromosome or a Y chromosome. The genetic material in the new individual will therefore contain either two X chromosomes (XX—one from the female, the other from the male) or one X chromosome and one Y chromosome (XY—the X chromosome from the female, the Y from the male). The XX combination designates a **genetic female** and the XY combination a **genetic male**. It is because, in most species of animals, males produce X- and Y-bearing sperm in approximately equal numbers that the number of females and males in the population are approximately equal.

In most instances a genetic female (XX) will develop into a fully normal, reproductively fertile female, and a genetic male (XY) will develop into a normal, fertile male. However, this development is not determined by genetics alone. Although genetic factors set the process into motion, hormones secreted by the developing fetus and later by the pubertal individual are largely responsible for the differentiation and development of most of the body into a female or male form. This process is discussed below, along with a brief description of the adult functions of the reproductive organs. (More detailed descriptions will be given later in the chapter.)

The Ovaries and Testes

The differentiation of the sex organs begins approximately six weeks after conception. *Before this time, the reproductive organs in a genetic male and those in a genetic female are indistinguishable.* The first organs to differentiate are the **gonads**, which are the **testes** in males and the **ovaries** in females.

Between approximately the fifth and seventh weeks of life, the **primordial gonads** in the fetus develop either into embryonic testes or into embryonic ovaries. (In embryology, primordial refers to the undeveloped early form of an organ.) This development appears to be triggered by the sex chromosomes: a genetic male (XY) will develop male gonads, or testes, whereas a genetic female (XX) will develop female gonads, or ovaries. Because the primordial gonads appear to have the potential to develop into *either* ovaries or testes, they are called **bipotential**. As we shall see, bipotentiality is a property characteristic of many sexual processes.

Functioning in the adult male, the two testes have many coiled **seminiferous tubules** within them where sperm are formed and grow. The testes also produce and secrete large amounts of a chemical called **testosterone**, also called *male hormone*. Testosterone is secreted into the blood—unlike sperm, which stay in the reproductive tract.

Functioning in the adult female, the two ovaries contain hundreds of thousands of spheroidal vesicles called **primordial follicles**. Each month, one or more of these follicles mature to the point where the egg it contains is expelled into the peritoneal cavity. This is called **ovulation**. In addition, the ovaries produce and secrete large amounts of the chemicals **estrogen** and **progesterone**, also called *female hormones*, into the blood.

The Internal Genitalia

The differentiation of the other reproductive organs begins a few weeks after gonadal differentiation. Between approximately the eighth and eleventh weeks of life, what are called the **internal genitalia** differentiate from their primordial form into either male organs or female organs.

The internal genitalia are also called the "genital ducts." In the male, these ducts become the **epididymis**, **vas deferens**, and the **seminal vesicles**. In the female they become the **fallopian tubes** and the **uterus** (including its lower cylindrical portion, called the uterine cervix).

Before the internal genitalia differentiate, genetic females and genetic males both have the same duct systems. In males, the **wolffian duct system** differentiates into the epididymis, vas deferens, seminal vesicles, and the ejaculatory duct. In females, the **mullerian duct system** develops into the uterus and the fallopian tubes.

Within the male fetus, the mullerian duct system, does not develop but instead regresses (disappears). Chemicals secreted by the embryonic testes are responsible for the development of the wolffian duct system and the regression of the mullerian duct system. In females, roughly the opposite occurs: the mullerian duct system develops and it is the wolffian duct system that does not develop. However, the differentiation of the female duct system does *not* depend upon chemicals secreted by the ovaries. This differentiation occurs because there are no hormones being secreted by the testes (which, of course, are not present in the genetic female). In other words, it is the *absence* of male hormones that leads to a differentiation of the genital ducts into the female form.

As with the ovaries and testes, the differentiation of the internal genitalia also involves bipotential organs. Thus, depending upon what happens to them, they can become either female or male in their development. If, for example, there is no secretion of hormones from the embryonic testes through some abnormality in testicular function, then female internal genitalia will develop even though the host is a genetic male. Conversely, if the embryonic female is exposed to male hormones—experimentally in animals, for example, or through abnormal secretions of the adrenal glands in humans—she will develop male internal genitalia even though she is a genetic female. Abnormalities such as these do not happen under normal conditions, yet they do occur under certain circumstances described later in this section.

The male reproductive organs are illustrated in Figure 10-1. In the adult, once sperm are formed in the testes, they pass into the **epididymis** where they become mature and develop their power of motility. Some sperm are stored here, but most pass into the

Figure 10–1. The adult male reproductive system.

Testes: the two testes have many coiled seminiferous tubules within them, where sperm are formed and grow. Once sperm are formed, they pass into the epididymis. The testes also produce and secrete a chemical called testosterone, also called male hormone. Testosterone is secreted directly into the blood and does not stay within the reproductive tract as do sperm.

Epididymis: the sperm become mature in the epididymis, where they develop their power of motility and become capable of fertilizing the ovum (egg). Some sperm are stored here, but most pass into the vas deferens.

Vas deferens: most sperm are stored in the vas deferens. The vas deferens goes from the epididymis to the prostatic urethra, where it ends as the ejaculatory duct.

Seminal vesicles: the seminal vesicles produce and store a number of chemicals that serve as nutrients for ejaculated sperm.

Prostate: the prostate secretes an alkaline fluid that increases the motility and fertility of sperm. It also secretes many other chemicals.

Penis: the penis contains erectile tissue that fills with blood when parasympathetic impulses dilate its arteries. It also contains the last part of the urethra as it courses from the bladder to the extremity of the penis. The urethra allows both urine and spermatic fluid to be discharged externally.

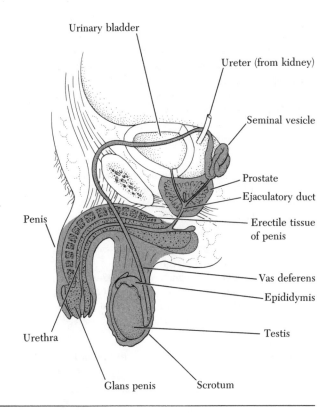

vas deferens where they are stored. The vas deferens goes from the epididymis to the prostatic urethra where it ends as the ejaculatory duct. The ejaculatory duct is a tubular structure formed by the union of the vas deferens and the excretory duct of the seminal vesicles. The seminal vesicles are organs that produce and store a number of chemicals that serve as nutrients for ejaculated sperm.

The female reproductive organs are illustrated in Figure 10-2. In the adult, once the fully formed egg is expelled from the ovary into the peritoneal cavity, it enters the fallopian tube, which is a tubular structure that starts at the ovary and ends in the uterus. The fallopian tubes help transport the egg to the uterus and also produce chemicals to maintain the egg. The uterus is a hollow, muscular organ whose strong muscles help to expel the newborn at the end of pregnancy in a process called labor. Its inner lining, called the endometrium, is made up of cells and tissues that accept and then maintain the egg whenever it is fertilized. The cells and tissues of the endometrium build up throughout each reproductive cycle, which is typically 28 days long, and then this growth is sloughed off. This sloughing-off process is called menstruation, which will be discussed later in the chapter as part of a more thorough discussion of

Figure 10–2. The adult female reproductive system.

Ovaries: the two ovaries contain hundreds of thousands of immature spheroidal vesicles called primordial follicles. Each month, one or more of these follicles is mature enough so that the egg it contains is expelled into the peritoneal cavity. From there the egg (ovum) enters the Fallopian tubes. The ovaries also produce and secrete chemicals called estrogen and progesterone, also called female hormones. Estrogens and progesterone are secreted directly into the blood.

Fallopian tubes: the Fallopian tubes start at the ovaries and end in the uterus. They are muscular canals containing ciliated cells and secretory cells. The ciliated cells help transport the ovum down the tube; the secretory cells secrete nutrients. Fertilization by a sperm cell usually takes place shortly after the egg enters the Fallopian tube. After passing through the Fallopian tube, the egg enters the uterus.

Uterus: the uterus is a hollow, muscular organ. Its inner lining, called the endometrium, grows and sloughs off this growth on a monthly, cyclical basis (menstruation). The secretory cells of the endometrium secrete and store nutrients that serve the ovum should it become fertilized. Once fertilized, the egg will implant itself in the endometrium, causing a placenta to form within the uterus (pregnancy). In pregnancy, the uterus, placenta, and fetus grow larger together. At the end of pregnancy, the strong muscles of the uterus help expel the baby during a process called parturition, or birth.

Vagina and clitoris: the clitoris, the urethral orifice, and the vaginal orifice are all externally visible parts of the vulva, the female genital apparatus. The clitoris and the tissue forming the entrance into the vagina contain erectile tissue similar to that in the penis. This tissue, as well as mucus-secreting glands just inside the vaginal orifice, respond to parasympathetic impulses evoked by sexual stimulation. The erectile tissue fills with blood and swells, while the glands secrete the mucus responsible for most of the lubrication occurring during sexual intercourse.

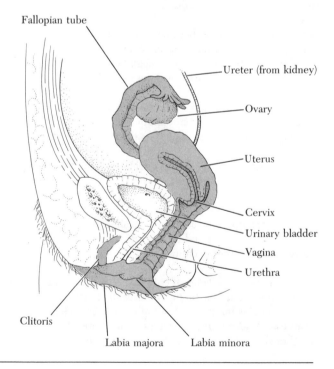

Fallopian tube

Ureter (from kidney)

Ovary

Uterus

Cervix

Urinary bladder

Vagina

Urethra

Clitoris

Labia majora   Labia minora

the role of the ovaries, pituitary gland, and brain in determining ovarian and menstrual cycles.

The External Genitalia

The differentiation of the **external genitalia** occurs at about the same time as does the differentiation of the internal genitalia, although its differentiation continues for a longer period of time. (Differentiation of the external genitalia starts between the ninth and twelfth weeks of life, and continues for a month or two.) In males, the external genitalia are the **penis** and the **scrotum**. In females, they are the **vagina**, **clitoris**, and the **labia** (folds which make up or are enclosed within the urogenital cleft).

The differentiation of the external genitalia does not involve selective growth of one or another system, as occurs with the internal genitalia. Rather, *the same tissue develops either into male external genitalia or into female external genitalia*. In males, differentiation into a penis and scrotum requires hormonal secretions from the embryonic testes. In females, differentiation of the external genitalia takes place in the *absence* of male hormones, a process similar to that noted earlier when we were discussing the differentiation of the internal genitalia.

The external genitalia are illustrated in Figures 10-1 and 10-2. Through scrotal reflexes that cause the muscles of the scrotum to contract or relax, the testes are pulled close to the body on cold days or they descend far from the body on warm days. In so doing, the scrotum maintains the temperature of the testes a few degrees lower than that of the body. This slightly lower temperature is necessary for complete growth and maturation of sperm. The penis contains erectile tissue which fills with blood when a male is sexually aroused, causing the penis to become hard and elongated so that spermatic fluid can be discharged. Urine is also discharged through the penis.

The clitoris and the tissue forming the entrance into the vagina (the introitus) contain erectile tissue which fills with blood when a female is sexually aroused. When erect during intercourse, the introitus tightens around the penis, increasing the sexual stimulation of the female and the male and thereby increasing the likelihood that orgasm will occur. In the female, the uterus and the fallopian tubes increase their motility during orgasm, which might help transport the sperm toward the ovum. In the male, orgasm is accompanied by ejaculation of the semen.

The differentiation of the gonads, internal genitalia, and external genitalia into male or female forms is summarized in Figure 10-3, which also indicates approximately when these events occur in fetal life. This figure also notes the involvement of hormones secreted by the embryonic testes, a topic discussed below.

The Role of Hormones in Early Sexual Development

We have seen the marked difference in how females and males develop. In the absence of hormonal influence, the bipotential genitalia of the fetus differentiate into female genitalia and under the influence of hormones secreted by the embryonic testes, they differentiate into male genitalia.

The hormones secreted by the embryonic testes are **testosterone** and a chemical called **mullerian-inhibiting substance**. The mullerian-inhibiting substance inhibits the development of the mullerian duct system, which otherwise would develop into the fallopian tubes and uterus. Testosterone causes the wolffian duct system to develop and it also causes the external genitalia to differentiate into the male form. Testosterone is the main male hormone. It is also subsumed by the term *androgen*, which includes other chemicals that act like testosterone. In the following pages we will see that testosterone has many effects in the male. Not only does it promote differentiation of the fetal organs into those of a male, but it is also responsible for most of the changes that occur in the male during puberty.

The main female hormones, called **estrogens** and **progesterone**, are not necessary for the fetal development of the female but are very much involved in most of the changes that occur during puberty, as will be discussed later.

Other Examples of Bipotentiality

Abnormal Sexual Development in Humans. The bipotentiality of the fetal reproductive organs prior to differentiation is dramatically illustrated by certain types of abnormal sexual development. One such pathological condition is called the **adrenogenital syndrome**. This abnormality, which involves abnormal functioning of the adrenal glands, develops when the fetus is approximately 12 weeks old. Normally at this time, the embryonic adrenal cortex is secreting cortisol (see pages 130–131, Chapter 7); in some cases, however, it secretes an androgenic substance called "androstenedione" instead. (Androstenedione acts very much like testosterone except that it is not as powerful a male hormone.)

STAGE OF FETAL
DEVELOPMENT:

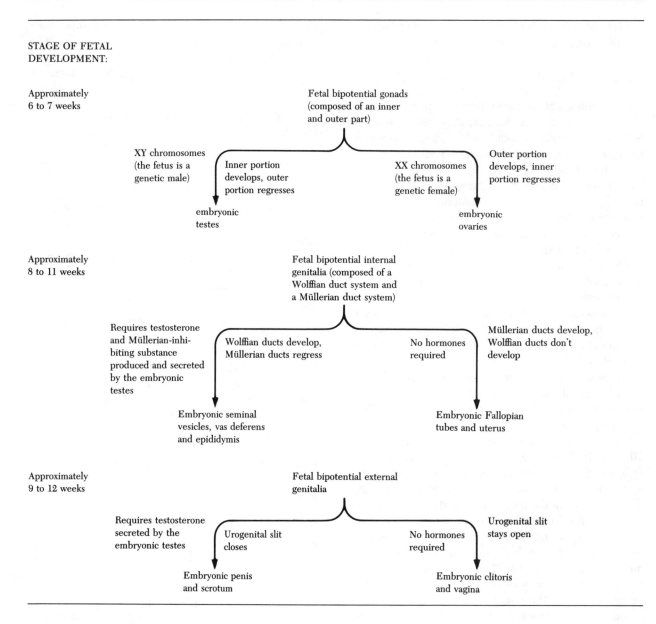

Figure 10–3. Differentiation of the fetal gonads, fetal internal genitalia, and fetal external genitalia into male or female forms. Note that in each case differentiation involves organs which, at first, are **bipotential** in their function.

In genetic females who have the adrenogenital syndrome, the female fetus is presented with excessive amounts of androstenedione at a time when the internal genitalia have already differentiated into the female form but the external genitalia are still differentiating. The result is that when the genetic female is born, her external genitalia will sometimes be indistinguishable from those of a male. That is, her clitoris looks like a penis, she has what looks like a scrotum, and the urogenital slit is closed so that the vagina is not apparent. Because there is considerable variability in the degree of masculinization present in the external genitalia of the newborn, some will be designated as males, some as females. More will be said about this syndrome later in the chapter (see page 237).

Another pathologic condition is called the **androgen-insensitivity syndrome**. This condition involves a genetically linked biochemical defect that prevents the male fetus from responding to testosterone, even though the hormone is secreted by his testes. The result is that male internal and external genitalia fail to develop. Female *internal* genitalia also fail to develop in this genetically male fetus because the embryonic testes continue to secrete mullerian-inhibiting substance. However, the *external* genitalia of many male infants afflicted with this syndrome are indistinguishable from those of a normal female. Born with a vagina and clitoris, the infant is often identified and raised as a female, the abnormality not discovered until "she" fails to menstruate at puberty. This syndrome will be further discussed later on in the chapter (see page 237).

This bipotentiality—that is, the possibility that reproductive functions can develop in either a male direction or in a female direction depending upon what happens to them—is also seen in studies of reproductive processes in animals.

Abnormal Sexual Development in Experimental Animals. In the male, *noncyclicity* is related to the fact that sperm undergo constant maturational processes after puberty, and these processes require continuous hormonal secretion. If a male rat is castrated within a few days after birth, it will not develop the noncyclic pattern at puberty, but develop the characteristic female capacity for *cyclic* reproductive functioning. This effect is clearly related to a lack of testosterone, since castration (removal of the .testes) removes the main source of this male hormone. When androgen levels are restored in these castrated males by injecting them with testosterone early in the neonatal period, they do not display cyclic reproductive functioning at puberty. Because male reproductive function does not depend on cyclic fluctuations in the levels of hormones as occurs in females (see the next section of the chapter), the *capacity* for cyclicity in the male can only be demonstrated under special experimental conditions (see, for example, Harris, 1964; Neill, 1972).

In the female, cyclicity is related to the periodic maturation and release of eggs by the adult ovary. If a newly-born female rat is given testosterone, she does not develop a cyclic reproductive pattern at puberty, but rather a constant (noncyclic) pattern as occurs in males. This same effect has been shown in mice and guinea pigs.

These studies serve to indicate that, at least in some species, the development of cyclicity (female) or noncyclicity (male) is also bipotential at first; that is, it could go either way depending upon whether male hormone is present or not. Although these results have been confirmed many times in rodents, they are not as obvious or as well undertood in humans and other primates.

Another example of bipotentiality involves *sexual behavior*. Again, in rats and other species (guinea pigs, hamsters, mice, and rabbits) it has been shown that the male brain seems to be "organized" by testosterone within a few days after birth to produce male sexual behavior. (As with the development of noncyclicity, these effects are observable only after the animal undergoes puberty.) If testosterone is not present during the neonatal period, the male will show more female sexual behavior after puberty— i.e., he will act toward males as does a female rat when she is in heat—than will a normal male. Similarly, if a female is given testosterone shortly after birth, she will show more male behavior—i.e., she will act toward females in heat as does a male—than will a normal female. Again, although these results are quite clear in the species mentioned, we still lack evidence that these same mechanisms operate in humans. Nevertheless, they provide at least some basis for assuming that homosexuality might have a physiological cause.

II. PUBERTY AND ADULT REPRODUCTIVE FUNCTION

With the exception of a gradual growth in size that parallels the overall growth of a child, the reproductive organs (which, as just explained, differentiate into female and male forms early in life), usually remain functionally dormant for a long period after birth. Then, typically between 9 to 12 years of age, a process called **puberty** occurs. Puberty usually begins and ends earlier in females than in males. In females, puberty generally occurs around 12 years of age, but individual variation is great and puberty starting at ages 16 or 17 is still normal. In males, puberty usually occurs at about 14 years of age, and, again, reaching puberty at age 20 is still normal.

In general, puberty involves four processes: a) accelerated growth of the reproductive organs, b) the development of secondary (non-reproductive) sexual characteristics such as body hair and a larger skeleton, c) the onset of activities that cause maturation of the egg in females and sperm in males, and d) the onset of sex drive and sexual behavior. The first three of these processes are discussed below. Sexual behavior is discussed in Sections IV, V, and VII.

*Androgens: from **andros**, which means man in Greek*

Testosterone: secreted by the testes of the male	*Contributes to:* Production of sperm Enlargement of the penis, scrotum, and testes Growth of the seminal vesicles, prostate, and other reproductive organs Growth of facial hair, axillary hair (armpits), pubic hair, and hair on other parts of the body (most notably, the chest) Growth and development of sebaceous glands (sometimes causing acne) and sweat glands in the skin Enlargement of the larynx, causing the voice to deepen Increased protein content in the body, related to increased musculature and large bones characteristic of men
Androstenedione: secreted by the adrenal glands of males and females (much weaker than testosterone)	*Contributes to:* The development of pubic and axillary hair in females Growth and development of sebaceous glands (sometimes causing acne) and axillary sweat glands in women

*Estrogens: from **estrus**, which means female sexual receptivity in Greek*

Estradiol: secreted by the ovaries of the female	*Contributes to:* Ovulation (release of the egg by the ovary) Enlargement of the vagina, uterus, and fallopian tubes Growth of the breasts Deposition of fat in the buttocks, thighs, breasts, and subcutaneous tissues Increased protein content of specialized tissues (uterus, breasts, bone) Increased bone growth; inhibition of bone growth (estrogens and androgens accelerate bone growth at first, but later—toward the end of puberty—they inhibit bone growth. Estrogens inhibit bone growth more powerfully than do androgens, explaining why growth ceases a few years earlier in females than in males. Estrogens also have the special effect of broadening the pelvis.)

*Gestagens: from **gestation**, which means pregnancy in Latin*

Progesterone: secreted mainly by the ovaries	*Contributes to:* The development of reproductive tissue (the lining of the fallopian tubes, the endometrium of the uterus, and the lobules and alveoli of the breasts) that is mainly secretory in nature

Table 10–1. The effects of sex hormones on the body. At puberty there is a marked increase in the secretion of estrogen and progesterone by the ovaries (females) and testosterone by the testes (males). In both sexes the adrenal glands enlarge and secrete more adrenal androgens. Note that the effects listed above encompass most of the changes that occur during puberty.

The Sex Organs and Sexual Characteristics

The main changes that occur in the sexual organs at puberty is that they become much larger and their secretory functions mature in order to make us fertile. The earlier bipotentiality of these organs has now been irreversibly lost. The development of secondary sexual characteristics that occurs at puberty are largely due to a markedly increased secretion of sex hormones by the ovaries and testes. These effects are summarized in Table 10-1, which indicates that estrogens and progesterone in the female and testosterone in the male are responsible for the development of many of the sexual characteristics of an adult. It is obvious that in most cases males and females will develop appropriate characteristics for their sex simply because a male has testes that secrete testosterone and a female has ovaries that secrete estrogens and progesterone.

Although the sex of our reproductive organs is fixed at an early age, this is not the case with the development of secondary sexual characteristics and the development of the breasts—*these remain bipotential.* Depending on which hormones are present at puberty, a female or male will develop either female or male characteristics. That is, a female with an adrenal tumor that secretes excessive amounts of adrenal androgen can develop severe hirsutism (excessive facial and body hair), recession of the hair line, shrinkage of the breasts, rather prominent musculature, and a deepening of the voice. Similarly, a male suffering from androgen-insensitivity syndrome (see page 217) will respond to the small amounts of estrogen that are normally secreted by his testes at puberty by developing large breasts and broad hips, and by *not* developing body hair or a deep voice. Also, if a male is injected with estrogen or a female is given large doses of androgen, their bodies will begin to conform to the "sex" of the hormone within a few weeks.

In most cases the above effects are reversible if the abnormal hormone secretions are stopped. For example, when the source of excessive androgen is removed in an otherwise normal female, menstrual function and fertility promptly reappear, the breasts begin to grow and become normal, the excessive musculature shrinks, the female distribution of body fat is reestablished, and an enlarged clitoris will slowly decrease in size. Some effects are not as reversible. The deep pitch of the voice may not be replaced by the normally higher pitch of females, and the excessive body hair, although it tends to decrease over a period of months and sometimes years, often never completely disappears. The restoration of these characteristics depends on the duration and severity of the excessive androgen condition. The point is, that in addition to the bipotentiality of our sexual organs, which differentiate into male or female forms while we are still fetuses, the changes that are expressed at a later age—i.e., at puberty—also involve tissues which are, for the most part, bipotential.

The Menstrual Cycle

Aside from the changes listed above, another dramatic change which occurs during puberty in females is the beginning of **menstruation.** Menstruation is a periodic discharge of the endometrial growth from the uterus through the vagina. As an average, this process takes place for a four-day period that occurs at approximately 28-day intervals. Again, there is considerable individual variability in these processes. Menstruation occurs for three days in some women and for as long as seven or more days in others. Similarly, the entire cycle can repeat itself in as short a period as 20 days or as long as 45 days. These variations are all completely normal. In most females, menstruation continues on a more or less regular basis from its onset (*menarche*) until she reaches an age of approximately 50 years. Around this time, the menstrual cycle becomes irregular and after a while (ranging from months to a few years) it ceases. The cessation of menstrual cycles is called *menopause.*

The menstrual cycle is related to events that have to do with the development of mature, fertile eggs by the ovaries. Before puberty, the ovaries do not produce fully mature eggs. Instead, they are composed of many round bodies, called **primordial follicles**, which contain the ova. During puberty the entire ovary, but especially the follicles, begin to grow. As they grow, the follicles secrete increasing amounts of estrogen into the blood. At a certain point in pubertal development, one follicle outgrows the others and eventually ruptures, releasing the ovum (egg) which is inside it. As mentioned earlier, the rupture of the follicle and the release of the ovum is called **ovulation**, a process that repeats itself approximately every 28 days until menopause. (Ovulation does not usually occur during the first few menstrual cycles; that is, cyclic variations in hormonal secretion are taking place, but no eggs are being released.) After ovulation occurs, the ovum enters the fallopian tube on its way to the uterus.

Within the ovary, the ruptured follicle undergoes a rapid physical and chemical transformation during the first few hours after the egg has been expelled from it. The cells of the follicle multiply and become greatly enlarged, forming a spherical mass in the ovary called the **corpus luteum**. The corpus luteum grows for about seven to eight days after ovulation, then, if the expelled egg is not fertilized, the corpus luteum starts to become smaller and, by about 12 days after ovulation, stops secreting estrogen and progesterone into the blood.

At the beginning of each cycle, the increased secretions of estrogen—produced by the maturing follicles—cause the inner lining of the uterus (the endometrium) to grow rapidly. Then, after the corpus luteum has formed from the single follicle that has expelled its egg, the increased secretion of progesterone and continued high secretion of estrogen cause the endometrium to further increase in size. The uterus now becomes a large, secretory organ capable of nurturing and housing a fertilized egg, should conception occur. As noted in the previous paragraph, if conception does not occur, the corpus luteum degenerates and ceases functioning after about 12 days (at approximately the 26th day of a 28-day cycle). Its degeneration, which causes a sudden reduction in the secretion of progesterone and estrogen, causes the endometrium to involute (shrink in size), in turn causing degeneration of its blood vessels and bleeding as these tissues are cast off and expelled with the aid of uterine contractions ("cramps" during menstruation). This marks the end of one cycle. Meanwhile, another follicle has begun to mature and will eventually rupture, causing ovulation and the formation of a new corpus luteum.

The events described above are repeated over and over in a cyclic fashion. (In pregnancy, the corpus luteum does not cease to function; it continues to secrete estrogen and progesterone which, in turn, act on the uterus to prepare and maintain it for its role of nurturing the newly conceived human being.) The maturation of the follicle is illustrated in Figure 10-4a, and the fluctuations in circulating levels of estrogen and progesterone are shown in Figure 10-4b. Before describing the events illustrated in Figure 10-4c, let's first discuss the pituitary gland and its role in female reproductive processes.

The Pituitary Gland and Its Role in Female Reproduction

The growth of follicles, ovulation, the development of the corpus luteum, and the secretion of estrogen and progesterone are all controlled by hormones secreted by the **pituitary gland**. The pituitary gland, which sits just below the hypothalamus, consists of two parts: the **anterior pituitary gland** and the **posterior pituitary gland** (see Figure 10-5). (The posterior portion is made up of neural tissue that originates embryologically as an outgrowth of the hypothalamus, and the anterior portion originates embryologically from the roof of the mouth and is not neural tissue.) The pituitary gland secretes at least eleven different chemicals into the blood. These are all hormones because, as mentioned earlier, a) they are secreted by glands into the blood and b) they have a specific physiologic action on one or another organ of the body. (Cortisol and other chemicals secreted by the adrenal glands, estrogen and progesterone secreted by the ovaries, and testosterone secreted by the testes are also hormones, as are epinephrine and norepinephrine secreted by the adrenal medulla, insulin secreted by the pancreas, and many others.)

Each of the pituitary hormones has a different function. Some of the main pituitary hormones are listed in Table 10-2. As Table 10-2 indicates, some of the pituitary hormones exert their action by controlling the function of other glands. For this reason, the pituitary gland is also called the "master gland" of the body. (In fact, if the pituitary gland is removed, the ovaries, the testes, the adrenal glands, the thyroid glands, and the mammary glands all cease functioning.) At the present time we are concerned with only two of these pituitary hormones: **follicle-stimulating hormone** (FSH) and **luteinizing hormone** (LH). Both of these hormones are secreted by the *anterior* pituitary gland into the blood, both are secreted in females and males (as are all the other pituitary hormones), and both act on the gonads (ovaries in females and testes in males).

In females, the main effect of FSH is to cause the follicles of the ovary to grow and mature. As discussed above, this growth increases the levels of estrogen in the blood, because follicles secrete more estrogen as they mature. (They also secrete progesterone, but to a much lesser extent.) The main effects of LH in females are to stimulate the final growth of the follicle, aid in its rupture and ejection of the egg (ovulation), and cause development and growth of the corpus luteum. Because of these actions, LH promotes the secretion of large amounts of both progesterone and estrogen. Starting about two days before ovulation, the rate of secretion of LH by the anterior pituitary gland increases tremendously, reaching a peak at approximately ten times higher than normal. This "LH burst," along with a smaller burst of FSH, is responsible for ovulation. If this sudden increase of secretion does not occur, ovulation does not occur and a corpus luteum does not form. This burst of LH secretion by the pituitary gland only develops at puberty, along with a general rise of plasma levels of LH and FSH, as illustrated in Figure 10-4c.

In summary, a secretion of hormones by the anterior pituitary gland is necessary for the ovarian cycle. Without FSH and LH there would be no follicular growth, no ovulation, no transformation of the follicle into a corpus luteum, no increases of estrogen and progesterone, no growth of the lining of the uterus, and no menstruation.

The Pituitary Gland and Male Reproduction

The secretion of hormones by the anterior pituitary gland is also necessary for testicular function in males. FSH is needed in order for sperm to mature in the testes. LH causes special cells within the testes to grow and secrete testosterone. (Aside from its other

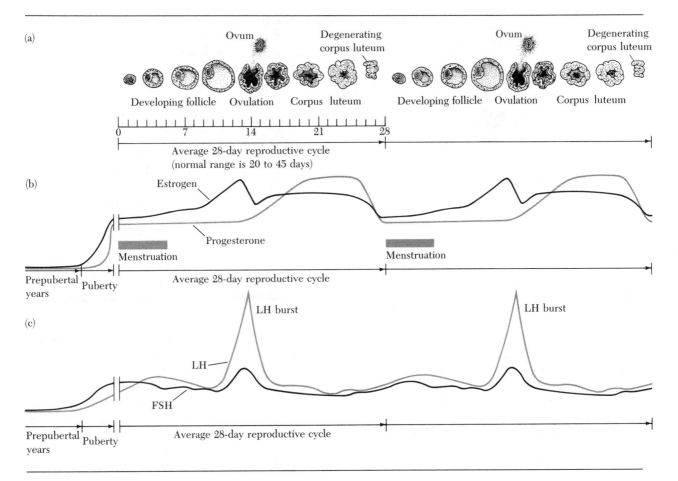

Figure 10–4(a). The ovarian cycle. During each reproductive cycle, which normally ranges from as short as 20 to as long as 45 days in length, about 20 follicles begin to grow. One follicle outgrows the others and the remaining follicles shrink and become nonfunctional. Ovulation is an event marked by rupture of the growing follicle, which releases a mature ovum (egg) into the peritoneal cavity. From there the ovum enters the fallopian tube. This process is repeated with each reproductive cycle.

Figure 10–4(b). Blood levels of estrogen and progesterone during the ovarian cycle. As the follicle grows, it secretes increasing amounts of estrogen and, to a lesser extent, more progesterone. Once formed from the follicle that has expelled its egg, the corpus luteum secretes large amounts of estrogen and large amounts of progesterone. Estrogen and progesterone levels fall quickly as the corpus luteum degenerates. This process is repeated with each reproductive cycle. Also shown is the dramatic rise (to adult levels) in estrogen and

progesterone that occurs during puberty. This increase occurs as a result of the growth of the entire ovary, but especially of the follicles.

Figure 10–4(c). Blood levels of FSH and LH during the ovarian cycle. The growth of follicles, ovulation, the development of the corpus luteum, and the secretion of estrogen and progesterone are all controlled by follicle-stimulating hormone (FSH) and luteinizing hormone (LH) released by the anterior pituitary gland. Starting about two days before ovulation, the rate of secretion of LH by the anterior pituitary gland increases tremendously. This "LH burst," along with a smaller burst of FSH, is responsible for ovulation. As also shown, during puberty FSH and LH rise to adult levels.

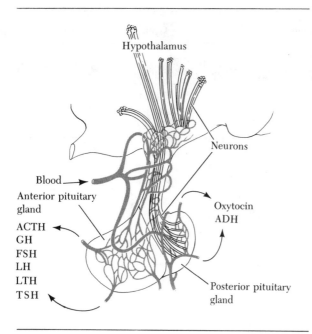

Figure 10–5. The pituitary gland. The *posterior* pituitary gland contains the endings of neurons that originate within the hypothalamus. The *anterior* pituitary gland is regulated by chemicals secreted in the hypothalamus and then carried to the anterior pituitary gland via tiny blood vessels. (The abbreviations are explained in Table 10-2.)

actions, testosterone is also required for full maturation of sperm.) Although, as in females, LH and FSH secretion increases at puberty, in males there is no event that corresponds to the onset of menstrual or ovarian cycles, nor is there any comparable LH "burst." As already discussed, cyclicity is not a functional requirement of the male reproductive system.

Before puberty, the testes contain only primitive germ cells, called **spermatogonia**. As puberty begins, these cells mature into **primary spermatogonia**, which then go through many stages of maturation to become **spermatozoa** (sperm). The maturation of sperm, called **spermatogenesis**, continues throughout a man's life as spermatogonia continually multiply and mature into spermatozoa. Following puberty, the secretion of FSH, LH, and testosterone continues steadily. In older men, there is often a reduction of reproductive functioning because of a slow reduction in the levels of circulating testosterone. Testosterone levels, highest at ages 25 to 30, decrease to about

one-half this value by the age of 60. There is no clear-cut cessation of reproductive functioning in males as occurs with females at menopause. These processes are summarized in Figures 10-6a through 10-6c.

Mechanisms That Control the Onset of Puberty

We are still a long way from understanding the mechanisms that control the onset of puberty. Two basic processes are involved: a) the rise in the secretions of FSH and LH by the anterior pituitary gland which occurs in both sexes, and b) the onset of periodic secretions by the anterior pituitary gland in females, especially the LH burst that occurs shortly before ovulation during each cycle. For a variety of reasons, which are listed below, it appears that *the onset of puberty is controlled by the brain.*

1) In itself, the pituitary gland is not fixed as either immature (prepubertal) or mature (pubertal). When the pituitary gland of an immature animal is transplanted into an adult animal, it secretes FSH and LH like an adult pituitary gland. Similarly, when an adult pituitary gland is transplanted into an immature animal, it secretes like an immature pituitary gland. Thus, whether the pituitary gland secretes in an adult or immature fashion is something outside its own control. The age of the bearer of the pituitary gland is the decisive factor rather than the age of the pituitary gland itself.

2) The pituitary gland is not fixed as cyclic or noncyclic (steady) in its secretion. When the pituitary gland of a male animal is transplanted into an adult female, it begins to secrete in a cyclic fashion. Similarly, when the pituitary gland of an adult female is transplanted into an adult male or into an immature female or male, it ceases secreting in a cyclic fashion and becomes noncyclic. Thus, the female (cyclic) or male (noncyclic) pattern of secretion is not fixed by the pituitary gland itself, but by the bearer of the gland. This, of course, means that *the pituitary gland is sexually bipotential.*

3) A variety of disorders involving the hypothalamus (such as tumors, developmental malfunctions, inflammations, and abnormalities such as hydrocephalus or meningitis), are sometimes associated with precocious sexual development. Puberty can begin in a child only one-year old, with onset of menstruation or evidence of mature testicular de-

Hormone (abbreviation)	Principal action
Follicle-stimulating hormone (FSH)	Stimulates the maturation of follicles in the ovaries and sperm in the testes. FSH also causes the follicles to secrete estrogen.
Luteinizing hormone (LH)	Causes ovulation and formation of the corpus luteum (which, before this, was the ruptured follicle) in the ovary and causes growth of the cells that secrete testosterone in the testes. The corpus luteum secretes large amounts of progesterone and estrogen.
Prolactin (LTH)	Stimulates milk production and secretion in the breasts of a woman who has given birth. Suckling of the breasts stimulates prolactin secretion.
Oxytocin	Stimulates contraction of smooth muscle, especially the uterus, during the birth process and the milk glands during suckling (causing milk ejection or "let-down").
Antidiuretic hormone (ADH)	Causes the kidneys to retain water when one is dehydrated or suffering from a decreased blood volume.
Adrenocorticotrophic hormone (ACTH)	Stimulates the adrenal cortex to secrete its hormones, including glucocorticoids and mineralocorticoids.
Thyroid-stimulating hormone (TSH)	Stimulates the thyroid gland to secrete thyroxine and triiodothyronine.
Growth hormone (GH)	Stimulates the growth of tissues and mobilizes fats for the production of energy.

Table 10–2. Major hormones secreted by the anterior or posterior pituitary gland. Oxytocin and antidiuretic hormone (ADH) are produced in the hypothalamus and then are transported within neurons to endings in the *posterior pituitary gland*. The other hormones listed above are not produced in the hypothalamus, but by secretory cells that make up the *anterior pituitary gland*.

velopment before the child is two years of age. In most of these cases, there is no visible disorder of the pituitary gland, but almost always there is a defect in the hypothalamus.

4) Selective destruction (by electrical lesions) within the hypothalamus of animals sometimes leads to precocious puberty, sometimes to delayed puberty. Also, electrical stimulation of the hypothalamus sometimes causes the pituitary gland to release LH, causing ovulation in some female animals otherwise unable to ovulate. In fact, a number of areas of the brain influence reproductive functions, as is discussed in the next section of the chapter.

5) The secretion of LH and FSH by the pituitary gland is modified by the amount of sex hormones being secreted by the ovaries or testes. In males, the *greater* the amount of testosterone secreted by the testes, the *less* the amount of LH secreted by the pituitary gland. In females, the same relation exists between estrogen and progesterone and FSH and LH—the *greater* the amount of estrogen and progesterone secreted by the ovaries, the *less* the amount of FSH and LH secreted by the pituitary gland. Thus, if androgen or estrogen is given to animals or humans for a prolonged period, LH secretion is reduced causing, in turn, a reduction or cessation of ovarian and testicular functions. Similarly, a decrease in the levels of androgens or estrogens causes an increased secretion of LH bringing about, in turn, increased activity of the ovaries or testes. This **negative feedback** mechanism is an obvious control mechanism that serves to maintain

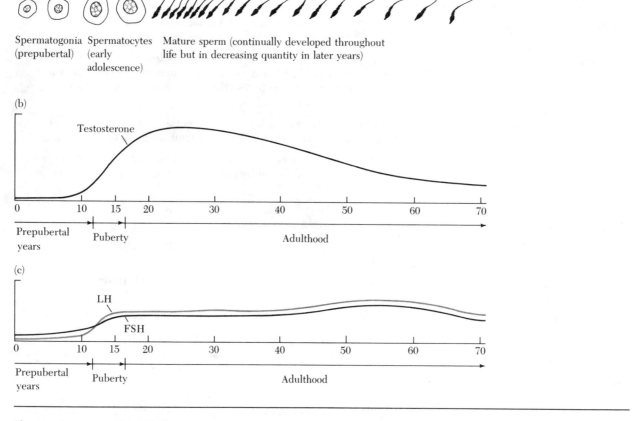

(a)

Spermatogonia   Spermatocytes   Mature sperm (continually developed throughout
(prepubertal)   (early   life but in decreasing quantity in later years)
                  adolescence)

(b)

Testosterone

0   10   15   20   30   40   50   60   70

Prepubertal
years   Puberty   Adulthood

(c)

LH

FSH

0   10   15   20   30   40   50   60   70

Prepubertal
years   Puberty   Adulthood

Figure 10–6(a). Spermatogenesis. Before puberty, the testes contain only primitive germ cells, called "spermatogonia." At puberty, these cells begin to mature in many stages, finally becoming mature spermatozoa (sperm). The maturation of sperm is a process that usually occurs continuously throughout a man's life, although fewer sperm are produced by older men. It takes about seven weeks for a fully mature sperm to develop.

Figure 10–6(b). Blood levels of testosterone. As a male reaches puberty, testosterone levels rise dramatically. Special cells within the testes, called "Leydig cells" (these are not sperm), grow and secrete testosterone. Testosterone levels remain high throughout adulthood, although they slowly decrease after age 30.

Figure 10–6(c). Blood levels of FSH and LH. The growth of sperm and the production of testosterone are controlled by follicle-stimulating hormone (FSH) and luteinizing hormone (LH) released by the anterior pituitary gland. During and after puberty, FSH and LH rise to adult levels. There is no LH burst as in females, nor is there any appreciable cyclicity.

the level of sex hormones in the blood. For example, if testosterone levels fall, LH secretion rises, in turn stimulating the testes to produce more of this androgen. Likewise, if testosterone levels are too high, LH levels fall, reducing the amount of testosterone produced by the testes.

From experiments done mainly on rodents (especially rats and mice), it is quite clear that the negative feedback mechanism mentioned above involves the brain. Nerve cells in the arcuate-median eminence region of the hypothalamus (see Figure 10-7) of both females and males respond to the level of sex hormones and either increase (if there is too little sex hormone) or decrease (if there is too much) LH and FSH production by the pituitary gland. Although this mechanism operates in both prepubertal and adult animals, there is a difference: *Before puberty the sex hormones are much more potent in inhibiting FSH and LH secretion than after puberty.* In other words, it appears that at puberty the brain becomes less sensitive to this inhibiting effect of the sex hormones, thereby allowing more FSH and LH to be secreted which, in turn, allows the levels of circulating sex hormones to increase.

6) In addition to the above negative feedback mechanism, in females there is also a **positive feedback** mechanism that involves estrogen and LH. In certain circumstances estrogen actually *increases* LH release rather than decreases it. This positive feedback mechanism is believed to be involved in triggering the LH burst before ovulation, and it appears to first begin at puberty. With positive feedback, increased estrogen causes increased secretion of LH by the anterior pituitary gland which, in turn, further increases the secretion of estrogen by the ovaries, leading to more LH, and so forth. This mechanism must be carefully regulated, because positive feedback will quickly lead to very high levels of circulating LH and estrogen. We do not know precisely how positive feedback is regulated, but the levels of circulating estrogen and progesterone, and the timing of the release of estrogen in the reproductive cycle are known to be important factors.

Again, experiments in rats and mice have demonstrated quite clearly that the positive feedback mechanism also involves the hypothalamus within the brain. In this case, however, the area is different from the one involved in negative feedback. It involves, instead, an interaction of estrogen and progesterone with neurons in the preoptic-anterior hypothalamic area, and this interaction results in increased LH output from the pituitary gland (see Figure 10-7).

In summary, the following picture emerges: at puberty, neurons in the preoptic-anterior hypothalamic area "mature" in females and become responsible for the cyclic release of LH. A positive feedback mechanism involving estrogen (secreted alone or in combination with progesterone) begins to function, and it does not develop in males. In *both* females and males, however, neurons in the arcuate-median eminence area "mature" and cause the negative feedback inhibition of LH and FSH by sex hormones to be less potent. This reduced potency of inhibition causes an increase in the levels of sex hormones. The positive feedback mechanism is only active shortly before ovulation, in contrast to the negative feedback mechanism which is constantly active in both sexes.

In the first section of this chapter, we briefly mentioned that the development of cyclic (female) or noncyclic (male) reproductive patterns is a process which is bipotential in the neonatal period of rodents. That is, depending upon whether or not testosterone is available during the first few days after birth, an animal will develop the capacity for noncyclic or cyclic reproductive functioning after puberty regardless of its sex (see page 217). From what has just been presented, it is obvious that, in this case, *the bipotential structure must be within the brain.* In other words, if androgen is not present at an early age (in some species, while the animal is still a fetus, in others, just after birth), the preoptic-anterior hypothalamic area can interact with estrogen much later (after puberty) to increase LH release. This differentiation is part of a mechanism responsible for cyclicity in females, but it also happens in males if testosterone is not present. Conversely, if androgen is present at this early age, the preoptic-anterior hypothalamic region is altered in its workings so that the animal (male or female) remains noncyclic after puberty.

As was noted previously, the above processes are quite clear in rodents, but there is considerable uncertainty as to whether the same mechanisms operate in humans and other primates. For example, there is no solid evidence that early exposure to androgen in human females abolishes the capacity for cyclic reproductive functioning after puberty. Furthermore, the pituitary gland of adult male monkeys will respond to estrogen by increasing LH levels, a positive feedback effect that is observed after these monkeys are castrated (Karsch, Dierschke, and Knobil, 1973). Much more research must be performed in primates before we fully understand these processes.

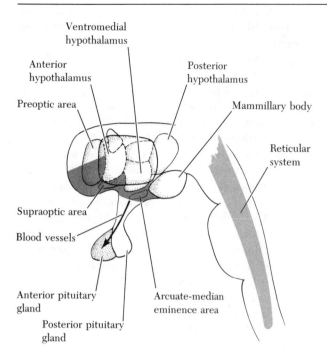

Preoptic-anterior hypothalamic-supraoptic area: this area contains LHRH (a neuropeptide). *Lesions* (especially in the preoptic area) abolish sexual behavior in male rats and guinea pigs and (especially in the anterior hypothalamic area) in female cats, rats, and guinea pigs. *Lesions* have also been reported to increase sexual behavior in female rats. *Lesions* abolish the preovulatory LH burst, causing a cessation of ovulation. There is also a reduction of LHRH in the median eminence region of the hypothalamus. Electrical *stimulation* causes LH release by the anterior pituitary gland and ovulation. Estrogen lowers the threshold for this positive-feedback response. Electrical *stimulation* has been observed to increase sexual behavior in male rats, guinea pigs, and monkeys and in female rats and guinea pigs. It also decreases sexual behavior in female rats and hamsters. *Implantation* of estrogen or testosterone increases sexual behavior in rodents.

Arcuate-median eminence area: this area contains LHRH (and also FSH-RF if it is a separate neuropeptide). *Lesions* cause atrophy (shrinkage) of the ovaries and testes due to their destruction of neurons that produce releasing factors. *Lesions* do not appear to affect sexual behavior except indirectly because of gonadal atrophy, which abolishes estrogen, progesterone, and testosterone secretions. (Sexual behavior is restored when these chemicals are injected into the lesioned animals.) *Implantation* of estrogen or testosterone causes atrophy of the ovaries or testes due to a negative-feedback suppression of LH release by the pituitary gland due, in turn, to decreased LHRH levels. Electrical *stimulation* can cause ovulation (especially if progesterone is present), and, in some cases, stimulation can cause sexual behavior.

Ventromedial hypothalamic area: in this area *lesions* disrupt or abolish sexual behavior in female hamsters, rats and guinea pigs. *Lesions* also abolish hypersexual behavior in male cats with temporal lobe lesions. *Implantation* of estrogen increases sexual behavior in female rats.

Mammillary-posterior hypothalamic region: here *lesions* have been observed to abolish sexual behavior in female rabbits and male rats. *Implantation* of estrogen causes ovarian atrophy via a negative-feedback effect on pituitary FSH and LH in female rats. Electrical *stimulation* has been observed to increase sexual behavior in male rats. In humans, tumors and other abnormalities in this area sometimes cause precocious puberty.

Upper spinal cord (extending from the hypothalamus into the reticular system of the upper spinal cord): in this area *lesions* have been reported to increase, decrease, and have no effect on sexual behavior in male rats. The increase is attributed to the removal of an inhibitory mechanism that influences spinal reflexes. Electrical *stimulation* has been reported to inhibit sexual behavior in male rats and has been reported to both induce and inhibit ovulation in female rats.

Figure 10–7. The role of the hypothalamus in sexual behavior and reproductive function. The shaded area indicates where the greatest amounts of LH-releasing hormone (LHRH) are produced. LHRH diffuses to the anterior pituitary gland through tiny blood vessels (heavy arrow). Note that sexual behavior and physiological responses are regulated by many areas of the hypothalamus.

III. WHAT CONSTITUTES "FEMALE" OR "MALE"?

Our sexual identity is not only molded by our sociological and cultural upbringing, but it is also very much influenced by our body's activities—especially our female/male body shape and size as it conforms to stereotyped norms, but also its workings as we understand them through education. From what has been presented thus far in the chapter, it is clear that our development and differentiation into females or males is a complex process. Sexual differentiation starts with conception, but continues while we are forming in the uterus and really isn't complete until after puberty. Let's review some of the considerations that have emerged thus far on the question of what constitutes "male" and "female" processes:

1) GENETICS AND GENDER. There is no doubt that females and males have different chromosomes, and that, as a result, there is an absolute difference between the sexes. However, it is incorrect to view this difference as a property that is expressed throughout our organs. For example, there is no genetic difference between male and female breasts, no genetic difference between the skin of females and males that causes hair to develop in males but not in females, and no genetic difference between the two sexes that decree a man's muscles to be larger than a woman's. In fact, even the differences in the internal and external genitalia are not directly attributable to genetic differences between the sexes.

2) REPRODUCTIVE ORGANS AND GENDER. There is no doubt that many of the organs of males and females differ from each other, and that these differences are absolute. The internal and external genitalia of women and men are quite different in their structure and function, as are the ovaries and testes, breasts, and other organs. It is also clear that almost all of these organs *could* have developed into those of the opposite sex, as is most dramatically seen in cases of masculine development in females suffering from the adrenogenital syndrome and in cases of feminine development in males suffering from the androgen-insensitivity syndrome (see pages 215–217). Moreover, some of our organs —such as the breasts, muscles, and hair—never lose their ability to change their "sexual characteristics" if they are exposed to the appropriate hormones.

3) HORMONES AND GENDER. There is no doubt that the sex hormones secreted in females

and males differ from each other. In fact, as discussed earlier, whether androgen is present or not is a decisive factor in our earliest sexual development. We have seen in many cases that if androgen is present, then differentiation occurs along male lines and if androgen is not present, then differentiation occurs along female lines. Female hormones are not necessary for the differentiation of organs along female lines until puberty, when estrogen is needed for maturation of the female reproductive system and development of the body into the mature female form. Different interpretations can be drawn from these facts: 1) Without male hormones, nature makes a female, or 2) Male development is a process that is superimposed upon a basically female development, or 3) Female development is a passive process (no outside factors are required), whereas male development is an active process (hormones are required).

4) CRITICAL PERIODS AND GENDER. The concept of the "critical period" stems from the fact that many developmental processes are much more vulnerable at one stage than at another. This differential susceptibility has been observed both behaviorally and physiologically. We discussed this briefly in Chapter 6 (pages 106–107) when we referred to the fact that visual deprivation at an early age is much more likely to cause permanent neural damage than if it occurs at a later age.

The concept of the critical period is also applicable to reproductive processes. If male hormones (androgens) are present in the fetus during approximately the 8th to 11th weeks of life, then differentiation of the internal genitalia will occur along male lines (see Figure 10-3). *Before or after this period, androgen has little effect on this differentiation.* The same occurs with the external genitalia a little later in development, although here the critical period is not as sharply defined. In rodents it is also clear that there are critical periods for the differentiation of sexual behavior and the capacity for reproductive cyclicity; their timing varies from species to species, but these critical periods occur later in fetal life than do the critical periods for differentiation of the genitalia. In rodents, they even extend into early postnatal life (from approximately 2 to 10 days after birth).

Although the principle of critical periods with respect to the differentiation of sexual behavior and cyclicity has not yet been clearly demonstrated in humans, these findings are important because they give support to the view—strongly espoused within the field of psychology—that early life is tremendously influential in molding our sexual identity. Furthermore, in a more general psychological sense, the fact that these periods exist during early rather than later life fits well with the notion that much of our psychological make-up is established by events taking place early in life.

In short, our understanding of the body points to the conclusion that female and male characteristics are on the one hand clearly separate and on the other hand unquestionably alike. There is certainly a broad basis for assuming that clear differences exist between the sexes, given that many organs, hormones, and patterns of hormonal secretions are not the same. Yet there is an equally broad basis for assuming that male and female processes are not unique to one or another sex, but are represented in both sexes simultaneously—perhaps even equally. This topic could be discussed at great length; here, it is sufficient to note that the information presented in this chapter allows both of these statements to be correct. This conclusion is not a paradox. It is simply a statement that the sexual system is uniquely bivalent in that it can develop two ways without absolute regard to genetics.

IV. THE INVOLVEMENT OF THE BRAIN IN REPRODUCTIVE PROCESSES AND SEXUAL BEHAVIOR

Reproductive processes are organized in a very special manner. The brain, the anterior pituitary gland, the gonads, and the other organs of the body are all interconnected by hormones. FSH and LH secreted by the pituitary gland affect the ovaries or testes, and the sex hormones secreted by the ovaries or testes affect the other organs. We will now briefly discuss those chemicals secreted by the brain that affect the anterior pituitary gland.

Neuropeptides

Many chemicals are produced by neurons in the hypothalamus. Some of these chemicals are called **neuropeptides** because they are short chains of amino acids (polypeptides) produced and secreted by nerve cells. Two of these neuropeptides, called "oxytocin" and "ADH" (see Table 10-2 and Figure 10-5), are transported within neurons to nerve endings in the *posterior* pituitary gland where they are then released into the general circulation. However, most of the neuropeptides produced in the hypothalamus are not transported to the posterior pituitary gland. Instead, they are secreted directly into the *blood* within the hypothalamus, then they travel a very short dis-

tance to the *anterior* pituitary gland. (See Figures 10-5 and 10-7, which also illustrates and notes those areas of the hypothalamus most involved in reproductive processes—a topic discussed later in this section.) These neuropeptides, variously referred to as **releasing factors**, **releasing hormones**, and **hypothalamic polypeptides**, are responsible for the release of many hormones from the anterior pituitary, including FSH and LH. At this time, about a dozen of these neuropeptides have been discovered and purified, and, for some, the exact chemical structure is known.

In general, each of the releasing hormones produced in the hypothalamus either stimulates or inhibits the release and synthesis of anterior pituitary hormones. For example, the neuropeptide that controls LH production and release from the anterior pituitary gland is called "LH-releasing hormone" (abbreviated LHRH). This peptide is produced in the medial preoptic area and the arcuate area of the hypothalamus (see Figure 10-7). From there, LHRH enters a small bed of blood vessels and diffuses into the anterior pituitary gland where it stimulates LH release. LHRH also stimulates FSH release. (Although the issue is not settled, some investigators believe that FSH-releasing factor and LHRH are the same peptide.)

Table 10-3 lists some of the neuropeptides and their actions. Although the principal actions of these neuropeptides is to promote the release of anterior pituitary hormones, experimental studies suggest that they also exert other actions. LHRH may stimulate sexual behavior, and thyrotropin-releasing hormone (TRH) and growth-hormone-inhibiting factor (GIF) may act, respectively, as a central nervous stimulant or as a depressant—increasing or decreasing general motor activity. TRH may also antagonize—and GIF promote—sleep and anesthesia (see Moss, 1979). It is not known, however, whether these responses reflect the workings of mechanisms operating under normal physiological conditions; they may, instead, reflect the effects of administering unnaturally high amounts of these neuropeptides (i.e., they may be pharmacological effects).

If the areas of the hypothalamus producing LH-releasing hormone and FSH-releasing factor are destroyed, the anterior pituitary gland will no longer release FSH and LH and the ovaries or testes will no longer function. These neuropeptides are included in a more general discussion of brain chemicals presented in Chapter 11. For now, it is sufficient to note that these chemicals control the release of hormones by the pituitary gland and that they come from the brain.

Hypothalamic releasing factor	Principal actions
LH-releasing hormone (LHRH)	Stimulates LH release and FSH release by the anterior pituitary. LHRH has also been observed to increase sexual behavior in male and female rats when it is injected into the hypothalamus.
FSH-releasing factor (FSH-RF)	Stimulates FSH release by the anterior pituitary gland. (Some people believe that this chemical is the same as LHRH.)
Thyrotropin-releasing hormone (TRH)	Stimulates thyroid stimulating hormone (TSH) secretion by the anterior pituitary gland. TSH controls the activity of the thyroid gland. TRH also stimulates prolactin release by the anterior pituitary and reportedly acts as a general stimulant when injected into the brain.
Corticotropin-releasing factor (CRF)	Stimulates adrenocorticotrophic hormone (ACTH) secretion by the anterior pituitary. ACTH controls the activity of the cortex of the adrenal gland.
Growth hormone-releasing factor (GRF)	Stimulates growth hormone (GH) secretion by the anterior pituitary gland.
Growth hormone-inhibiting factor (GIF—also called somatostatin)	Inhibits growth hormone, thyroid stimulating hormone, and prolactin release by the anterior pituitary gland. GIF has also been reported to act as a general depressant when it it injected into the brain.
Prolactin-releasing factor (PRF)	Stimulates prolactin release by the anterior pituitary gland.
Prolactin-inhibiting factor (PIF)	Inhibits prolactin release by the anterior pituitary gland.

Table 10–3. Major releasing factors produced and secreted within the hypothalamus. These neuropeptides travel a very short distance within special blood vessels and then exert their action by influencing the release of hormones from the anterior pituitary gland.

Hierarchical Organization with Feedback

The organs most involved with reproductive functions —the brain, the pituitary gland, the ovaries or testes, and the other reproductive organs in the body—are morphologically separate from one another, yet linked together by chemicals. As mentioned earlier, releasing factors link the brain to the pituitary gland, FSH and LH link the pituitary gland to the ovaries or testes, and the sex hormones link the ovaries or testes to additional reproductive organs as well as to other tissues of the body.

This entire organization operates as a *hierarchy*. If the brain cells that produce LH- and FSH-releasing factors are destroyed, everything "below" the brain in this organization stops functioning. The anterior pituitary stops producing and releasing LH and FSH, without which the ovaries or testes stop secreting female or male sex hormones (estrogen, progesterone, and testosterone). In turn, the reduced or abolished levels of sex hormones severely alter the organs that depend on these hormones. On the other hand, if

an organ "further down" in the hierarchy is destroyed, there is very little damage to those organs "higher up." For example, if the ovaries are removed, the organs dependent on estrogen and progesterone (such as the uterus and breasts) shrink in size and/or cease producing their chemicals, but the anterior pituitary gland continues to release LH and FSH and the hypothalamus continues to produce LH- and FSH-releasing factors (even though the level and pattern of these secretions has been changed because the sex hormones are no longer exerting their positive and negative feedback actions).

The hierarchical organization of the reproductive system is illustrated in Figure 10-8. Although this aspect was not emphasized in Chapter 7 where we discussed the adrenal glands, as illustrated in Figure 10-8, these glands are subject to the same type of organization as are the thyroid gland and its secretions, the breasts and their sensitivity to prolactin, and other endocrine functions.

The regulation of the reproductive system is not solely dependent upon the workings of this hierarchical system. As discussed earlier in the chapter and

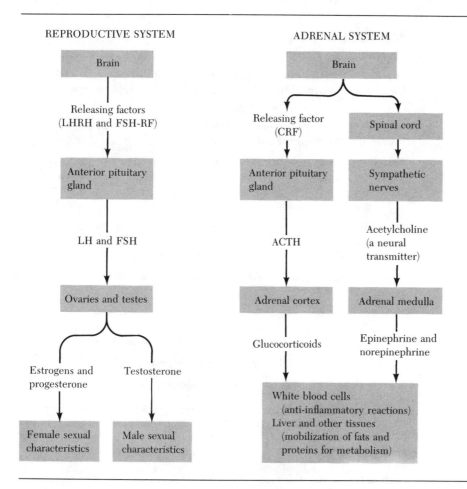

Figure 10–8. The hierarchical organization of mechanisms regulating the reproductive (left) and adrenal (right) systems. Every organ "below" another organ is subject to the secretions of the higher organ. (Although the functions of the adrenal glands are not discussed in this chapter, the hierarchical organization of the adrenal system is shown here to illustrate that it is subject to the same type of regulation as the reproductive system.)

mentioned again above, these hormones also exert a "feedback" effect on the brain. Although many of the details are not well understood in humans, it is quite clear in rodents that estrogen and testosterone act on the brain to

a) facilitate LH release preceding ovulation in females—a "positive-feedback" effect mediated by estrogen (see page 225),

b) inhibit LH release in females and males—a "negative-feedback" effect of estrogen and testosterone (see pages 223–225), and

c) inhibit FSH release in females—a "negative-feedback" effect of estrogen.

Depending on the dose and when it is administered in the ovarian cycle, all of these responses can be experimentally increased or decreased by injecting female animals with appropriate amounts of progesterone.

In addition, it is clear that estrogen and testosterone act on the brain to stimulate *sexual behavior* in many species. Testosterone also has this effect in human males, but the evidence is not as convincing that estrogen stimulates sexual behavior in females as it does in many—if not all—nonhuman species. (This point will be discussed further in the next section of the chapter.) The influence of sex hormones on brain functions concerned with sexual behavior and reproductive processes is illustrated schematically in

Figure 10-9, which also illustrates the hierarchical organization discussed previously. As Figure 10-9 illustrates, the reproductive system is a highly integrated network composed of many interconnecting, interwoven parts. Note also that in addition to the sex hormones, LH, FSH, and the releasing factors appear to affect the brain.

Areas of the Brain Involved in Reproductive Processes and Sexual Behavior

No one area of the brain influences *only* reproductive function, or *only* sexual behavior. These processes are inseparably interconnected with each other. As we have noted with many other functions, reproductive function is also a result of the integration of many systems whose workings are extremely refined. For example, neurons in the anterior hypothalamus and the preoptic area are involved not only in the production of neuropeptides that control the release of LH by the anterior pituitary gland, but also in the selective concentration of sex hormones (which has been demonstrated by analyzing slices of brain for uptake of labelled—that is, radioactive—hormones such as estrogen and testosterone), as well as in sexual behavior. Despite these connections, damage to these brain areas can selectively disrupt sexual behavior without affecting ovulation or spermatogenesis, and reproductive fertility can be abolished without disrupting sexual behavior. Thus, even though under normal conditions many different components are integrated to accomplish these functions, they actually involve separate mechanisms, as has been demonstrated experimentally.

A tremendous amount of research has been performed to elucidate the mechanisms responsible for sexual behavior, and yet we are still a long way from understanding these mechanisms. One reason is that sexual behavior involves a great number of variables, particularly in humans. Even on a physiological level, sex hormones influence sexual behavior in different ways. For example, not only do the sex hormones affect specific nerve cells that appear to stimulate sexual behavior, but, because these same hormones are responsible for the development of our sex and other organs, they contribute to the perceptions of "maleness" or "femaleness" as viewed by others as well as by ourselves. In terms of reproductive functions, the entire brain is involved. Spinal reflexes integrated within the **lower spinal cord**, arousal responses integrated within the **reticular system** of the upper spinal cord, and **autonomic reflexes** are all involved, as well as the **hypothalamus** and the **limbic**

system. These are discussed, in turn, below, as is the involvement of the **cerebral cortex**.

Spinal Reflexes. The act of copulation depends largely upon reflexes that are integrated within the lower portions of the spinal cord. Animal studies have shown that when the spinal cord is cut so that its lower portions are no longer connected to the rest of the brain, stimulation of the genitals causes erection, pelvic thrusting, and ejaculation. These reflexes have also been observed in paraplegic males (suffering from a lesion or transection of the spinal cord); this activity does not evoke orgasm, however, indicating that higher regions of the brain are necessary for this experience.

The Autonomic Nervous System and the Reticular System. The autonomic nervous system is very much involved in sexual responses. Penile erection, vasocongestion of the clitoris, vaginal lubrication, secretions by the prostate and seminal vesicles, erection of the nipples, and other erotic responses are due to activation of the parasympathetic branch of the autonomic nervous system. The sympathetic branch is also involved, not only in ejaculation and the orgasmic response (including contraction of smooth muscle of the genital ducts and glands in males, and the vaginal muscles, fallopian tubes, and uterus in females), but also in reducing bladder and digestive reflexes (see Table 7-2, Chapter 7).

The arousal responses associated with sexual excitement—increased respiration, increased heart rate, and increased muscle tension—all involve the reticular system, discussed in Chapter 8. Interestingly, experimental observations suggest that the reticular system's involvement extends beyond its regulation of arousal responses: studies in animals have shown that electrical stimulation of the reticular system within the upper spinal cord can both induce and inhibit ovulation, that nerve cells in this region are capable of selectively concentrating radioactively labelled estrogens or testosterone, that destruction of its cells sometimes increases, sometimes decreases sexual behavior, and that electrical stimulation inhibits sexual behavior. These findings suggest the workings of refined systems, but their elucidation awaits further research.

The Hypothalamus. The hypothalamus is essential to normal reproductive function. Without the releasing factors it produces, the pituitary gland and the reproductive organs cease functioning—they even stop secreting the hormones they normally produce. But the hypothalamus is important for another reason: *because of its anatomical position, the hypothalamus is the final common pathway in the brain to the*

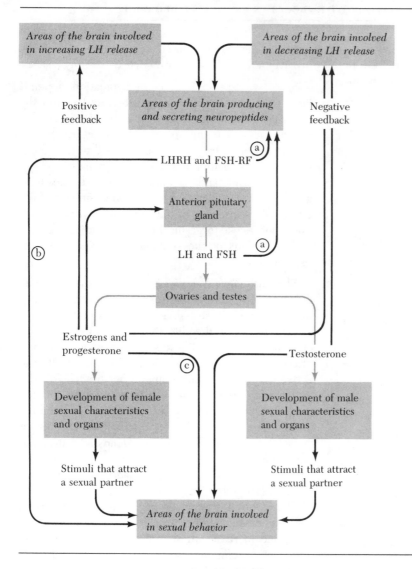

Figure 10–9. The effects of hormones on brain mechanisms regulating reproductive functions. The shaded arrows reflect the hierarchical organization illustrated in Figure 10–8. The involvement of the brain is emphasized by the use of italic type.

(a) There is good evidence that FSH, LH, and the releasing factors themselves can reduce the quantity of releasing factors found in the hypothalamus. It is not known, however, whether this effect is purely pharmacological or actually part of a mechanism controlling pituitary secretion under normal physiological conditions.

(b) There is evidence in rodents that LH-releasing hormone increases female and male sexual behavior when it is injected into the brain. The importance of this finding remains to be ascertained. (In humans, LHRH has been observed to both increase and have no effect on sexual behavior; see Moss, 1979.)

(c) Estrogen and progesterone definitely increase sexual behavior in subhuman species. In humans, however, sexual behavior appears to be normal even when estrogen and progesterone levels are negligible.

pituitary gland. That is, any activity within the brain that influences pituitary secretion must do so by exerting an action in the hypothalamus. This relation holds not only for reproductive processes but also for stress responses and the release of ACTH, which stimulates the adrenal cortex (see Figure 10-8 and Chapter 7). The hypothalamus is also essential for normal sexual behavior.

A study of Figure 10-7 will quickly reveal that most areas of the hypothalamus influence not only sexual behavior but also, in one way or another, the release of anterior pituitary hormones (in this case, LH and FSH), and thereby affect the activity of all the reproductive organs.

The Limbic System. The limbic system appears to modulate the activity of lower areas of the brain, especially the hypothalamus. Even though the neural circuitry necessary for sexual behavior is not abolished by lesions of the limbic system, this system is likely to be involved in selecting behaviors *appropriate* for sexual activity. As you will recall, a similar assertion was made in Chapter 7 when we were discussing the activities of the limbic system and lower areas of the brain with respect to defensive behaviors (see page 143 and Figure 7-12).

Animals with lesions in the amygdala or adjacent pyriform cortex are often hypersexual, expressed in monkeys by increased masturbatory activity and a loss of the ability to discriminate in selecting appropriate sex partners. That is, lesioned males will mount other males, the experimenter, animals of other species, and even stuffed toys. In humans there are also some reports of increased sexual activity in patients suffering from damage to this region (see Marlowe, Mancall, and Thomas, 1975). It has also been reported that abnormal excitation of this area of the brain (as occurs in patients suffering from temporal lobe epilepsy) sometimes reduces the sex drive. Thus, although the evidence is scanty, it appears that the limbic system may be involved in modifying sexual functions in humans.

A summary of the involvement of the limbic system is presented in Figure 10-10. Again, as emphasized in this figure, the areas of the limbic system that influence sexual behavior are also areas that modify the activity of the pituitary gland and, as a result, the activity of the other reproductive organs in the body. This influence is not as powerful as that exerted by the hypothalamus, however.

The Cerebral Cortex. Although we know the cerebral cortex is quite important for sexual behavior, its role is even less well defined than that of the limbic system. In male cats, rats, and rabbits, the frontal cortex appears to be important inasmuch as lesions in this region can abolish or severely disrupt sexual behavior. Interestingly, the same effects have not been observed in female animals. Damage to the cerebral cortex in female rats, rabbits, cats, and guinea pigs does not alter their ability to engage in sexual behavior. These data are sometimes cited as evidence that the cortex is not necessary for female sexual behavior but is necessary for male sexual behavior. Although this conclusion appears to be generally true in some species, it would be risky to generalize this finding to humans.

In many subhuman species, male copulation consists of his mounting the female from the rear, grasping and palpating the sides of her body with his forepaws, and engaging in pelvic thrusting movements. These complex behaviors require fine muscular coordination, so it is not too surprising to find that the frontal lobes participate in this response (see Chapter 9). Furthermore, the male must often respond to sensory stimuli from the female indicating that she is behaviorally receptive. Again, one would expect the cortex to be involved in receiving and responding to these sensory stimuli, which are mainly visual and olfactory (see Chapter 6 for a discussion of sensory stimuli).

In contrast, copulation in the female animal is quite simple. While the male is mounting her, the female stands quite still, usually with her hindquarters raised and her tail deflected. This response, called "lordosis," is elicited by tactile stimulation of the genital area of the female, and is chiefly a spinal reflex under the control of the hypothalamus where it is subject to the effects of estrogen and progesterone. The cortex is not necessary for this behavior.

The copulating behaviors just described in female and male animals are very different from each other. This is not the case in humans, where, in many respects, female and male sexual behavior is similar. Not only does the female actively participate in the process of penile insertion, but she also engages in pelvic thrusting and other behaviors only seen in the male of most animal species. The similarity in their sexual behavior also supports the view that in humans the cerebral cortex is probably just as important in females as in males. Certainly, both men and women are sexually aroused by many cognitive processes that involve the cortex—verbal communication, erotic visual stimuli, and reading material.

The fact that females and males are so similar in their behavior might be related to the finding that androgens reportedly increase sex drive in human females moreso than do estrogens, a topic that will be further discussed in the next section.

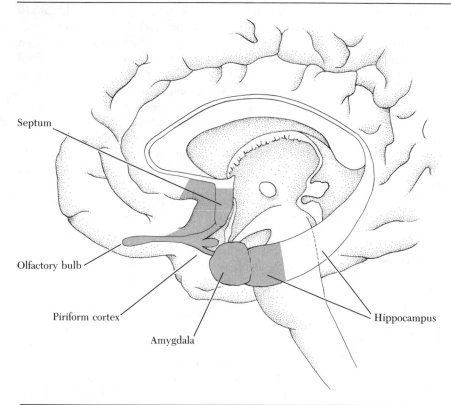

Figure 10–10. Limbic structures most clearly involved in reproductive processes.

Amygdala and adjacent piriform cortex: *lesions* have been reported to cause hypersexual behavior in male cats, lynx, and monkeys. (In cats, this effect is abolished with ventromedial hypothalamic lesions. Therefore, damage to the limbic system probably causes hypersexual behavior by modulating behavioral, autonomic, and reproductive processes integrated in lower parts of the brain, such as the hypothalamus.) Hypersexual behavior includes an indiscriminate choice of sex objects, ranging from furniture to teddy bears. This effect is likely to be related to the role of the temporal cortex in visual discrimination. In human males and females suffering from temporal lobe epilepsy, *removal* of the temporal lobes has been reported to restore below-normal sexual behavior to normal levels, and sometimes to levels much higher than normal. *Lesions* have also been observed to cause precocious puberty in female rats and to block ovulation in adult female rats, both indicating that the amygdala can also modify the release of hormones from the pituitary gland. Electrical *stimulation* of one area of the amygdala delays puberty in female rats and decreases plasma LH and FSH levels, whereas, electrical stimulation of a different area causes ovulation in rabbits, cats, and rats, and raises plasma LH and FSH levels. Patients suffering from temporal epilepsy (where there is an abnormal irritative focus that makes the temporal lobe overexcitable) often have decreased sex drive. As mentioned above, removal of the temporal lobe sometimes increases sex desire and sex behavior.

Olfactory bulbs: *lesions* have been observed to delay puberty in rats and mice; in humans born without olfactory bulbs, genital development is often retarded.

Hippocampus: *lesions* have been reported to increase, decrease, and have no effect on sexual behavior in cats and rats. *Lesions* have also been reported to raise plasma LH and FSH levels in female rats. In general, these effects are not as dramatic as those observed with damage to the amygdala. Electrical *stimulation* has been observed to cause precocious puberty in female rats. Also, electrical *stimulation* has been reported to block ovulation and prevent the LH burst that precedes ovulation (including blocking ovulation otherwise produced by stimulating the preoptic area of the hypothalamus). Again, these responses indicate that the limbic system modulates the activity of the hypothalamus.

Septum: *lesions* have been reported to cause irregular reproductive cycles, delay the onset of puberty, and increase sexual behavior in female rats. Electrical *stimulation* has been observed to increase plasma LH and FSH levels. Humans have reported that electrical *stimulation* in this area sometimes evokes pleasurable sexual sensations. Electrical *stimulation* has also been reported to decrease sexual behavior in female hamsters.

V. HORMONES AND SEXUAL BEHAVIOR

In most animals the correlation between sex behavior and sex hormones is very strong. In general, when a male is castrated (testes removed) his sexual behavior declines but can be restored with testosterone. Similarly, when a female is ovariectomized (removal of the ovaries) her sexual behavior declines, but, again, it can be restored with appropriate injections of estrogen and progesterone. This amazing finding—that an animal's sexual responsiveness is determined by hormones secreted by the reproductive organs—is one of the clearest examples we have that chemicals can control specific behavioral processes. The fact that minute quantities of hormones, contained within tiny pellets that are implanted into the brain, can evoke sexual behavior in animals when these pellets are placed in specific brain regions (see Figure 10-7) provides additional evidence that hormones do, in fact, direct behavior.

Although the relationship between sexual behavior and reproductive hormones is well established in animals, this is not the case in humans. This lack of a relationship between sexual behavior and hormones is expressed in a number of ways, some of which differ markedly from what occurs in animals. For example:

1) Sexual behavior in humans is not closely tied to the possibility of fertilization as dictated by the ovarian cycle. In many species, the female will accept a male only during the period when estrogen and progesterone levels rise and ovulation occurs. In other species, sexual behavior occurs only during a specific time period—the breeding season—when male and female hormones are secreted to make the animals fertile. In contrast, sexual behavior in humans occurs during any part of the menstrual cycle and at any time of the year. (Of course, in humans, sexual behavior is not simply purposeful in procreative terms; it also serves the important function of cementing bonds between people.)

2) In human females, removal of the ovaries or the occurrence of menopause result in a marked reduction in the levels of estrogen and progesterone, yet there is very little (if any) reduction of sexual behavior or desire. By contrast, in subhuman species removal of the ovaries usually abolishes or markedly reduces sexual behavior. These findings do not necessarily mean that sexual behavior in human females is free from dependence upon hormones.

There is some evidence that sexual desire in females—before and after menopause—is associated with androgens rather than estrogens or progesterone, and that the adrenal glands might secrete enough androgen to maintain sexual desire. The evidence is somewhat weak, however, and the contribution of adrenal androgen to sexual behavior in human females needs further study.

3) In human males, although castration usually leads to a gradual decline in sexual behavior, the results can vary greatly. In some cases, castrated males (who have no testes and therefore little, if any, testosterone) appear to engage in normal sexual behavior even 18 years following castration (for more details, see Money, 1961).

It is interesting to note that male animals also show great variability in the amount of sexual behavior that persists after castration. Most male rats cease to copulate within a few weeks, and cats and dogs within a few months, although individual animals may continue for much longer periods (dogs have been reported to copulate even five years after castration). When an animal is castrated, testosterone levels fall very rapidly and, within a few hours, there is virtually none left in the blood. Thus, in either animals or humans, the persistence of sexual behavior for weeks, months, sometimes even years after castration cannot be explained by a correspondingly slow reduction in testosterone levels. Nevertheless, it is certain that testosterone is involved, because sexual behavior is restored in almost all cases when this androgen is given to castrated males (animals or humans).

4) In humans, whether or not sexual behavior occurs is largely determined by non-reproductive factors such as those imposed by prior learning, culture, society, compatibility of personalities, and so forth. One possible conclusion to be drawn from these differences is that humans are emancipated from, or less dependent upon, their "biology" than are other animals. Another, perhaps more likely, conclusion is that humans respond to many more factors than do animals; hormonal influences, therefore, are just one factor out of many. In other words, rather than a freedom from biological imperatives, as humans we experience many emotions, thoughts, and physical states that animals do not—states which exert a tremendous influence over our arousal and autonomic responses. For example, even though an immediately threatening situation can evoke fear and other defensive reactions that inhibit sexual activity in animals, the

associated activation of the sympathetic nervous system and cessation of erotic responses in humans is expressed in many more situations—many imagined, some far removed from our immediate environment—than occurs in animals. Anxiety, fear, and other defensive reactions are often associated with impotence or premature ejaculation in males and difficulty in achieving orgasm in females. Conversely, erotic stimuli based on fantasy or other cognitive processes can stimulate the parasympathetic nerves that contribute to sexual arousal. Moreover, "competition" from many other (nonsexual) arousal mechanisms can detract humans from sexual activity. A person who is very worried about his or her career or an impending exam, or who is engaged in heavy physical exercise, is much more likely not to respond to erotic stimuli. In women, such anxieties are sufficient to cause irregularities in the menstrual cycles. (See also the comments on infertility at the beginning of this chapter.)

5) Sex hormones, by themselves, do not evoke behavior, but, rather, they make it more likely that behavior will occur when the appropriate stimuli are present. This **permissive action** of hormones, which operates in humans as well as in most animal species, simply means that these chemicals somehow sensitize the appropriate nerve cells and/or areas of the brain so that sexual behavior is more likely. Other stimuli are also necessary—the most obvious, of course, being the presence of a sexual partner, but erotic thoughts, reading materials, or tactile stimulation are also effective. We must emphasize that this permissive action also applies to the behavioral effects of other chemicls. For example, when our blood glucose levels are low, it is more likely that we will eat (see Chapter 3), but this behavior cannot take place unless food is available.

We are still a long way from understanding the exact mechanisms whereby sex hormones influence sexual behavior. Limited as our knowledge is in this general area, it is nevertheless much more extensive in the field of reproduction and sexual behavior than it is for any other specific behavior we know to be influenced by chemicals.

VI. HORMONES AND OTHER BEHAVIORS

The only type of behavior we have discussed so far in relation to hormonal effects is heterosexual behavior (behavior involving male and female). Although we will cover them only briefly, other behaviors subject to hormonal influence must be mentioned: aggressive, maternal, general motor, and homosexual behavior.

Aggression

In Chapter 7 we discussed rage and attack behaviors as they relate to the autonomic nervous system and the brain. We listed a number of different types of aggression, including sham rage, rage, and predatory attack (see pages 136–137, Chapter 7). There are several examples where aggression appears to be related to sexual processes. For instance, in most species, males are more aggressive than females. Also, in many species (deer, seals, horses, goats, sheep, and many others) fighting between males of the same species occurs most often during the breeding season. Many studies indicate that castration reduces aggressive behavior in male animals of some species, and it is quite clear that this reduction can be restored by administration of testosterone.

Androgen is by no means a single causative factor in aggression, however, for castrated animals are quite capable of being aggressive. Moreover, aggression is often linked to states that are not associated with an increase in androgen levels—hunger, for example. Therefore, the fact that androgen appears to increase aggressiveness in some cases is actually just a small part of a process which includes many other factors. The complexity of this behavior is probably one reason why there is no conclusive evidence that aggression is linked in any unique way to male hormones in humans.

Maternal Behavior

The physiological aspects of maternal behavior have been most studied in rodents. Female mice show very consistent behaviors: nest-building during and after pregnancy, cleaning of newly-born pups after birth, nursing, periodic licking of the anogenital region of pups to stimulate urination and defecation, and pup retrieval (bringing pups back to the nest when they stray from it). In rodents and many other species, these behaviors (or behaviors similar to them) are correctly called "maternal" since the mother, and clearly not the father, is the involved parent. In humans, however, in spite of the traditional "absenteeism" of fathers who work and the more recent acceptance of single mothers, both parents generally care for the young—at least when compared to some lower species where male parent behavior toward their young ranges from indifference to aggression. We will briefly mention what is known of maternal behavior from animal studies.

In rodents, nest-building has often (but not always) been reported to be dependent on circulating levels of progesterone and **prolactin**. During pregnancy, very high levels of progesterone are secreted by the corpus luteum within the ovary and then, as pregnancy progresses, by the placenta. After pregnancy, progesterone levels fall and prolactin levels immediately rise. Prolactin is a hormone produced and released by the anterior pituitary gland. Like the other hormones secreted by the anterior pituitary, it, too, is under the control of neuropeptides produced and secreted within the hypothalamus (see Tables 10-2 and 10-3). The main effect of prolactin is to stimulate the production of milk in the breasts. (Lactation is maintained by the suckling of the infant, a stimulus that initiates neural impulses which are propagated to the hypothalamus of the mother. This process will be discussed in more detail later in the chapter.)

Other aspects of maternal behavior also have been associated with the increased secretion of prolactin, progesterone, and (perhaps) estrogen. Injections of these hormones in experimental animals will sometimes induce pup retrieval and other maternal behaviors. Interestingly, however, other chemicals may be involved inasmuch as plasma taken from lactating rats, or rats giving birth, will induce maternal behavior in virgin female rats much more rapidly than will injections of any of these hormones. Other indications that maternal behavior in rodents may not depend critically on reproductive hormones is that these behaviors have been found to persist even in the absence of hormones. Again, much more research remains to be done before the mechanisms responsible for maternal behavior are understood.

General Motor Activity

From research findings, mostly in rats, it is quite clear that androgen and estrogen have an effect on general motor activity; specifically, administration of these hormones has been found to increase wheel-running activity, and removal of the testes or ovaries reduces it. We do know that both testosterone and estradiol (an estrogen) increase the excitability of the reticular system and other regions of the brain known to have a strong influence on muscular activity, and it may be that these effects are mediated by the reticular system. Progesterone appears to decrease the excitability of the reticular system in female rats, and also has been reported to decrease wheel-running activity. In humans, it has been suggested that one reason why pregnant women often tire easily is because of the tremendous increase in circulating levels of progesterone that occurs during pregnancy.

Homosexual Activity

There is no substantial evidence that persons who engage in homosexual activities are any different from others with respect to the type and quantity of hormones in their blood. Nor is there evidence that homosexuals (or heterosexuals) will alter their sexual preferences when hormones—female or male—are administered to them. In animal studies, when female hormones are given to adult males or when male hormones are given to adult females, no dramatic change occurs in sexual behavior with regard to the selection of a partner; that is, the animal is much more likely to select an animal of the opposite sex than change its behavior to correspond to the "sex" of the administered hormone. Even though most animals will mount other animals of the same sex, and administration of hormones from the opposite sex may increase this "homosexual" mounting behavior slightly, by far the more potent effect is on heterosexual behavior.

In humans, the influence of society and the family in determining the sexual identity of a person is extremely strong. Persons suffering from the adrenogenital syndrome or the androgen-insensitivity syndrome have provided much information on this subject. For example, when masculinized females (see pages 215–216) are raised as girls, they identify themselves as females and their erotic interests focus on men. Similarly, when masculinized females are raised as boys, they identify themselves as men and their erotic interests focus on women. These gender identities seem to be as strong as in others who do not suffer from the adrenogenital syndrome. Males suffering from the androgen-insensitivity syndrome (see page 217) are often raised as females, and here, too, we see that these genetic males identify themselves as women and direct their sexual activity and fantasies toward men (see Money and Ehrhardt, 1972). Another line of evidence comes from adult men who are treated with estrogen for prostate cancer. These men often experience decreased sexual desire (due to the sickness itself, but also because of reduced testosterone levels and a reduced sensitivity to testosterone caused by the estrogen), but they do not become interested in homosexual activity nor do they appear to entertain homosexual fantasies.

There is some evidence that men who have been raised as girls because of retarded development of their external genitalia do redirect their sexual interests at puberty when their external genitalia develop masculine form (see Imperato-McGinley, Peterson, Gautier, and Sturla, 1979). It is not clear, however, whether these data argue against the importance of society and family in establishing gender identity because these men, in fact, were raised by parents and a society which knew they would become masculinized at puberty (see Money, 1976). In any event, these data certainly provide no evidence that the administration or exposure to hormones of the opposite sex make a person homosexual.

Effects of Hormones Early in Life

All of the behaviors noted above might be influenced, however, by the hormones present during our very early development. As mentioned previously (see page 217, studies in rodents provide good evidence that early exposure to androgens (within the first few days after birth) encourages male sexual behavior in females and that early removal of androgen (by castration) encourages female sexual behavior in males. Similar observations have been made with respect to aggression and maternal behavior—*early* exposure to androgen increases aggression and decreases maternal behavior in females, whereas early removal of androgen in males causes increased maternal behavior and decreased aggression. Although these results are very interesting, their relevance to human functioning is not clear and awaits further research.

VII. PHYSIOLOGICAL/PSYCHOLOGICAL INTERACTIONS

The organs involved in making us reproductively fertile and the organs involved in sexual behavior are, in some cases, the same. This, of course, means that our reproductive system and reproductive behavior are inseparably interconnected. And there are many examples of this. For instance, testosterone from the testes is needed for the production of fully fertile, motile sperm, but, in most men, it also maintains normal levels of sexual desire. Similarly, the external genitalia not only allow successful union of the egg and sperm, but these organs also produce sensations of pleasure when they are used for copulation. Also,

the anterior and basal regions of the hypothalamus are necessary for both sexual behavior and a functioning pituitary gland. In addition, the changes in our body that occur at puberty reflect increased levels of circulating sex hormones, but they also contribute to making our physique feminine or masculine and therefore potentially more attractive to a sexual partner.

It is therefore apparent that there is an elaborate network of physiological and behavioral processes that are dependent on one another for their existence. Furthermore, *an enormous number of these processes are subject to our conscious experience.* This fact not only makes reproduction an important part of our lives because we experience many facets of its functioning, but also it enables us to carry out the necessary voluntary behaviors that are involved. The interactions that exist among reproductive processes are illustrated in Figure 10-11, which indicates those processes that are part of our conscious experience. Although at first glance this diagram may appear to be somewhat complex, most of the processes included have already been discussed.

There are many other examples of the interdependence of physiology and behavior in sexual and reproductive function besides those illustrated in Figure 10-11. In some animal species, ovulation occurs only with external stimulation. These females are called **reflex ovulators** and they differ from **spontaneous ovulators**—females whose ovulation is not linked to external stimulation. Humans are spontaneous ovulators, as are dogs, cattle, sheep, and other species. Rabbits and cats are examples of reflex ovulators. In general, the act of copulation by the male is the stimulus that causes ovulation in reflex-ovulating females. The stimulation of the vagina and perhaps other tactile stimuli caused by the male's sexual activity evoke the production of LH-releasing hormone by the hypothalamus which then results in LH release by the anterior pituitary gland. (It is, of course, the LH that causes the follicle to rupture and that produces ovulation—see page 220 and Figure 10-4.) *Thus, in some mammalian species, the act of copulation does more than assure the egg and sperm will meet; it causes ovulation to occur.* (This is indicated by the dashed arrow in Figure 10-11.)

In experimental work in rats, researchers have been able to change a spontaneous ovulator to a reflex ovulator (see Bunn and Everett, 1957). Similarly, there are reports that rabbits—reflex ovulators—will sometimes ovulate spontaneously (Sawyer and Everett, 1959). Because of these demonstrations, there is

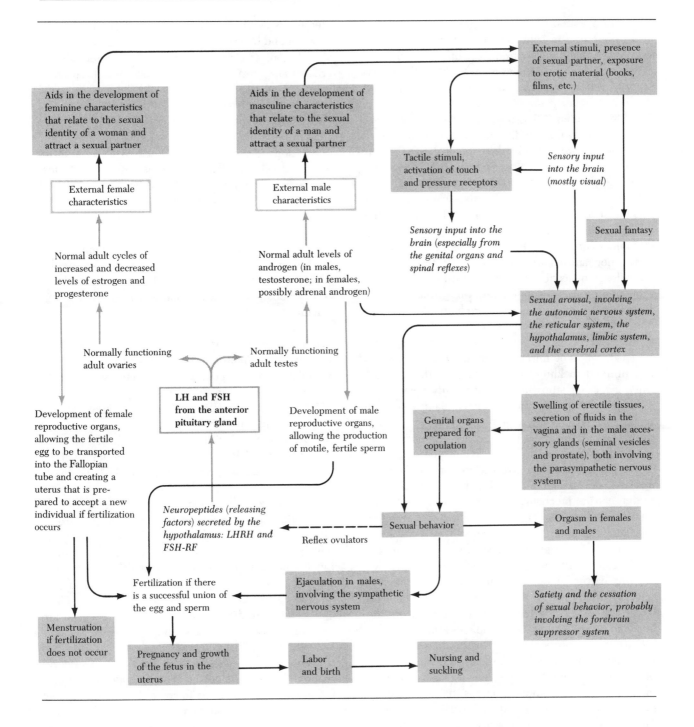

Figure 10–11. Continuity of physiology and behavior in reproductive processes. Note the large number of boxed processes representing those consciously experienced. The involvement of the brain, which is even greater than shown (see, for example, Figure 10–12 for the brain's role in nursing and suckling), is emphasized by the use of italic type. The shaded arrows reflect the hierarchical organization illustrated in Figures 10–8 and 10–9.

reason to question whether the physiological mechanisms operating in spontaneous and reflex ovulators are, in fact, that different from each other. In humans, existing evidence both favors and denies the possibility of reflex ovulation, so we must wait for more research to clarify this issue. If reflex ovulation is possible in humans, it is probably a very weak effect that would only operate in unusual circumstances.

Another example of the clear integration of physiology with behavior involves nursing. In this case, the operating mechanisms apply to humans as well as to animals. As described previously, when an infant suckles, it sets off touch receptors in the nipples that generate neural impulses which are propagated up the spinal cord to the hypothalamus of the mother. Here, mechanisms are set into motion that result in the release of oxytocin from the posterior pituitary gland and prolactin from the anterior pituitary gland. The prolactin stimulates milk production and secretion in the breasts and the oxytocin forces the milk glands in the breasts to contract, causing milk ejection or "let-down." The importance to the nursing process of continued suckling is exemplified by the fact that when a mother stops nursing, it is only a couple of weeks before the anterior pituitary gland ceases to secrete prolactin and, as a result, milk production stops. Conversely, if she continues to nurse, the breasts can produce milk for several years in some cases. The mechanisms involved in nursing are summarized and further discussed in Figure 10-12.

Some of the mechanisms we have been discussing represent more than an inseparable functioning of physiological and behavioral processes within us. *They also reflect the kind of symbiotic relationships we are capable of having with others.* Not only do we see this particular bond in the nursing mother and suckling infant where the infant is getting its food while the mother is obtaining the stimulation she needs to produce milk, two people engaged in sexual activity also express this kind of symbiotic pairing. Each person is not only being aroused him/herself, but is also arousing the other and evoking responses in each other's reproductive organs that makes fertilization (and, in reflex ovulators, ovulation) possible. These symbiotic relationships also have psychological and physiological ramifications. For example, a quiet, undisturbed mother is more likely to release her milk while the baby is suckling, and her serenity at this time is obviously more conducive to an emotional bonding with the baby than if she were upset and the infant had to struggle to get milk.

We do not know the mechanisms responsible for sexual activity being a pleasurable experience. When electrodes are placed within the hypothalamus of a male rat and he is allowed to self-administer electrical stimulation, the rate of stimulation sometimes increases after testosterone levels are raised. In other cases, the brain areas that evoke increased sexual behavior when electrically stimulated are also areas that evoke self-stimulation. Sometimes a rat will stop self-administering electrical stimulation just after copulation. Castration, also, leads to a cessation of electrical self-stimulation in some cases, and testosterone injection in these castrated rats has been found to restore it. Scanty as the evidence is, and risky as it may be to use animal studies as a springboard for interpretations concerning "pleasure" in humans, these data do indicate that sexual mechanisms and reward mechanisms are integrated and are represented in similar, if not identical, regions of the brain (see Hoebel, 1979; Caggiula, 1970; Hoebel, 1969; Caggiula and Hoebel, 1966).

Of course, you should not asume from the foregoing that all reward areas of the brain are sexual. As discussed in Chapter 4 (see page 53), electrical self-stimulation is not necessarily connected with specific behaviors, and it can be connected with one type of behavior but not another. Eating, drinking, breathing, smelling, and sexual behavior are all processes that are integrated with reward mechanisms, yet each one of these behaviors can exist independently of the other. For example, an electrode within the hypothalamus might elicit sexual behavior and self-stimulation, and these responses might be dependent upon adequate amounts of circulating testosterone. However, this electrode might not elicit eating behavior, nor will self-stimulation be dependent upon blood glucose levels, as occurs when the electrode is within a different region of the hypothalamus (see Chapter 3 and Caggiula, 1970; Hoebel, 1979). Once again, these findings point to the fact that we are looking at the workings of highly refined systems rather than singular phenomena. *"Reward" is a process that is often a part of other processes being integrated at that time, and it is not one thing.* This point has been discussed in some detail with respect to other seemingly singular processes such as hunger, thirst, consciousness, arousal, attention, sleep, dreams, volition, and "will" (see Chapters 4, 6, 8, and 9). For more information, the reader is referred to these chapters as well as to the next chapter, where the chemical basis of "reward" is discussed in some detail.

We could devote the entire chapter (if not an entire book) just to the integrative mechanisms involved in sexual processes. In other words, the examples dis-

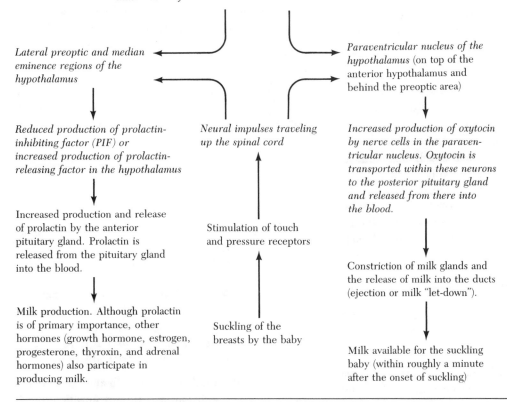

Neural impulses from various areas of the brain: Although the neural pathways are not well understood with respect to psychological states and their relation to one's ability to nurse, various stimuli such as seeing a baby and hearing a baby cry can cause milk ejection into the ducts (milk "let-down"). Also, emotional or defensive reactions that cause arousal and activation of the sympathetic nervous system can inhibit milk ejection.

Lateral preoptic and median eminence regions of the hypothalamus

Paraventricular nucleus of the hypothalamus (on top of the anterior hypothalamus and behind the preoptic area)

Reduced production of prolactin-inhibiting factor (PIF) or increased production of prolactin-releasing factor in the hypothalamus

Neural impulses traveling up the spinal cord

Increased production of oxytocin by nerve cells in the paraventricular nucleus. Oxytocin is transported within these neurons to the posterior pituitary gland and released from there into the blood.

Increased production and release of prolactin by the anterior pituitary gland. Prolactin is released from the pituitary gland into the blood.

Stimulation of touch and pressure receptors

Constriction of milk glands and the release of milk into the ducts (ejection or milk "let-down").

Milk production. Although prolactin is of primary importance, other hormones (growth hormone, estrogen, progesterone, thyroxin, and adrenal hormones) also participate in producing milk.

Suckling of the breasts by the baby

Milk available for the suckling baby (within roughly a minute after the onset of suckling)

Figure 10–12. Relationship of nursing, milk production, and milk "let-down" or ejection to neural processes. Note that suckling of the breasts causes the pituitary gland to release hormones that stimulate milk production and eject milk into the ducts where it is available to the infant. The involvement of the brain in these processes is emphasized by the use of italic type.

cussed above serve merely to indicate that physiology and psychology are inseparably interconnected in our reproductive functioning.

VIII. RELATION TO HEALTH

Throughout this book it has been relatively easy to grasp that the processes being considered have a relationship to our health. We have seen that de-

pending upon how they are used (or misused), eating, drinking, breathing, sensory experiences, defensive mechanisms, arousal, sleep, and muscular movement all help to maintain our health (or make us sick). What about sexual processes? It is difficult to answer this question, because sexual functions are not, in themselves, necessary for an individual's survival. Sexual deprivation, or the abolishment of sexual activity and reproductive capacity, does not make an animal or human sick, nor does it interfere with a person's ability to maintain health or have a long life. The same can be said of "too much" sex; it does not, in itself, alter the health of an individual. We will discuss some possible relationships between sex and health below, with the cautionary note that our knowledge in this area is very limited.

The most obvious purpose of sexual processes is the continuation of the species. Without reproductive organs capable of producing fertile eggs, fertile sperm, a place where the fetus can grow, and a means for the baby to be born, there would be no propagation of our species. This assertion, of course, also applies to sexual behavior—without it there would be no future generations of human beings (except, of course, through artificial insemination).

In this sense, reproductive fertility and sexual activity are necessary for the health of humankind, for humanity would cease to exist without them. If we assume the health and survival demand to be at this broader level, we can begin to see similarities between sexual processes and those processes discussed in Chapters 3 through 6, where we discussed "foods." For example:

1) Food-related processes share with sexual processes the fact that their total abolishment will lead to the cessation of humankind. If all humans were deprived of solid food, liquid, or air, humanity would cease to exist.

2) Brain mechanisms serving sex drive and sexual behavior are like those serving hunger, eating, thirst, and drinking in that they are strongly represented in the hypothalamus, less strongly but clearly in the limbic system, and least strongly in the cerebral cortex. Moreover, for all of the foregoing functions, neural activity in these areas of the brain is, in part, determined by the activity of specific function-related organs dispersed throughout the body.

3) There is a connection between sexual activity and self-stimulatory reward, as there is with eating, drinking, breathing, and other ancillary functions (like smelling and predatory attack, both of which are related to food).

4) As with satiety mechanisms involved in eating, drinking, and breathing, where the cessation of behavior is tied in with the ingestion of solid food, liquids, or air (breathing rate is reduced, but of course doesn't stop when we breathe too quickly),

some similar mechanism operates with sexual behavior. At the very least, satiety involves an interaction of the brain and the reproductive organs, especially those that participate in orgasm.

5) As an emotion that serves object-related needs, sexual desire is responsive to many different sensory modalities at once. We discussed something similar in regard to taste, olfaction, touch, pressure, temperature, and pain, all of which contribute to our desire for food (see page 105). We also mentioned that a seemingly "nonspecific" stimulus, such as gently pinching a rat's tail, will make it eat more. The same has been observed with regard to sexual behavior—gently pinching its tail will sometimes make a rat that was sexually unresponsive because of a hypothalamic lesion increase its sexual activity. In humans, of course, many different types of sensory experience (including pain in some individuals) contribute to sexual arousal.

6) In general, the fulfillment of sexual desires involves an interaction with stimuli that are *external* to ourselves. These stimuli, which we will call *sexual stimuli*, usually come from interactions with other people. As with eating, drinking, breathing, and sensory activities that allow us to assimilate solid food, water, air, and sensory stimuli, we have a host of *approach behaviors* to maximize the likelihood that we will assimilate sexual stimuli.

Can sexual stimuli be called "food"? The organization of sexual behavior and the organization of eating, drinking, and other behaviors that depend on organic needs is strikingly similar, as indicated above. In other words, even though sex in itself is not essential to the life of an individual, sexual functions are organized in a manner quite similar to that associated with essential foods.

However tenuous the relationship between sex and health with respect to individuals, the situation is not as vague in relation to society as a whole. Just as too much or too little assimilation of solid foods, water, air, or sensory stimuli can harm us as individuals, similarly, too much or too little sex can harm society. Too much reproduction leads to the problem of overpopulation, which exists in many countries. Too little reproductive capacity and sexual behavior could also harm society. Although not a current problem, it is well known that once there are too few of a species, the species becomes "endangered" because its reproductive practices might not be sufficient to maintain subsequent generations. In this respect, our knowledge of reproduction has great relevance to "health." For example, developing methods of birth control and encouraging reproductive fertility—in the world context as in the context of the individual family—depends very much on our understanding of physiological, psychological, and cultural aspects of reproductive processes and behaviors.

In Chapter 5, we discussed breathing as an organic need. We also referred to the belief, shared by many, that breathing can be used as a means of achieving an inner state conducive to spiritual growth (see pages 70–71). Many spiritual disciplines believe the same thing about sex. The general presumption is that "proper" use of "sexual energy" extends *beyond* fulfilling our immediate physical needs. At a physiological level, there is certainly plenty of evidence presented in this chapter to indicate that sexual processes involve the workings of many refined systems within the brain. Furthermore, there is no doubt that many emotional and mental states can affect sexual processes, and vice versa. We therefore cannot deny the possibility that the brain may have the capacity to integrate physical, emotional, and mental processes of a sexual nature in ways that could change people beyond affecting their immediate needs. At the very least, it appears as if the desire for intimate relationships is a potent factor in forcing us to look beyond our immediate needs to the life of another person. There is no doubt, for example, that sexual functions have a great influence on our relations with other people, and that they involve organic needs that are quite different from those related to eating, drinking, breathing, sleeping, and so forth. *These basic survival functions do not require that people be attracted to us or we to them.* We could state that the capacity for intimate relationships is an "organic" requirement for healthy persons. Although the requirement may not be met by all individuals, the organic need does not disappear.

The need for intimate relations requires many types of interactions, involving aspects of ourselves as well as our attitudes toward others. Our own self-image as females or males, for example, is as important as (and, at times, may even govern) our ability and willingness to understand and care for other people. On the other hand, our ability and willingness to care for other people is frequently a function of how well we can set aside our own wishes and thoughts and "relate" to a person who is *not* in the same state as we are. It is interesting to note that these considerations usually become much more relevant to us during adolescence than before. In other words, during and after puberty we can no longer satisfy all of our organic needs on our own terms as we were generally able to do as "carefree" children—assuming that food, shelter, and clothing have been readily available to us during our childhood. An inability to understand and care for others is surely one of the reasons why some intimate relationships "fall apart." In this connection, it is interesting to note that our ability to understand ourselves and other people is certainly an indication of how "grown up" we are.

IX. CONCLUSIONS

As emphasized throughout this book, physiological and behavioral functions are inseparably interconnected. Because many sexual functions first become fully active when we are old enough to remember what we were like before they had much effect on us, sexual maturation illustrates this truth on an experiential level perhaps more than any other physiological/psychological aspects of development. The study of reproduction has become a multidisciplinary effort, incorporating endocrinology (the study of hormones and the glands that produce them), neurophysiology (the study of the brain and other functional aspects of the nervous system), psychology (the study of behavior), embryology (the study of the development of the embryo and fetus), comparative zoology (the study of various animal species) and chemistry. Investigators in this field comprise "physiological psychologists," "neuroendocrinologists," "psychobiologists," "biopsychologists," and a host of other compound names, all of which confirm the interconnections that are so prominent in this area.

We will now take a more general look at the chemical nature of the brain. Here we will discuss the effects of drugs and processes such as dependence and addiction, but we will also see that chemicals produced by the brain influence every function discussed so far in this book.

Recommended Reading

BEACH, F. *Human Sexuality in Four Perspectives*, edited by Beach, F. Baltimore: Johns Hopkins University Press, 1977, 330 pages. *This highly readable book covers human sexual development, sexual differentiation, sexual deviations, and physiological mechanisms. There is also some discussion of sexual functions in other cultures and other species.*

BERMANT, G. and DAVIDSON, J. *Biological Bases of Sexual Behavior.* New York: Harper & Row, 1974, 306 pages. *This well-written paperback covers the influence of hormones, the brain, the environment, and sexual development on sexual behavior. There are many comparisons between the sexual behavior of humans and that of other mammals.*

KATCHADOURIAN, H. and LUNDE, D. *Fundamentals of Human Sexuality.* New York: Holt, Rinehart and Winston, 1980 (3rd edition), 534 pages. *This paperback covers the basic anatomy and physiology of reproduction but is mostly a presentation of facts and mechanisms of human sexual behavior. Sexual disorders, sex and society, sex and the law, and pregnancy and childbirth are also discussed.*

MONEY, J. and EHRHARDT, A. *Man and Woman, Boy and Girl: The Differentiation and Dimorphism of Gender Identity from Conception to Maturity.* Baltimore: Johns Hopkins University Press, 1972, 311 pages. *A well-written book which covers a broad spectrum of events related to the sexual differentiation of men and women. Sexual differentiation is discussed in relation to genetics, embryology, neuroendocrinology, endocrinology, psychosexual developmemnt and other topics. Experimental and clinical data are both presented. Recommended for those who wish detailed information.*

The Chemical Nature of the Brain

We have repeatedly emphasized that psychological and physiological processes are inseparably interrelated, one with the other, in contributing to our experience. In the course of this discussion, we have indicated how the brain, the other organs of the body, and behaviors all interconnect with each other. Although these interconnections can be described in general terms (like the interrelation between an empty stomach, hunger, and eating), they are extremely refined in their actual workings (in the case of eating, involving interactions among neural circuits in the hypothalamus and limbic system, blood nutrient levels, reward and satiety mechanisms, the autonomic nervous system, the digestive tract, olfactory and other sensory input, and other processes).

The more we understand how the body works, the more obvious it becomes that the refinement of systems involved in these interactions is much greater than previously suspected. During the past twenty years, there has been a tremendous expansion of our knowledge of the chemical nature of the brain. Dozens of chemicals have been discovered that are produced and released by nerve cells within the brain. It appears that *each* neuron is regulated in its production and release of these chemicals, and that neurons specialize in which of these chemicals they secrete. These chemicals, in some highly organized manner, then modify the response of other neurons or, as discussed in the previous chapter, influence other organs such as the pituitary gland—again, in a highly organized manner (see page 228, Chapter 10).

In some cases the neurons that produce a particular chemical appear to form specific pathways as they course through the brain. For example, *norepinephrine* is produced and released not only by the endings of neurons that comprise the sympathetic nervous system and by the medulla of the adrenal glands, but also by several well-defined systems of neurons within the brain. Within the upper spinal cord, for example, norepinephrine is manufactured only in certain regions. Neurons in these regions project their axons to the hypothalamus, limbic system, cerebral cortex, cerebellum, and lower regions in the spinal cord within well-defined pathways. (For a review of the anatomy and physiology of the norepinephrine system, see Moore and Bloom, 1979). In other cases, such as that of *acetylcholine*, the neurons that secrete a chemical are more widely dispersed; that is, they are located in many isolated areas and their axons do not always make up pathways.

It will be many years before we begin to fully understand and appreciate how these chemicals are organized, what their functions are, and how they interact with neurons and other chemicals within the brain. Each year we continue to discover more chemicals operating within the brain. Until most of these chemicals are discovered and their functions understood, it will not be possible to get a clear picture of the brain's chemical workings; it is therefore quite premature to draw firm conclusions about how the brain is chemically organized to serve physiological and psychological processes. Nevertheless, a few remarks will give the reader an idea of why the study of neurochemicals is currently an exciting area for those attempting to understand physiological/psychological interactions.

I. NEURAL CHEMICALS

As mentioned above, dozens of chemicals (currently around fifty) are known or suspected to be involved in the myriad workings of the brain. Some of these are noted in Table 11-1, which is by no means a complete list. In order to qualify as a **neural chemical**, a substance must be produced, stored, and released by neurons. It also must exert an effect on nerve cells by increasing or reducing their activity, or it must affect the functioning of other tissues, such as altering the

Neural chemical	Main sites and principal actions
Acetylcholine	Acetylcholine is used in many different neural systems. It is released by nerves that innervate skeletal muscle, causing these muscles to contract. It is also released by parasympathetic nerves, causing various effects on organs, as discussed in Chapter 7 (see Table 7–1). In addition, acetylcholine is found in neural endings throughout the brain and spinal cord, where it is released to excite or inhibit other neurons.
Norepinephrine	Norepinephrine is released by most sympathetic nerves and causes various effects on organs, as discussed in Chapter 7 (see Table 7–2). It is also found in neural endings throughout the brain and spinal cord where it is released to excite or inhibit other neurons. Neurons that produce norepinephrine are organized in discrete anatomical pathways that course through the brain.
Dopamine	Dopamine is found in neural endings throughout the brain, where it is released to excite or inhibit other neurons. As with norepinephrine, neurons producing dopamine are organized in discrete anatomical pathways. Dopamine is also believed to be the prolactin-inhibiting factor secreted by neurons within the hypothalamus because it inhibits prolactin secretion by the anterior pituitary gland (see Table 10–3).
Epinephrine	Epinephrine is released by nerve endings in the medulla of the adrenal gland (see Chapter 7). It is also found in neurons in the spinal cord, thalamus, and hypothalamus.
Serotonin	Serotonin is found in many tissues of the body as well as in neurons throughout the brain and spinal cord, where it is released to excite or inhibit nerve cells. Neurons that produce serotonin are also organized in discrete anatomical pathways that course through the brain.
Enkephalins and endorphins	Enkephalins and endorphins are also called "endogenous opiates" (see pages 248–249) and are produced in neurons throughout the spinal cord and brain.
Substance P	Substance P is found in neurons in the spinal cord, brain, and autonomic nervous system. It appears to be involved in the neural transmission of pain (see page 249). Substance P excites and, in some cases, inhibits neurons.
Hypothalamic chemicals that stimulate or inhibit the release of pituitary hormones (see Table 10–3).	LH-releasing hormone (LHRH) is mostly found in neurons confined to the hypothalamus and upper spinal cord (see Figure 10–7). Somatostatin and thyrotropin-releasing hormone (TRH) are also found in other parts of the brain.
Gamma-aminobutyric acid (GABA)	GABA is found throughout the brain, but especially in neurons in the cerebellum, spinal cord, and cerebral cortex. When released, GABA usually inhibits neural activity.
Histamine	Histamine is found in white blood cells where it is released in allergic and inflammatory reactions (see Figure 7–3). Histamine is also found in the hypothalamus and pituitary gland and to a lesser extent in other parts of the brain.
Glycine	Glycine is an amino acid found throughout the body. In the spinal cord it appears to inhibit neural activity.

Table 11-1.   Some of the major chemicals produced by neurons in the brain. These chemicals act as transmitter agents under two conditions: when they are released by neurons to influence the activity of other neurons, and when they are released by neurons to immediately influence the activity of the tissues they innervate (as occurs with acetylcholine and norepinephrine produced by the endings of neurons that serve the autonomic nervous system). In addition, neural chemicals act as hormones when they are first released into the blood. Many other neural transmitter agents are known to exist besides those listed, and undoubtedly many more remain to be discovered.

secretion of pituitary hormones (as occurs with hypothalamic releasing factors—see Table 10-3, Chapter 10) or affecting the activity of many of the internal organs (as occurs with acetylcholine, norepinephrine, and epinephrine when they are released from the neuronal endings of the autonomic nervous system—see Tables 7-1 and 7-2, Chapter 7).

We know much more about *acetylcholine* and *norepinephrine* than we do of any other neural chemicals, largely because they are released by neurons innervating the organs and muscles of the body and, therefore, are readily accessible. Figure 11-1 illustrates and discusses some of the events that occur at the endings of the neurons that secrete norepinephrine. Various *drugs* are known to influence the activity of neural chemicals and those affecting norepinephrine are noted in this figure. As indicated, these drugs are quite specific in how they affect the activity of norepinephrine. In fact, it is this specificity which led to the differentiation of receptors into "alpha" and "beta," a distinction that is extremely important in our understanding of immunological reactions and the effects of sympathetic stimulation on various organs (see Chapter 7). We will discuss the effects of drugs at greater length in Section III of this chapter.

Although the detailed workings are different— different chemical processes are involved and different drugs affect these systems—the basic manner in which neurons secrete *epinephrine, dopamine, serotonin,* and *acetylcholine* is similar to that of *norepinephrine*. We will not describe these workings in detail (see recommended readings for this chapter); we will, however, mention specific properties of some of these chemicals as they fit into our discussion of neural chemicals and their effects on behavior.

As previously mentioned, very little is known about most of the neural chemicals listed in Table 11-1. In fact, aside from the actions of epinephrine, norepinephrine, and acetylcholine when released by peripheral nerves (those innervating muscles and organs), very little is understood about the actions of these chemicals within the brain. Our lack of knowledge is partly because of the difficulty of studying chemical activity inside the brain, where the neurons are harder to isolate, but it is also because the identity and anatomical organization of these chemicals within the brain has been discovered only very recently.

However little we understand of the regulatory roles played by the various neural chemicals, we understand even less about their relation to behavior. Nevertheless, some findings are very interesting and are discussed below as part of a general discussion of some of the apparent functions of these chemicals. Much of the information presented is relatively recent and, as such, still under intense investigation; accordingly, many findings are referenced and an extensive list of recommended readings is included at the end of the chapter.

II. APPARENT FUNCTIONS OF NEURAL CHEMICALS

As mentioned earlier, the more we understand of the functions of the neural chemicals, the more it becomes clear that they are responsible for regulating exquisitely refined systems operating within the brain and other parts of the body. Some aspects of these refined workings are listed below as they apply to physiological and behavioral functions.

1) NEURONS USUALLY SPECIALIZE IN WHICH CHEMICALS THEY PRODUCE. For many years it was assumed that each nerve cell makes use of only one chemical, which it produces and releases. That is, a neuron that secretes *norepinephrine* does not secrete *serotonin* or *acetylcholine*, and vice versa. Although generally correct, in some cases it appears that neurons can secrete more than one chemical, or change their secretion from one chemical to another (Potter, Furshpan, and Landis, 1983; Landis, 1983).

2) DEPENDING ON WHICH CHEMICALS THEY PRODUCE, NEURONS WITHIN THE BRAIN ARE ORGANIZED IN DISCRETE ANATOMICAL PATTERNS. Neurons secreting the chemicals listed in Table 11-1 are all found in the hypothalamus, yet they are not randomly dispersed. Those that secrete *norepinephrine, serotonin, dopamine,* and *epinephrine* are each a part of a "system" of neurons that courses through the brain, some having their origin in specific regions of the upper spinal cord where they produce one or another of these chemicals. Neurons that secrete *acetylcholine* are organized in a similar manner, but they are also found in clusters that appear throughout the brain or in pathways such as that linking the septum and the hippocampus. Thus, each neural chemical appears to be found in neurons that are discretely located within the spinal cord and/or brain.

3) IN SOME CASES, DIFFERENT CELLULAR MECHANISMS CAN BE ACTIVATED BY THE SAME CHEMICAL. The effects of *epinephrine* and *norepinephrine* on alpha and beta receptors in the organs—an effect discussed on pages 129–130 of Chapter 7—illustrates this observation clearly. It appears that the same types of receptors exist within the brain. For example, when norepinephrine levels are raised within the lateral hypothalamus of rats, eating behavior is inhibited, but when levels are raised within the medial hypothalamus, eating behavior increases. The first effect (suppressed eating) appears to be mediated via beta receptors whereas the second (increased eating) appears to be mediated via alpha receptors (Hoebel and Leibowitz, 1981).

4) THE SAME NEURAL CHEMICAL CAN HAVE MANY DIFFERENT ACTIONS. The actions of any given chemical probably depend on its location within the brain and which receptors it activates. For example, *norepinephrine* released by neurons within the brain affects not only eating behavior but also the secretion of many pituitary hormones. Similarly, *dopamine* has been reported to increase the intensity of electrical self-stimulation (activating "reward" systems) but it has also been found to cause increased or decreased sexual behavior (increasing it in males, both increasing and decreasing it in females—Crowley and Zemlan, 1981) and inhibit prolactin secretion by the anterior pituitary gland. *Endorphins* can produce analgesia—a decreased or abolished sensitivity to pain—but they also affect body temperature and can produce insomnia.

It is clearly apparent that neural chemicals affect many physiological and psychological functions, and that the workings of refined mechanisms are involved. Some of these functions are discussed briefly below. (It is not the purpose of this book to present detailed information concerning processes whose workings are so poorly understood.)

Regulation of Pituitary Hormones

Norepinephrine within the brain influences the secretion of pituitary hormones, but *dopamine, serotonin, histamine, acetylcholine,* and the *endorphins* do so as well, as do the *releasing factors* discussed in the previous chapter. Although it is apparent that each of the releasing factors exerts a different action on the pituitary gland and that dopamine inhibits prolactin secretion, the specific regulatory roles of other neural chemicals (and, for that matter, dopamine) are not known.

Pain

For a long time we have known that opiates such as morphine reduce or abolish the perception of pain, an effect called "analgesia." During the past fifteen years we have begun to understand some of the mechanisms involved in this process. It appears that narcotics such as morphine, heroin, codeine, and methadone exert their analgesic action by binding to specific receptors associated with neurons in the periaqueductal gray region of the upper spinal cord (see Figure 7-11, Chapter 7). These narcotic drugs, by increasing the activity of these neurons, leads to reduced sensations of pain. The receptors involved are called "opiate receptors" (because opiates bind to them), and we now know that neurons naturally produce a family of peptides, collectively called *endorphins,* which bind to these same receptors.

Enkephalins are part of the endorphin family. These are small molecules, consisting of five amino acids that are linked together. Enkephalins are produced and released by neurons in the periaqueductal gray region of the upper spinal cord, but they are found in other regions of the brain as well—the hypothalamus, frontal cortex, amygdala, septum, and caudate nucleus. Larger endorphins—made up of more amino acids—are found mostly in the hypothalamic-pituitary region, and a still larger endorphin—called *beta-lipotropin*—is secreted by the anterior pituitary gland into the blood. The enkephalins bind to opiate receptors in the brain and they produce analgesia when injected into the periaqueductal gray region of the upper spinal cord.

It is becoming increasingly clear that enkephalin-secreting neurons are only a part of a larger system that mediates pain. Neurons that release *serotonin* and neurons that secrete a chemical called *substance P* are also involved, as are others (see Calne, 1978).

Sexual Behavior

Many different neural chemicals also appear to influence sexual behavior. In the last chapter we mentioned that the neuropeptide, *LH-releasing hormone* (LHRH), not only stimulates LH release, but also induces sexual behavior when it is injected into the hypothalamus of rats (Moss, 1979). Earlier in this chapter, we noted that *dopamine* also influences sexual behavior, and it appears that *serotonin* does so as well (serotonin within the brain has been reported to inhibit sexual behavior in female and male rats, and in female monkeys and hamsters—see Crowley and Zemlan, 1981). *Endorphins* have been observed to both increase and decrease sexual behavior. In addition to these effects, the sex hormones testosterone and estrogen (see Chapter 10) also influence the secretion of neural chemicals within the brain.

Eating

As discussed in Chapter 3, the medial hypothalamus is part of a system that regulates satiety and the cessation of eating whereas the lateral hypothalamus is involved with hunger and eating. We mentioned that electrical stimulation of the medial hypothalamus can make an animal stop eating and that destroying this area causes an animal to overeat and become obese. Similarly, when glucose is injected into this area, an animal will stop eating—another indication of satiety.

Earlier we noted that neurons which secrete *norepinephrine* appear to participate in these responses; so do those that release *serotonin, gamma-aminobutyric acid* (GABA, see Table 11-1), and *endorphins*. The mechanisms operative here are beginning to become somewhat clear. It appears, for example, that norepinephrine within the medial hypothalamus inhibits this part of the satiety system and thus causes animals to eat more. Norepinephrine within this region of the brain also leads to increased secretion of acid by the stomach and increases insulin secretion. Low glucose levels and low endorphin levels within the medial hypothalamus also induce eating behavior, and it appears that these effects are related to the activation of norepinephrine-secreting neurons. In other words, norepinephrine participates with a host of other chemicals in a variety of well-integrated responses.

Reward

Throughout this book we have noted that reward mechanisms are well-integrated with specific functions. For example, hunger and eating, thirst and drinking, breathing, smell and taste sensations, and sexual behavior are all clearly connected to reward mechanisms as measured by electrical self-stimulation studies of the brain. We have also seen that the "reward value" of these processes is related to many factors, including the level of various chemicals produced by the activity of specific organs and tissues in the body—glucose for eating, angiotensin for drinking, carbon dioxide for breathing, testosterone for sexual behavior, to name a few. It has become increasingly clear that chemicals produced and released by nerve cells in the brain participate in the regulation of reward mechanisms as well.

Neurons that release *norepinephrine* and *dopamine*, for example, appear to be related to reward mechanisms, the evidence for dopamine being somewhat more convincing than that for norepinephrine. *Endorphins* also appear to be involved. That is, when rats are allowed to press a lever that delivers *enkephalins* or morphine into the hypothalamus, the rate of self-administration is high (see Olds and Fobes, 1981). Also, when rats self-administer electrical stimulation, the rate of self-stimulation can sometimes be reduced by injecting these rats with naloxone, a drug that blocks some of the effects of morphine and the endorphins (see Belluzi and Stein, 1977; Olds and Fobes, 1981). This effect is not surprising, given that narcotic drugs (which, you will recall, bind with the same receptors as do endorphins) are generally known to be rewarding to individuals who take them. On the other hand, not all studies show morphine to be rewarding. In fact, when the electrode is placed within the lateral hypothalamic area, some studies show that morphine will decrease the rate of self-administered electrical stimulation (see Lomax and Ary, 1978). It is also interesting to note that the rewarding effect of endorphins apparently exists separately from their analgesic action of reducing pain (see Mayer and Liebeskind, 1974).

In previous chapters we emphasized that "reward" is not a singular process. Rather, as with consciousness, arousal, attention, sleep, and voluntary behavior, "reward" is part of whatever is being integrated at that time. Limited as it is, our understanding of the workings of neural chemicals clearly strengthens this interpretation. For example, when *norepinephrine* is injected into the amygdala of *hungry* rats this serves as a potent reward. However, norepinephrine is ineffective as such a motivator when injected into the amygdala of rats that are *not* hungry (see Jurkowlaniec and Bialowas, 1981). Also, injections of *serotonin* into the medial hypothalamus will make rats avoid a high carbohydrate diet—leaving their preference for protein undisturbed—whereas *norepinephrine* will make rats prefer carbohydrates (Hoebel and Leibowitz, 1981; Tretter and Leibowitz, 1980). These results confirm that "reward" involves highly refined systems that differ in their workings from one function to another. In other words, this refinement is characterized not only by the specific experience (experientially, the "reward" of drinking water when one is thirsty is clearly different from the "reward" of sex or the "reward" of breathing after having held one's breath for a while), by anatomy (different areas of the hypothalamus are rewarding depending on the function, such as eating or sex), and by the functioning of specific organs (expressed in the form of hunger pangs, a dry mouth, high or low levels of testosterone, insulin, and carbon dioxide, all of which influence reward mechanisms), but also by the effects of neural chemicals.

Stress

In Chapter 7 we discussed the involvement of the brain, the autonomic nervous system, the adrenal glands, and the immune system in defensive behaviors and stress responses. We saw that these systems are strongly connected to each other and that their interactions produce a variety of effects in the body. It is obvious that changes do occur within the brain during stress reactions; it is not surprising, therefore, that these reactions appear to involve changes in the release of neural chemicals as well.

Stress influences the release of *corticotrophin-releasing factor* (CRF, which causes the pituitary gland to release ACTH which then stimulates the cortex of the adrenal glands—see Table 10-3 and Chapter 7), *serotonin, norepinephrine, epinephrine, dopamine,* the *endorphins,* and possibly other chemicals produced within the brain, including *acetylcholine* and *histamine.* In general, stress appears to increase the synthesis of these chemicals within neurons, increase their release, and decrease their degradation. At the present time, we cannot state that any particular chemical system is uniquely involved —they all appear to be. Whatever the chemical systems, however, they appear to be operating in a very refined manner.

For example, stress appears to increase the amount of *dopamine* found in one area of the ventromedial hypothalamus and to increase the amount of *serotonin* in another area of the *same* structure. Thus, there are "microcircuits" of neurons that react selectively to

stress by secreting one or another chemical. Also, the changes that occur in the amount of *epinephrine* found in the hypothalamus and upper spinal cord in response to stress appear to be more marked than those associated with other neural chemicals. In addition, it seems that there are very selective changes in the receptors that receive these chemicals once they are released. In some cases, repeated stress causes a decreased sensitivity of beta receptors within the brain and, in other cases, an increased sensitivity of alpha receptors (U'Prichard and Kvetnansky, 1980). Both of these receptors are influenced by *norepinephrine* (see page 130, Chapter 7 and Figure 11-1). Norepinephrine has been reported to decrease ACTH secretion by the anterior pituitary gland (you will recall that ACTH stimulates the adrenal cortex to release glucocorticoids—see pages 130–131, Chapter 7 and page 230, Chapter 10) whereas *dopamine, histamine,* and the *endorphins* have been reported to increase ACTH secretion. Much more research must be performed before we are sure of what these findings mean. Nevertheless, they clearly indicate that stress activates complex, refined mechanisms within the brain.

What do we conclude from all of this? As stated in the beginning of this chapter, it is premature to draw conclusions until much more is known of the specific roles played by neural chemicals in determining neural function. Given the intricate structure and varied functions of the brain, the fact that *each* neuron releases one or more of the many chemicals known to be produced within neural cells, and the strong likelihood that each of these chemicals exerts a specific influence on whichever neurons and/or organs they act upon, the number of possible effects is so vast as to be almost beyond comprehension. Furthermore, it appears that the entire brain and all of its functions are organized in this highly refined manner.

III. DRUGS

Most of our knowledge about the functions of neural chemicals has been gained as a direct result of the discovery and synthesis of drugs that influence these chemicals. Because the adrenal glands and the autonomic nervous system have important and powerful effects on our organs and immune system, influencing conditions such as high blood pressure, asthma, allergic reactions and many others (see Chapter 7), efforts have been more or less continuous to develop drugs capable of modifying their effects. In this connection, hundreds of drugs that influence the release and/or action of acetylcholine, norepinephrine, and epineph-rine have been developed over the past forty years.

The basic manner in which drugs modify the release and/or action of *norepinephrine* is discussed and illustrated in Figure 11-1. As noted, drugs can exert their actions in various ways. In the case of norepinephrine, they can block its production (as with alpha-methyl-para-tyrosine, disulfiram and FLA-63), interrupt its storage in nerve endings (as with reserpine and tetrabenazine), stimulate its release and prolong its action (as with amphetamine and cocaine), block its effects on alpha receptors (as with phentolamine), block its effects on beta receptors (propranolol), stimulate its effects on alpha receptors (clonidine), or stimulate its effects on beta receptors (terbutaline).

Even though different drugs affect different systems, their actions are generally similar to those described above. There are many drugs that selectively influence the production, release, and actions of acetylcholine, histamine, dopamine, serotonin, and epinephrine. For example, apomorphine is a drug that increases the activity of receptors sensitive to *dopamine*. Pilocarpine increases the activity of receptors sensitive to *acetylcholine*, and atropine decreases this sensitivity. P-chlorophenylalanine (pCPA) blocks the synthesis of *serotonin*, whereas SKF 64139 blocks the synthesis of *epinephrine*. Although very few drugs have been developed that influence recently discovered chemicals, there are a few. Naloxone, for example, is a drug that blocks the effects of the *endorphins*.

Drugs that affect the activity of neural chemicals are used for a variety of medical purposes. In addition to their use in modifying the activity of organs or the immune system, they are also used to modify neural activity within the brain. For example, in persons suffering from Parkinson's disease, a disease characterized by tremors, rigidity of the limbs, difficulty in initiating movements, and a general lack of associative movements (such as not swinging the arms when walking), parts of the brain function abnormally—in particular, the basal ganglia (see page 198) and the upper spinal cord, where abnormally low levels of *dopamine* are found. Administration of L-dopa in large doses allows it to enter neurons within the brain where it is then converted into dopamine (see step 2, Figure 11-1). Although the administration of L-dopa is not a cure, it has been very effective in treating many patients with Parkinson's disease.

For reasons of perspective, we have pointed out that many drugs exert specific effects on one or another neurochemical system, but it is not within the scope of this book to discuss the many actions of drugs. Even though their actions are not as easy to classify as those catalogued in patients with Parkinson's disease, drugs have clear effects on psychotic behavior, schizophrenia, and depression, and they appear to exert their effects by modifying the activity of neural chemicals within the brain. We will briefly discuss these actions.

Hallucinations and Psychotic Behavior

Many drugs have hallucinogenic actions. These include psilocybin, mescaline, bufotenine, amphetamine, cocaine, and lysergic acid diethylamide (LSD). All of these drugs influence the activity of neural chemicals, but what specific effect they may share has not yet been discovered. In many cases, hallucinogenic drugs stimulate receptors that are sensitive to *serotonin;* however, effects on *norepinephrine*, *dopamine*, and *histamine* are also frequently reported.

Large doses of hallucinogenic drugs sometimes produce delusions and hallucinations that are practically indistinguishable from those seen in some cases of schizophrenia. In general, schizophrenia is a mental disorder characterized by these symptoms in addition to behavior such as withdrawal from the outside world, "inappropriate" emotional reactions, and progressive deterioration of the patient's mental state over time. Delusions, in contrast to hallucinations, are said to occur when a person experiences beliefs that are clearly contrary to reality—beliefs that "everyone is trying to harm me or kill me" or that one is especially exalted, the president or ruler of a country, perhaps. Hallucinations refer to perceptions of objects or experiences of events that cannot be detected by anyone else (and would be with certainty if actually present). For example, a person might frequently misidentify another person as a demon, or hear the sound of sirens. Such symptoms have been observed most often in response to amphetamine, L-dopa, cocaine, and methylphenidate (Ritalin). Although these drugs all stimulate the action of *dopamine*, it is premature to discuss exact mechanisms until we know much more about the various roles neural chemicals play in regulating neural functions.

In many cases, hallucinogenic substances have chemical structures that are very similar to those of known neural chemicals (see Figure 11-2). Because of these similarities, some investigators have concluded that one cause of schizophrenia may be the abnormal production or metabolism of neurochemicals within the brain. In other words, psychosis-producing substances may be manufactured in the brain of the schizophrenic. There are some findings to support

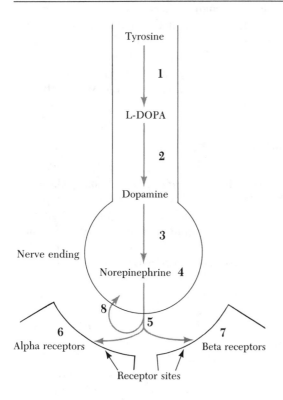

(1) Conversion of the amino acid tyrosine to L-DOPA (dihydroxyphenylalanine) is facilitated by the enzyme tyrosine hydroxylase. The drug α-methyl-para-tyrosine (AMPT) inhibits this enzyme and therefore prevents the synthesis of DOPA.

(2) Conversion of DOPA to dopamine takes place via the enzyme DOPA decarboxylase.

(3) Conversion of dopamine to norepinephrine takes place via the enzyme dopamine-β-hydroxylase. The drugs disulfiram and FLA-63 inhibit this enzyme and prevent the synthesis of norepinephrine (dopamine will be released instead).

(4) Norepinephrine is stored in vesicles (small spheroidal "bubbles" surrounded by a membrane; these vesicles hold fluid that contains the chemical). The drugs reserpine and tetrabenazine displace norepinephrine from the vesicles, allowing it to escape and be quickly destroyed.

(5) Norepinephrine is released from the nerve ending. The drug amphetamine facilitates this release.

(6) Norepinephrine acts on alpha receptors. Alpha receptors are blocked by the drugs phentolamine, yohimbine, and phenoxybenzamine. The drug clonidine stimulates alpha receptors.

(7) Norepinephrine acts on beta receptors (less so than does epinephrine, however). Beta receptors are blocked by the drug propranolol and stimulated by isoproteronol (which also stimulates alpha receptors to a slight extent) and terbutaline.

(8) Norepinephrine is "pumped" back into the nerve ending. This process is called re-uptake, and it is the main mechanism for terminating the effects of norepinephrine. The drugs amphetamine and cocaine inhibit the re-uptake of norepinephrine and dopamine. The tricyclic antidepressants (imipramine, amitryptyline, and desipramine are some of these) also inhibit re-uptake. Desipramine selectively inhibits norepinephrine re-uptake while the other tricyclics also inhibit dopamine and serotonin re-uptake.

Figure 11–1. Some of the events occurring at noradrenergic nerve endings. These nerve endings exist within the brain and at the end of nerves comprising the sympathetic nervous system. Noradrenergic neurons secrete noradrenalin, also called norepinephrine (NE). The basic manner in which neurons secrete other chemicals—such as acetylcholine and serotonin—is similar to that involving norepinephrine, although different enzymes and neurons are involved and different drugs are effective.

Note that **drugs** can selectively influence many of these events. In some cases the drugs listed have effects on other neural chemicals as well. Reserpine and tetrabenazine also block the storage of serotonin and dopamine in neurons that release these chemicals, whereas amphetamine and cocaine also inhibit the re-uptake of dopamine. The drugs mentioned in this figure are only a small fraction of those known to influence norepinephrine.

NEURAL CHEMICALS   SIMILAR HALLUCINOGENS

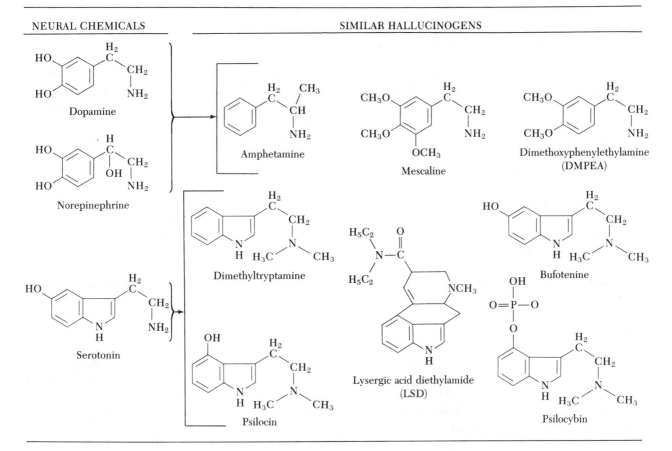

Figure 11–2. Chemical structure of hallucinogenic substances that are similar in structure to the known neural chemicals, dopamine, norepinephrine and serotonin.
(Adapted from Barchas, Akil, Elliott, Holman and Watson, *SCIENCE*, Vol. 200, page 969, 1978).

this theory but, at the present time, the evidence is not very convincing. Nevertheless, this hypothesis is very exciting.

Antischizophrenic Drugs

If drugs can produce symptoms of schizophrenia, it is not surprising that there exist other drugs that can reduce these symptoms. Most (if not all) of the many antischizophrenic drugs appear to block *dopamine* receptors. Perhaps the best known drug is chlorpromazine (Thorazine). Chlorpromazine not only blocks dopamine receptors, but it also has been reported to block the effects of *serotonin, acetylcholine, histamine,* and other chemicals. Drugs such as spiroperidol and pimozide are quite specific in antagonizing the effects of dopamine, and they are very potent antischizophrenic agents. Apparently, neurons that interact with dopamine within the brain play an important role in schizophrenia, but we do not know what this role is.

The antischizophrenic drugs are sometimes called "major tranquilizers." Some, but not all, of these drugs are classified as sedatives. Their antischizophrenic action (reducing hallucinations, delusions, and disordered thoughts) can occur with or without sedation. It is therefore incorrect to view the antischizophrenic drugs as agents whose primary action is merely to tranquilize the patient.

Antidepressant Drugs

Depression is characterized by feelings of hopelessness, lethargy, despair, and sadness. In extreme cases, called "psychotic depression," the depressed state is combined with a general view of life that is divorced from reality—frequently there are feelings of deep personal guilt over offenses and shortcomings that are imagined or for which one is not responsible and over which one has no control. There are often strong feelings of wanting to "get out" via suicide.

There is a class of drugs called "tricyclic antidepressants" (their chemical structure contains three rings—hence the tricyclic name) which are quite effective against depression. Imipramine, discovered in 1957, was one of the first of these drugs to be developed. Now there are many, including amitryptiline, doxepine, and the tetracyclic antidepressant, mianserin. It is generally believed that most antidepressants exert their action by intensifying the effects of *norepinephrine* and/or *serotonin* within the brain by prolonging their action after they are released. Not all of the antidepressants have this action, however. Furthermore, some drugs increase the activity of norepinephrine and/or serotonin in the brain but are not antidepressant drugs. Many of the antidepressant drugs appear to block the effects of *histamine*, yet, again, not all of them do this. At this point, all we can state with certainty is that some drugs are clearly antidepressant and that these drugs in some way affect the activity of neural chemicals. We do not understand how these chemicals work.

As the discovery of new neural chemicals and the development of drugs capable of influencing the activity of these chemicals continues, we will certainly learn much more about mental disorders. In the meantime, what little we do know serves to confirm that physiology and psychology are as inseparably connected in psychopathologic functions as in normal functions such as eating, drinking, breathing, sensory perception, and sex.

IV. RELATION TO HEALTH

The discovery of drugs that help in the treatment of mental disease and Parkinson's disease are clear examples of the chemical nature of the brain being put to use to promote health. But there are much more subtle relationships. Of these, perhaps the most important to health, in a negative sense, is the development of dependence and addiction to certain chemicals.

Dependence and Addiction

It is well known that receptors in neurons and other tissues can undergo an altered sensitivity to the chemicals that affect them. This fact was discussed in Chapter 7, where we mentioned that a reduced sensitivity of beta receptors to the effects of epinephrine and norepinephrine is probably one reason why stress can intensify inflammatory or immune reactions in some people.

One way to alter the sensitivity of receptors is to *repeatedly* expose them to the same chemical. In some cases, continued exposure to a chemical *reduces* the response of neurons and organs to that chemical. This process is called **tolerance**. Tolerance implies a decreased sensitivity of receptors to the chemical involved, and, although we know it is the result of a process occurring within cells, it remains a poorly understood phenomenon. As tolerance develops, *more* of a chemical (a higher dose) is required to produce the same effect as before.

As a person develops tolerance for a chemical, there is a chance of becoming **dependent** on it. Furthermore, if the higher levels of the chemical are suddenly reduced, there can be **withdrawal symptoms**. When withdrawal symptoms are physical, a person is in a state of **physical dependence**. When a person craves the chemical, this craving is called **psychic dependence**.

A person who is physically dependent on a chemical always develops tolerance to it and experiences psychic dependence. On the other hand, psychic dependence and physical tolerance can develop with little or no obvious physical withdrawal symptoms once the chemical is removed. Thus it appears that psychic dependence can occur without physical dependence. Even so, we cannot categorically state that these two types of dependence exist independently of each other. Physiological and psychological dependence are discussed in more detail below, where we will briefly comment on the effects of progressively less addictive chemicals—heroin, alcohol, nicotine (from smoking tobacco) and caffeine (coffee, tea, and cola drinks).

Heroin Addiction. Almost all persons who use heroin develop tolerance to the effects of this chemical, which is converted into morphine once it enters the brain. (Heroin enters the brain more readily than does morphine.) In addition, heroin users develop an irresistible need for the drug (psychic dependence) and severe and painful physical symptoms when the drug is withdrawn (physical dependence). Heroin suppresses respiration, gastrointestinal movement, and the activities of the autonomic nervous system; causes sedation, pupillary constriction, and euphoria; and produces analgesia. As tolerance develops, many of these effects of heroin are reduced unless increasingly higher doses are taken. The symptoms of withdrawal are opposite to the effects of the drug—activation of the autonomic nervous system (autonomic storm), pupillary dilation, hyperventilation, intestinal spasms (stomach cramps and diarrhea), an acute sensitivity to pain (generalized physical discomfort), gooseflesh (explaining the phrase "cold turkey"), insomnia, and states of depression.

Although heroin dependence is clearly a physiological condition that is almost always connected with strong withdrawal reactions, psychological factors appear to be involved as well. For example, in one study (see Wikler, 1981), subjects on heroin, morphine, or methadone (a synthetic narcotic) were given nalorphine and, as expected, withdrawal reactions occurred within a few minutes. (Nalorphine, like naloxone, is an opiate antagonist. We will discuss naloxone when we discuss the relationship between addictive drugs and the activity of neural chemicals later in this section.) When saline (a salt solution compatible with blood but containing no drugs) was substituted for nalorphine, the subjects, thinking the injection was nalorphine, *still* suffered from withdrawal symptoms. This conditioned response persisted for several weeks and then stopped; that is, saline no longer evoked withdrawal symptoms in subjects who were still taking opiates. When the subjects were questioned, it was revealed that they had been watching each other and had figured out after several weeks that if withdrawal symptoms did not appear within 2 to 3 minutes, the shot was a "blank" (saline). (This conclusion was based on the fact that the conditioned withdrawal symptoms took longer to develop, so if they did not get sick within a few minutes then the shot was not nalorphine.) Commenting on this observation, Wikler points out that the subject's realization that they were getting a blank was sufficient to change their reaction from withdrawal symptoms to no withdrawal symptoms. In a separate experiment, when an odor and sound were presented to subjects during mild withdrawal from methadone, following repeated pairing of the noise and odor, signs of withdrawal were eventually elicited as a conditioned response (i.e., withdrawal reactions occurred without administering naloxone—see O'Brien, Testa, O'Brien, Brady, and Wells, 1977). Again, this finding points to the conclusion that psychological factors are involved in withdrawal reactions to narcotics. (In this case, involving one's reaction to the environment as defined by the odor and sound.)

Alcohol Addiction. In humans, the main route of alcohol elimination is the oxidation of ethanol by the liver. Ethanol is converted into acetaldehyde, which is then converted into acetate. In turn, many organs convert acetate into acetyl CoA, which is readily metabolized into carbon dioxide and water (see Figures 3-1 and 3-1A). The large amounts of energy released during this metabolic process are used to produce the high-energy molecule, ATP (see Chapter 3). Because so much energy is produced as ethanol is degraded, up to two-thirds of the body's total energy needs may be satisfied by substituting alcohol for other foods. (This explains why many alcoholics neglect eating for several weeks at a time.)

In alcoholics, blood and liver acetaldehyde levels are higher after drinking ethanol than in nonalcoholics (see Salaspuro, Lindros, and Nuutinen, 1983). Unfortunately, high levels of acetaldehyde are harmful. Directly disturbing the intricate activities of the cells of the liver, the heart's ability to synthesize protein, and reacting to produce unnatural chemicals when combined with other chemicals (including those produced in the brain), acetaldehyde can damage many tissues. If alcohol is consumed, accumulation of acetaldehyde from ethanol can be greatly increased by administering such drugs as disulfiram (Antabuse) and calcium cyanamide (Temposil, Dipsan). The accompanying results—flushing, increased heart rate, headache, hyperventilation, vertigo, nausea, and vomiting—are very disagreeable and they form the basis for using these drugs to promote an aversion for alcohol in alcoholics. One theory holds that in the early, adaptive stage of alcoholism, a vicious cycle begins whereby the alcoholic must drink more to maintain a level of alcohol sufficient to override and block the harmful effects of the rising level of acetaldehyde (Milam and Ketcham, 1981).

Although we *do* understand some of the reasons why the ethanol consumed by chronic heavy drinkers of alcohol is damaging to the body, very little is understood about the process of alcohol addiction. Many persons who are heavy drinkers develop clear-cut tolerance to this chemical and have very few withdrawal symptoms once they stop drinking. On the basis of these cases, one might conclude that alcohol dependence is mainly a psychological process; yet alcohol withdrawal in some addicts consistently produces very serious physical symptoms, including convulsions, high fever, and delirium, as well as less serious effects such as nervousness, tremors, restlessness, nausea, vomiting, and insomnia. Rather than concluding that alcohol dependence is merely a psychological condition that is sometimes connected to particularly strong withdrawal reactions, we could equally state that dependence is a physiological process which is sometimes connected to particular psychological reactions (sometimes increasing, sometimes reducing withdrawal reactions). Along these lines, when a person whose alcohol or drug addiction has been arrested undergoes stress, or is in the company of others who are still addicted, or is depressed, there may be a reappearance of physical withdrawal symptoms even though there has been physiological recovery (Wikler, 1981). Under these conditions, the former dependent may start taking these chemicals again as an obvious and known way to get rid of the very unpleasant withdrawal reaction. In other words, there is no doubt that a person's psychological state can modify dependency reactions, even inducing physical withdrawal symptoms long after a person has been free of addiction.

Nicotine Addiction. Chronic smokers of tobacco develop tolerance to the chemicals involved (mostly nicotine in the case of tobacco), and many people are psychically dependent on this habit—they will crave nicotine even though tobacco is known to be harmful. (Tobacco contains hundreds of chemicals; of these, nicotine is most clearly associated with addiction, "tar" with cancer.) Although withdrawal symptoms are much less severe for nicotine than for opiates and other drugs, they are clear-cut. Symptoms include nausea, headache, tension, irritability, depression, anxiety, constipation, restlessness, difficulty concentrating, insomnia, a drop in heart rate and blood pressure, a decrease in high-frequency activity in the EEG, and many other common reactions (such as drowsiness). It is therefore apparent that although some persons may experience very few withdrawal symptoms when they stop smoking, this does not necessarily mean that we are looking at the workings of psychological processes free from physiological processes. As with alcohol, we could also state the converse—that we are looking at physiological dependence modified by psychological reactions. For instance, it is entirely possible that when a person who has long since stopped smoking enters a stressful, anxiety-provoking situation, unpleasant feelings would be evoked by the workings of some mechanisms that are *identical* to those evoked during withdrawal. If this person were to start smoking, the unpleasant feelings would be reduced. This is a conditioned response based on prior experience. (Approximately 70 percent of heavy smokers appear to smoke more when exposed to emotionally stressful situations—Kissen, 1960; McArthur, Waldron, and Dickinson, 1958.) The relationship between nicotine dependence and stress has been demonstrated in rats, where animals given nicotine performed better in stressful situations than they did when the nicotine was withdrawn. This response was dependent on the intensity of the stress; when the situation was only mildly stressful, there

was no difference in performance when the rats were given saline instead of nicotine (Hall and Morrison, 1973).

Caffeine Addiction. The effects of chronic caffeine consumption, studied mostly among coffee drinkers, are not as well documented as those of heroin, alcohol, and tobacco smoking. In some reports, the development of tolerance is clear, but not in others. Similarly, although most investigators report physical dependence or withdrawal reactions to caffeine, some do not. Symptoms of caffeine withdrawal include headache, irritability, depression, drowsiness, and lethargy. Again, many chronic coffee drinkers crave coffee if they are deprived of it, but many do not. Thus, dependence on caffeine generally appears to be a weak effect, both physiologically and psychologically. Nevertheless, the fact that a substantial proportion of adults throughout the world habitually drink caffeine—either in coffee, tea, or cola drinks—is some indication that a degree of dependence develops.

Clearly, the development of tolerance to a drug, physiological and psychological dependence, and withdrawal symptoms are all interrelated. Furthermore, the intensity of these processes varies with different drugs, being strongest with opiates and alcohol, being less strong with drugs like caffeine. Of course, not all chemicals induce tolerance and dependence; however, dependence and withdrawal reactions clearly apply to opiates, alcohol, barbiturates and, to a lesser extent, to amphetamine.

Addiction in Relation to Neurochemical Processes. Physical withdrawal symptoms, dependency, and the development of tolerance are complex processes that involve the brain as well as the organs in the rest of the body. Within the brain, the systems most likely to affect mechanisms of tolerance and dependence are those determined by the workings of neural chemicals. There are at least two ways that tolerance and dependence may develop:

a) The drug may alter the activity of neural chemicals and, in turn, this altered activity may lead to a condition of tolerance and dependence. Amphetamine and cocaine, for example, may be exerting their effects by stimulating the release of *norepinephrine* and by prolonging its actions, thereby causing the receptors sensitive to norepinephrine to change their responses. Because this explanation assumes the primary cause of tolerance and dependence to be the altered activity of neural chemicals, it suggests the possibility that tolerance and dependency can be induced *without* drugs. In other words, one could develop tolerance and dependence to chronic stress responses or any other chronic condition that repeatedly affects neural activity and the activity of neural chemicals. (This possibility will be discussed later in this section.)

b) The drug may exert its effects by acting on receptors that respond normally only to naturally-occurring neural chemicals. Heroin, morphine, and methadone may exert their effects, for example, by activating receptors *otherwise* responsive to the *endorphins*. This explanation assumes the development of tolerance and dependence to be caused by the abnormal functioning of receptors affected by chemicals that are not "natural" for the body.

Although precise workings are not understood, it is likely that both of these mechanisms are involved, and there may be others. Studies of the effects of heroin, alcohol, nicotine, and caffeine clearly point to the involvement of neural chemicals. We will mention only general findings that confirm the liklihood of these neurochemical workings; at this point, a detailed discussion would be premature.

We mentioned earlier that naloxone (and, to a lesser extent, nalorphine) reverses the effects of opiates such as morphine, heroin, methadone, and codeine by blocking the effects of these drugs on the receptors to which they attach within the brain. This drug has helped us to understand the effects of the opiates because it abolishes or greatly reduces such effects as analgesia and, as mentioned, naloxone can also induce withdrawal reactions in opiate addicts. The *endorphins*—probably *enkephalins* produced by neurons in the brain—appear to act on the same receptors as do the opiates. There are a number of reasons for this assumption:

a) When injected into the brain, the endorphins act like opiates in their ability to produce analgesia (see page 248);

b) With repeated administration, the endorphins are capable of inducing tolerance and dependency reactions;

c) As with the opiates, the effects of the endorphins are blocked by naloxone.

Because the activity of *norepinephrine* and *dopamine* within the brain increases when opiates are administered, these neural chemicals also appear to be involved in the process of dependence and tolerance to opiates.

Alcohol also increases the activity of *norepinephrine* and *dopamine* within the brain. In addition, alcohol also affects the activity of *acetylcholine*, *serotonin* and other chemicals (see Ellingboe, 1978). Confirmation of the involvement of these chemicals comes from reports indicating that withdrawal reactions to alcohol abstinence are relieved by drugs that increase the levels of norepinephrine and dopamine within the brain (Griffiths, Littleton, and Ortiz, 1974; Collier, Hammond, and Schneider, 1976). Alcohol may also promote the production of abnormal chemicals such as tetrahydropapaveroline (THP), which may be produced in the brain through an interaction of dopamine with acetaldehyde. THP may act on neural receptors to produce addiction to alcohol (Myers and Melchior, 1977).

With smoking, it is clear that nicotine affects the release of various neural chemicals, especially *norepinephrine*, *dopamine*, *acetylcholine* and *serotonin*. Similarly, caffeine has been reported to affect the activity of *norepinephrine*, *dopamine*, *acetylcholine*, and *serotonin* within the brain (see Gilbert, 1976).

Although much more research needs to be done before we understand the various mechanisms involved—for example, mechanisms responsible for opiate dependence and withdrawal are somewhat different from those involved in alcohol dependence (see, for example, Goldstein and Judson, 1971)—it is nevertheless clear that we are looking at complex interactions of drugs and the neural chemicals and receptors they influence.

Habits, Addiction, and Stress

In general, our behaviors are quite habitual. The postures we asume as we sit and stand, our patterns of speech and eating, even the way we "arrange" ourselves before we go to sleep, are more or less the same each time we perform these (and many other) functions. Although most of our habits are quite harmless, some of them can be detrimental to our health. In fact, drug addiction can be considered as a particularly "bad" habit. In other words, although drug addiction is a special circumstance, as a habit it is likely to involve processes that occur in the same patterns as our other everyday habits. These are some of the properties common to all habits:

a) We consider the repetition involved in our habits to be necessary or rewarding. In learning to drive a car, for example, we did it repeatedly so that the mechanics of driving would become "habitual."

b) Once developed, any change in our habits is

discomforting, especially if we are "forced" to change. The irritability and restlessness we experience when we are "forced," for example, to drive with the seat pulled far forward (or, for others, far back) is not that different from what we experience when we wish to smoke a cigarette but must wait for a more appropriate time and place. In many respects, therefore, changing a habit leads to some kind of withdrawal reaction. (You will probably experience this discomfort if you cross your fingers for a brief period of time as you are now reading.)

c) Even though unhealthy, we will often stick to our habits. Some of us will not change our driving posture, for example, until our back pains become so severe that something must be done about it.

As with addiction, is there a possible connection between the formation of habits and the activity of neural chemicals? We do not know enough about these processes to answer this question. Nevertheless, that neural chemicals appear to be involved in regulating various aspects of every behavior studied to date is some indication that such might be the case. In rats, for example, it has been shown that neurons in one region of the hypothalamus contain alpha receptors whose stimulation by *norepinephrine* elicits eating, whereas neurons in another region of the hypothalamus contain beta receptors whose stimulation (by *epinephrine* and, presumably, *norepinephrine*) inhibits eating (Leibowitz and Brown, 1980 a,b). If, for some reason, "tolerance" were to develop to the effects of chronically high levels of epinephrine and/or norepinephrine on beta receptors, the effect could be suppressed inhibition of eating, resulting in the "habit" of increased eating. The workings of the above mechanism are purely speculative, yet there is evidence that long-term activation of the beta receptors of a rat's brain decreases the number of these receptors and simultaneously increases the number of alpha receptors (Maggi, U'Prichard, and Enna, 1980).

Another indication of the involvement of neural chemicals in the development and maintenance of habits comes from studies of stress. Earlier we mentioned that stress increases the production and release of *norepinephrine, epinephrine, endorphins,* and other chemicals within the brain. Recently, it has been shown that *repeated* stress reduces the number of beta receptors in the brain (see U'Prichard and Kvetnansky, 1980; Telegdy, Fekete, and Varszegi, 1980). In Chapter 7 we mentioned that beta receptors are normally activated by epinephrine and norepinephrine. When this fact is combined with the fact that these (and other) neural chemicals are also involved in eating, satiety, and reward—they might

even be involved in the feelings of euphoria that accompany the use of cocaine and amphetamines—we can see how stress, or anything else that affects the actions of these chemicals, could affect these behaviors. A person who stops smoking, or stops drinking alcohol or coffee, for example, could begin to overeat and thereby activate the same mechanisms as before, in effect maintaining the addiction through the sustained action of neural chemicals within the brain. In other words, the neurophysiological effects of stress could promote the formation and maintenance of habits or addictions. We already mentioned that when one is particularly troubled or anxious, cravings for alcohol, tobacco, and narcotics increase—especially in those already addicted (or, those who were addicted earlier in their lives—see Wikler, 1981). Similarly, persons who are anxious and/or depressed often resort to excessive intake of caffeine. In this case, however, one cannot prove a clear cause-effect relationship between stress and caffeine consumption—the increased levels of caffeine may serve to increase the anxiety and depression (see Greden, Fontaine, Lubetsky, and Chamberlin, 1978). We should note, however, that a vicious cycle may be operating: the increased intake of caffeine, nicotine, and possibly other drugs may increase the anxiety which the person is seeking to subdue by taking these chemicals.

Although the relationship between stress, habits, and addiction cannot yet be connected to precise physiological mechanisms, one can readily appreciate their relevance to health. Someone who undergoes repeated stress might develop an "addiction" for coffee, alcohol, cigarettes, eating particular foods, or using other means of obtaining solace—all of which serve to maintain the altered secretion of neural chemicals *even after the stress-provoking situation is gone.* This possibility even extends to the "habit" of being in an overly aroused state. The neurons of several neurochemical systems are known to have their origin in the upper spinal cord from which they then course throughout the brain above or into the spinal cord below. These neurons are discretely organized in various areas, but many of these areas are intimately connected to the reticular system or are actually a part of it. In Chapter 8 we discussed the fact that the reticular system within the brain is especially involved in mechanisms of increased and decreased arousal. We also noted that arousal mechanisms are extremely powerful, being intimately connected to stress responses and many other processes. As one would expect, neurons within the upper spinal cord that produce *norepinephrine, dopamine, serotonin,* and *acetylcholine* have all been implicated in sleep and arousal mechanisms. Moreover, many drugs that influence neural chemicals also influence mechanisms of arousal (for example, amphetamine causes the reticular system to become more active and keeps a person awake whereas withdrawal from opiates or alcohol often causes insomnia). In other words, a system of neurons within the brain that is heavily involved in mechanisms of arousal is also a system that is affected by—and produces—many neural chemicals. This association corresponds to the fact that the development of an overly aroused state is by far the most common "habit" one develops during stress, and, as discussed in Chapter 8, prolonged arousal is a "habit" that is often very difficult to reverse.

In short, there should be no question that the ability of cells to alter their response after repeated exposure to the same chemical is extremely relevant to our health. Chronic overeating, prolonged arousal (with its effects on the autonomic nervous system and immune system), smoking and other forms of drug abuse, chronic states of resentment and anxiety, and many other unhealthy behaviors are clearly "bad habits," certainly antithetical to health and well-being.

Diet and Neural Chemicals

During the past ten years it has become increasingly clear that the synthesis of neural chemicals by neurons is in part regulated by a person's diet. This observation has many implications which relate to health. We will briefly mention what is known.

Many neural chemicals are made from amino acids. In order for neurons in the brain to receive these amino acids, they are transported into the brain from the *blood*. In general, the greater the amount of these particular amino acids found in the blood, the greater the production of neural chemicals. For example, tryptophan, phenylalanine, and tyrosine are amino acids. In the brain tryptophan is converted into *serotonin*, tyrosine is converted into *dopamine, norepinephrine*, or *epinephrine*, and phenylalanine is converted into tyrosine. When blood tryptophan levels rise, so do brain serotonin levels. Similarly, when blood phenylalanine or tyrosine levels rise, so do brain levels of dopamine, norepinephrine, and epinephrine.

The single most important factor in determining the level of these amino acids in the blood is what we eat. What we eat is especially critical here because most of the amino acids used to make neural chemicals (including tryptophan and phenylalanine) are *essential* amino acids—that is, they must be furnished by *dietary* protein because our body does not make them itself.

Different diets can lead to high or low levels of *serotonin, norepinephrine, acetylcholine*, and other neural chemicals in the brain (see Wurtman, 1980, 1982 for reviews of these effects). Even though it is premature to discuss what is occurring in any detail, it is already clear that we are looking at the workings of intricate systems. For example, in the consumption of protein, a person is incorporating many different amino acids all at once, and many of them *compete with each other to get into the brain*. (For this reason, if, because of a neurological disorder, one or another neural chemical needs to be increased, it has been suggested that the amino acid—in this case, a precursor to the neural chemical—be given in a nearly pure form.) Also, the types of amino acids competing for entry into the brain differ according to the foods we eat. Because consumption of carbohydrates causes the release of insulin, and insulin decreases blood levels of many amino acids, a high carbohydrate diet will affect which amino acids are most likely to get into the brain. Similarly, high and low protein diets will alter the proportion of circulating amino acids and therefore affect the likelihood that one or another of them will get into the brain. For example, when a person consumes a high-protein meal, brain *serotonin* levels decrease (because of the reduced entry of the amino acid, tryptophan). Conversely, when a person consumes a low-protein meal, brain serotonin levels increase. Changes also occur in other neural chemicals (see Wurtman, 1980, 1982).

The above findings are simply an indication that what a person eats can affect the production and release of neural chemicals within the brain. When this fact is coupled with the fact that the actions of neural chemicals are very refined, it is not difficult to recognize how a person's eating habits could have profound effects on arousal levels, emotional states, and many other aspects of his/her physiology and psychology. It is important to realize that this effect is not a simple matter of conversion of foods into usable energy. Rather, it is a result of a particular use of neural chemicals within the brain that results in a modification of the brain's activities.

V. CONCLUSIONS

The material presented in this chapter makes it amply clear that neural chemicals play an important role in modifying physiological and psychological functions and that physiological and psychological functions play an important role in modifying the activity of neural chemicals. As the identity and functions of neural chemicals gradually become better known, we will understand much more about these interrelations than we do now. Further research, for example, will certainly reveal the workings of extremely refined systems. That is, so-called "singular" processes such as "addiction," "dependence," "habit," "stress," "depression," "reward," and "schizophrenia" will have to be considered as varied in their nature, defined by particular interactions of specific mechanisms occurring at one time rather than as simple phenomenological entities.

The above statement does not negate the importance of psychological factors involved in the formation of habits, chronic emotional states, or drug addiction. To the contrary, it makes psychology perhaps much more important than many of us realize. When a person enters a stressful, anxiety-provoking situation, to be sure, the unpleasant feelings evoked can be reduced by whatever "bad" habit—compulsive eating, smoking, even becoming very tense and excited —the person has habitually used in the past. However, the same symptoms can also be alleviated in other ways: by removing oneself from the situation or by dealing differently with the immediate stress. Consider, for example, the power of cognitive thought— dramatically illustrated by the finding, discussed earlier, that the discomfort an addict's withdrawal reactions bring about can disappear as soon as the person realizes that a "blank" is being administered instead of the appropriate drug (see page 255). Such findings have many implications. We sometimes perceive events in our lives to be threatening when there is no need to be defensive; that is, the threat of the circumstance is a product of our imagination. Were we to experience the "goings on" of ourselves and/or the situation we find ourselves in differently, perhaps unpleasant (withdrawal) reactions—promoted by chronic (habitual) defensive responses and the connected actions of neural chemicals—could thereby be reduced so as to allow us to more comfortably break bad habits such as smoking, overeating, being excessively tense, and many other reactions. Of course, many counselling and psychotherapeutic techniques rely on enabling people to recognize that their fears, anxieties, and concerns often stem from experiences that are no longer relevant to their present or future life. With this realization, many people are able to relinquish a wide variety of harmful "habits" that keep one restricted, afraid, unhealthy, or sick.

Recommended Reading

BLOOM, F. "Neuropeptides." *Scientific American*, 245,4, 148-168, 1981. *A good presentation of what neuropeptides are, how they were discovered, and how they are measured.*

CROW, T. and DEAKIN, J. "Brain reinforcement centers and psychoactive drugs." In: *Research Advances in Alcohol and Drug Problems*, Volume 4, edited by Israel, Y., Glaser, F., Kalant, H., Popham, R., Schmidt, W., and Smart, R. New York: Plenum Press, 1978, pp 25-76. *This article reviews the involvement of neural chemicals and drugs with reward mechanisms within the brain. It is especially valuable for the student who wishes to study reward mechanisms in detail, for it includes 184 references pointing the student to the literature in this field.*

CROWLEY, W. and ZEMLAN, F. "Neurotransmitter systems." In: *Neuroendocrinology of Reproduction*, edited by Adler, N. New York: Plenum Press, 1981, pp 65-85. *This article explains how some neural chemicals are produced, and discusses their influence on behavior, their anatomical make-up within the brain, and drugs that influence these chemicals.*

DOLE, V. "Addictive behavior." *Scientific American*, 243,6, 138-154, 1980. *This article discusses some of the problems encountered when treating drug addicts. It also presents an extensive report on the effectiveness of methadone in counteracting a craving for narcotics.*

GILBERT, R. "Caffeine as a drug of abuse." In: *Research Advances in Alcohol and Drug Problems*, Volume 3, edited by Gibbins, R., Israel, Y., Kalant, H., Popham, R., Schmidt, W., and Smart, R. New York: John Wiley & Sons, 1976, pp 49-176. *A detailed review of the effects of caffeine, covering its chemistry and metabolism, effects throughout the body, effects in the brain, and effects on behavior, tolerance, dependence, and interactions with other drugs. Included are 420 references documenting work done in this field.*

GROWDON, J. "Neurotransmitter precursors in the diet: their use in the treatment of brain diseases." In: *Nutrition and the Brain*, edited by Wurtman, R. and Wurtman, J. New York: Plenum Press, 1979, pp 117-181. *This article is a review of mechanisms whereby diet influences the synthesis of neural chemicals. In addition to covering basic principles, the author discusses possible relations to mental and nervous diseases, and their treatment. Recommended only for readers with advanced interest.*

KORNETSKY, C. and MARKOWITZ, R. "Animal models of schizophrenia." In: *Psychopharmacology: A Generation of Progress*, edited by Lipton, M., DiMascio, A., and Killam, K. New York: Raven Press, 1978, pp 583-593. *A review of the effects of antischizophrenic drugs (mostly chlorpromazine) and the effects of LSD and amphetamine as hallucinogens and psychotic agents. These chemicals are discussed as a part of a general discussion of their relation to schizophrenia.*

MILAM, J. and KETCHAM, K. *Under the Influence: A Guide to Myths and Realities of Alcoholism.* Seattle: Madrona Press, 1981. 210 pages. *A well-written book, covering such topics as the body's reactions to alcohol, physiological and psychological reasons why a person might become alcoholic, the early, middle, and late, stages of alcoholism, and its treatment.*

OLDS, M. and FOBES, J. "The central basis of motivation: intracranial self-stimulation studies." *Annual Review of Psychology*, 32, 523-574, 1981. *This is a clear, concise review of the physiology, behavior, and anatomy of self-administered electrical stimulation and its relation to reward. Recommended to any reader who wishes detailed information in this area.*

POMERLEAU, O. "Behavioral factors in the establishment, maintenance and cessation of smoking." In: *The Behavioral Aspects of Smoking*, edited by Krasnegor, N. National Institute on Drug Abuse Research (NIDA) Monograph 26, 1979, pp 47-67. *This article reviews factors responsible for the establishment, maintenance, and cessation of smoking as well as dependence and withdrawal reactions.*

ROUTTENBERG, A. "The reward system of the brain." *Scientific American*, 239,5, 154-164, 1978. *A general discussion of reward areas of the brain, covering their anatomy, neurochemistry, and relationships to learning and memory.*

RUSSELL, M. "Tobacco smoking and nicotine dependence." In: *Research Advances in Alcohol and Drug Problems*, Volume 3, edited by Gibbins, R., Israel, Y., Kalant, H., Popham, R., Schmidt, W., and Smart, R. New York: John Wiley & Sons, 1976, pp 1-47. *A detailed review of the effects of nicotine, covering its actions throughout the body, in the brain, and dependence, withdrawal, and tolerance reactions. Included are 150 references pointing students to the literature in this field.*

Appendix

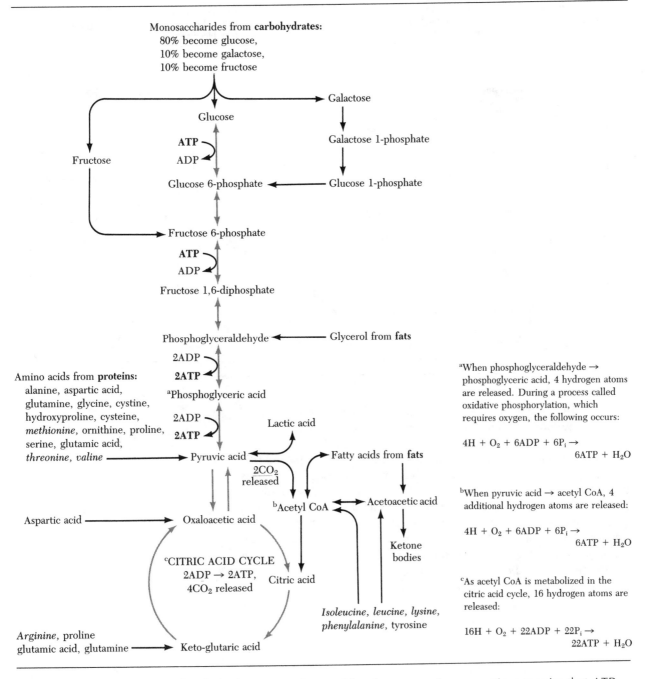

Monosaccharides from **carbohydrates:**
80% become glucose,
10% become galactose,
10% become fructose

Galactose

Glucose

ATP
ADP

Fructose

Galactose 1-phosphate

Glucose 6-phosphate ◄──── Glucose 1-phosphate

Fructose 6-phosphate

ATP
ADP

Fructose 1,6-diphosphate

Phosphoglyceraldehyde ◄──── Glycerol from **fats**

2ADP
2ATP

Amino acids from **proteins:**
alanine, aspartic acid,
glutamine, glycine, cystine,
hydroxyproline, cysteine,
methionine, ornithine, proline,
serine, glutamic acid,
threonine, valine ──────►

[a]Phosphoglyceric acid

2ADP
2ATP

Lactic acid

Pyruvic acid

$2CO_2$
released

Fatty acids from **fats**

[b]Acetyl CoA ◄──► Acetoacetic acid

Aspartic acid ──────► Oxaloacetic acid

Ketone
bodies

[c]CITRIC ACID CYCLE
$2ADP \rightarrow 2ATP$,
$4CO_2$ released

Citric acid

Isoleucine, leucine, lysine,
phenylalanine, tyrosine

Arginine, proline
glutamic acid, glutamine ──────► Keto-glutaric acid

[a]When phosphoglyceraldehyde →
phosphoglyceric acid, 4 hydrogen atoms
are released. During a process called
oxidative phosphorylation, which
requires oxygen, the following occurs:

$$4H + O_2 + 6ADP + 6P_i \rightarrow 6ATP + H_2O$$

[b]When pyruvic acid → acetyl CoA, 4
additional hydrogen atoms are released:

$$4H + O_2 + 6ADP + 6P_i \rightarrow 6ATP + H_2O$$

[c]As acetyl CoA is metabolized in the
citric acid cycle, 16 hydrogen atoms are
released:

$$16H + O_2 + 22ADP + 22P_i \rightarrow 22ATP + H_2O$$

Figure 3–1A. Metabolism of carbohydrates, proteins, and fats for energy. Some reactions require that ATP be converted into ADP and therefore require energy (which is released in this conversion). Other reactions are the reverse: energy is produced for the body as ADP is converted into ATP. As a separate process, note that hydrogen atoms are released and used to produce ATP as phosphoglyceric acid and acetyl CoA are formed (notes a and b), and as citric acid is metabolized in the citric acid cycle (note c). The amino acids that are essential are indicated by the use of italic type. Tryptophan, not shown, is also an essential amino acid.

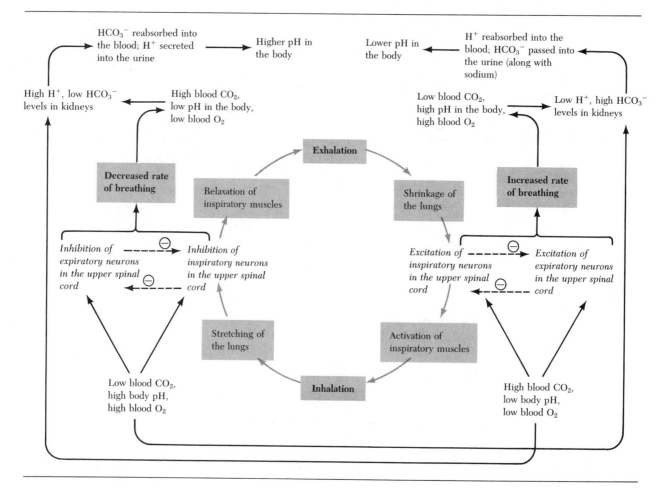

Figure 5–4A. Kidney function, respiration, and body pH. High blood CO_2 and low body pH are accompanied by an excess of hydrogen ions (H^+) and a reduction of bicarbonate ions (HCO_3^-) in the blood. As this blood passes through the kidneys, the excess H^+ is passed into the urine, while the HCO_3^- is reabsorbed into the blood. This process raises body pH to near-normal levels. Thus, low body pH is handled by the body in two ways: by increasing the rate of respiration and by specific kidney action. Once pH is restored to normal, either by the kidneys or by breathing, then breathing rate and kidney function return to normal. When the situation is one of low blood CO_2 and high body pH, the reactions are reversed.

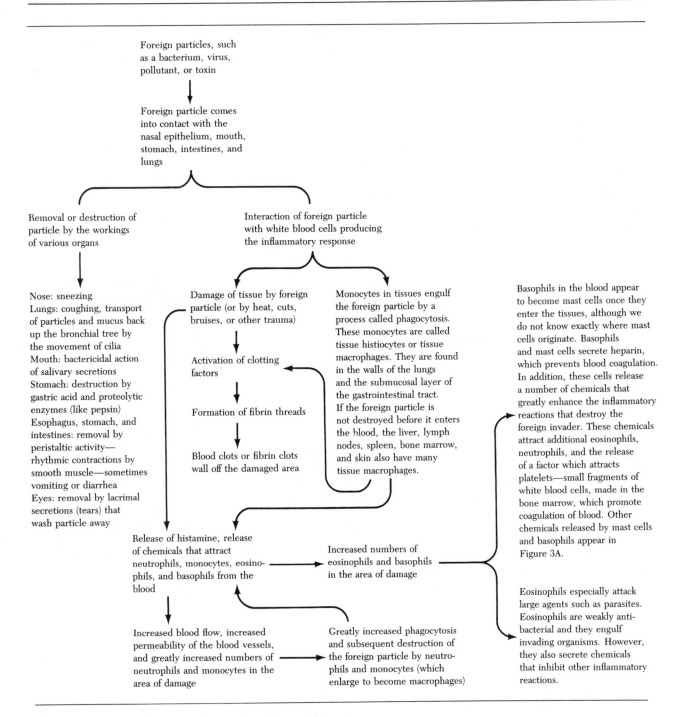

Figure 7–1A. Mechanisms of natural or innate immunity.

Foreign particles come into contact with lymphoid tissue in the nasal epithelium, mouth, stomach, intestines, lungs, skin, lymph nodes, thymus, spleen, and bone marrow. The lymphoid tissue contains T and B lymphocytes

Foreign particles are phagocytized by tissue macrophages. This process helps to expose specific protein complexes contained by the invader. These complexes are called antigens.

The foreign particle (antigen) interacts with some T or B lymphocytes to form sensitized T or sensitized B lymphocytes. These lymphocytes are differentiated to respond specifically to the foreign agent involved and not to other agents.

Activation of a clone of sensitized T or B lymphocytes: the antigen causes a proliferation of lymphocytes all specifically sensitized to the particular foreign particle involved

The sensitized T lymphocyte destroys the invader through a host of mechanisms:
A direct attack, which involves the release of toxic enzymes by the lymphocyte into the invader
An indirect attack, which involves the release of chemicals by the T lymphocytes into the surrounding fluid. These chemicals attract large numbers of macrophages, eosinophils, and basophils. They also stimulate mast cells to release their mediators, and mobilize B lymphocytes.

Some of the sensitized T or B lymphocytes remain dormant in the lymphoid tissue, thereby greatly increasing the number of lymphocytes that can be activated by the foreign particle if it is encountered again. These lymphocytes are called memory cells.

The sensitized B lymphocytes enlarge and further differentiate to become plasma cells. Hundreds of plasma cells are formed from each B lymphocyte. The antibodies secreted by the plasma cells react specifically with the antigen (foreign particle) which sensitized the B lymphocyte originally. The antibodies destroy the invader through a host of mechanisms:
A direct attack on the invader, causing rupture of the cell or inactivation of the invader by clumping (agglutination) and precipitation of the antigen-antibody complex.
An indirect attack whereby a host of enzymes called the complement system are activated by the antigen-antibody complex to produce chemicals that attract neutrophils and macrophages and also increase their ability to phagocytize the invader. These chemicals are also bactericidal, they neutralize viruses, inactivate organisms by making them clump together (agglutination), mobilize more B lymphocytes, and stimulate mast cells to release their mediators.
An indirect attack whereby the antibodies attach to mast cells in the tissues and basophils in the blood, causing these cells to release a host of chemicals that comprise the anaphylactic system. Some of these chemicals attract neutrophils, eosinophils, macrophages, and platelets. Other chemicals are histamine, prostaglandins, bradykinin, the slow-reacting substance of anaphylaxis, and toxic enzymes that attack the invader.

Figure 7–2A.   Mechanisms of acquired or adaptive immunity.

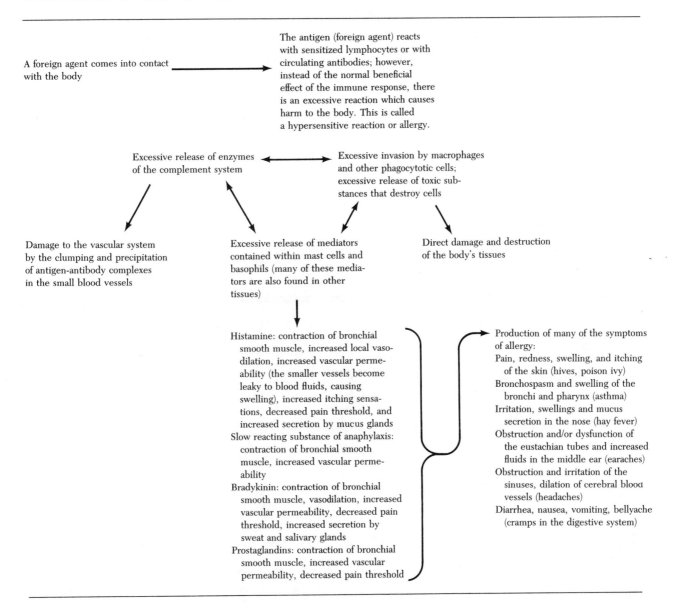

A foreign agent comes into contact with the body

The antigen (foreign agent) reacts with sensitized lymphocytes or with circulating antibodies; however, instead of the normal beneficial effect of the immune response, there is an excessive reaction which causes harm to the body. This is called a hypersensitive reaction or allergy.

Excessive release of enzymes of the complement system

Excessive invasion by macrophages and other phagocytotic cells; excessive release of toxic substances that destroy cells

Damage to the vascular system by the clumping and precipitation of antigen-antibody complexes in the small blood vessels

Excessive release of mediators contained within mast cells and basophils (many of these mediators are also found in other tissues)

Direct damage and destruction of the body's tissues

Histamine: contraction of bronchial smooth muscle, increased local vasodilation, increased vascular permeability (the smaller vessels become leaky to blood fluids, causing swelling), increased itching sensations, decreased pain threshold, and increased secretion by mucus glands

Slow reacting substance of anaphylaxis: contraction of bronchial smooth muscle, increased vascular permeability

Bradykinin: contraction of bronchial smooth muscle, vasodilation, increased vascular permeability, decreased pain threshold, increased secretion by sweat and salivary glands

Prostaglandins: contraction of bronchial smooth muscle, increased vascular permeability, decreased pain threshold

Production of many of the symptoms of allergy:
Pain, redness, swelling, and itching of the skin (hives, poison ivy)
Bronchospasm and swelling of the bronchi and pharynx (asthma)
Irritation, swellings and mucus secretion in the nose (hay fever)
Obstruction and/or dysfunction of the eustachian tubes and increased fluids in the middle ear (earaches)
Obstruction and irritation of the sinuses, dilation of cerebral blood vessels (headaches)
Diarrhea, nausea, vomiting, bellyache (cramps in the digestive system)

Figure 7–3A. Hypersensitive (allergic) reactions of the immune system.

References

ADAMS, R. "Sleep and its abnormalities." In *Harrison's Principles of Internal Medicine*, edited by Isselbacher, I., Adams, R., Braunwald, E., Petersdorf, R., and Wilson, J. New York: McGraw-Hill, 1980, pp 126-131.

AHLSKOG, J. and HOEBEL, B. "Overeating and obesity from damage to a noradrenergic system in the rat." *Science*, 182, 166-169, 1973.

ALTMAN, N., SACHAR, E., GRUEN, P., HALPERN, F., and ETO, S. "Reduced plasma LH concentration in postmenopausal depressed women." *Psychosomatic Medicine*, 37, 274-276, 1975.

AMIT, Z., STERN, M., and WISE, R. "Alcohol preference in the laboratory rat induced by hypothalamic stimulation." *Psychopharmacologia*, 17, 367-377, 1970.

AX, A. "The physiological differentiation between fear and anger in humans." *Psychosomatic Medicine*, 15, 433-442, 1953.

BALL, G., MICCO, D., and BERNTSON, G. "Cerebellar stimulation in the rat: complex stimulation-bound oral behaviors and self-stimulation." *Physiology and Behavior*, 13, 123-127, 1974.

BARCHAS, J., AKIL, H., ELLIOTT, G., HOLMAN, R., and WATSON, S. "Behavioral neurochemistry: neuroregulators and behavioral states." *Science*, 200, 964-973, 1978.

BAXTER, C. and BALDWIN, R. "A functional role for amino acids in the adaptation of tissues from the nervous system to alterations in environmental osmolality." In *Amino Acids as Chemical Transmitters*, edited by Fonnum, F. New York: Plenum Press, 1978, pp 599-627.

BAXTER, C., TACHIKI, K., BLASER, S., BALDWIN, R., and GOSENFELD, L. "Lithium and brain function: a new hypothesis." In *Enzymes and Neurotransmitters in Mental Disease*, edited by Usdin, E., Sourkes, T., and Youdim, M. New York: John Wiley & Sons, 1980, pp 155-167.

BELLUZI, J. and STEIN, L. "Enkephalin may mediate euphoria and drive-reduction reward." *Nature*, 266, 556-558, 1977.

BERMAN, A., BERMAN, D., and PRESCOTT, J. "The effect of cerebellar lesions on emotional behavior in the rhesus monkey." In *The Cerebellum, Epilepsy, and Behavior*, edited by Cooper, I., Riklan, M., and Snider, R. New York: Plenum Press, 1974, pp 277-284.

BERNTSON, G., POTOLICCHIO, S., and MILLER, N. "Evidence for higher functions of the cerebellum: eating and grooming elicited by cerebellar stimulation in cats." *Proceedings of the National Academy of Sciences*, 70, 2497-2499, 1973.

BEUTLER, L., THORNBY, J., and KARACAN, I. "Psychological variables in the diagnosis of insomnia." In *Sleep Disorders: Diagnosis and Treatment*, edited by Williams, R. and Karacan, I. New York: Wiley, 1978.

BLACK, D. "Pathological laughter: a review of the literature." *Journal of Nervous and Mental Disease*, 170, 67-71, 1982.

BLASS, E. and EPSTEIN, A. "A lateral preoptic osmosensitive zone for thirst in the rat." *Journal of Comparative and Physiological Psychology*, 76, 378-394, 1971.

BLASS, E. and NUSSBAUM, A. "Septal hyperdipsia: specific enhancement of drinking to angiotensin in rats." *Journal of Comparative and Physiological Psychology*, 87, 422-439, 1974.

BOOTH, D. "Effects of intrahypothalamic glucose injection on eating and drinking elicited by insulin." *Journal of Comparative and Physiological Psychology*, 65, 13-16, 1968.

BOOTH, D. "Feeding inhibition by glucose loads, compared between normal and diabetic rats." *Physiology and Behavior*, 8, 801-805, 1972.

BRODY, M. and JOHNSON, A. "Role of the anteroventral third ventricle region in fluid and electrolyte balance, arterial pressure regulation, and hypertension." In *Frontiers in Neuroendocrinology*, edited by Martini, L. and Ganong, W. New York: Raven Press, 1980, pp 249-292.

BUENDIA, N., SIERRA, G., GOODE, M., and SEGUNDO, J. "Conditioned and discriminatory responses in wakeful and in sleeping cats." *Electroencephalography and Clinical Neurophysiology*, supplement 24, 199-218, 1963.

BUGGY, J. and JOHNSON, K. "Preoptic-hypothalamic periventricular lesions: thirst deficits and hypernatremia." *American Journal of Physiology*, 233,1, R44-R52, 1977.

BUNN, J. and EVERETT, J. "Ovulation in persistent-estrus rats after electrical stimulation of the brain." *Society of Experimental Biology and Medicine*, 96, 369-371, 1957.

BUTTERS, N. and ROSVOLD, H. "Effect of septal lesions on resistance to extinction and delayed alternation in monkeys." *Journal of Comparative and Physiological Psychology*, 66, 389-395, 1968.

CABANAC, M. "Physiological role of pleasure." *Science*, 173, 1103-1107, 1971.

CABANAC, M. "Temperature regulation." *Annual Review of Physiology*, 37, 415-439, 1975.

CAGGIULA, A. "Analysis of the copulation-reward properties of posterior hypothalamic stimulation in male rats." *Journal of Comparative and Physiological Psychology*, 70, 399-412, 1970.

CAGGIULA, A. and HOEBEL, B. "'Copulation-reward site' in the posterior hypothalamus." *Science*, 153, 1284-1285, 1966.

CALNE, D. "Pain and analgesic mechanisms." In *Psychopharmacology: A Generation of Progress*, edited by Lipton, M., DiMascio, L., and Killam, K. New York: Raven Press, 1978, pp 777-781.

CANTU, R. and DREW, J. "Pathological laughing and crying associated with a tumor ventral to the pons." *Journal of Neurosurgery*, 24, 1024-1026, 1966.

CAREY, R. "Quinine and saccharin preference-aversion threshold determinations in rats with septal ablations." *Journal of Comparative and Physiological Psychology*, 76, 316-326, 1971.

CARON, J., CAPPOEN, J., CHOPIN, C., LEFEBVRE, J., and WAROT, P. "Les intoxications par l'eau apres acces polydipsiques." *Revue Neurologique*, 133, 485-495, 1977.

CHAN, P. and FISHMAN, R. "Elevation of rat brain amino acids, ammonia and idiogenic osmoles induced by hyperosmolality." *Brain Research*, 161, 293-301, 1979.

CHERNER, R. "Abnormal thirst." *Consultant*, 22, 341-346, 1982.

CLEMENTE, C. and CHASE, M. "Neurological substrates of aggressive behavior." *Annual Review of Physiology*, 35, 329-356, 1973.

COHEN, L. "Perception of reversible figures after brain injury." *A.M.A. Archives of Neurology and Psychiatry*, 81, 765-775, 1959.

COHEN, M. "Central determinants of respiratory rhythm." *Annual Review of Physiology*, 43, 91-104, 1981.

COLLIER, H., HAMMOND, M., and SCHNEIDER, C. "Effects of drugs affecting endogenous amines or cyclic nucleotides on ethanol withdrawal head twitches in mice." *British Journal of Pharmacology*, 58, 9-16, 1976.

COVEY, C. and ARIEFF, A. "Disorders of sodium and water metabolism and their effects on the central nervous system." In *Contemporary Issues in Nephrology: Sodium and Water Homeostasis*, edited by Brenner, B. and Stein, J. New York: Churchill-Livingstone, 1978, pp 212-241.

CREER, T. "Personality, mother/child relationships, learning factors, and other considerations." In *Asthma Therapy*. New York: Springer Publishing Co., 1979, pp 53-86.

CROWLEY, W. and ZEMLAN, F. "The neurochemical control of mating behavior." In *Neuroendocrinology of Reproduction*, edited by Adler, N. New York: Plenum Press, 1981, pp 451-484.

DANIELE, R. "Asthma." In *Cecil's Textbook of Medicine*, edited by Wyngaarden, J. and Smith, L. Philadelphia: W. B. Saunders, 1982, pp 359-363.

DEWS, P. and WIESEL, T. "Consequences of monocular deprivation on visual behavior in kittens." *Journal of Physiology*, 206, 437-455, 1970.

DUBOVSKY, S., GRABON, S., BERL, T., and SCHRIER, R. "Syndrome of inappropriate secretion of antidiuretic hormone with exacerbated psychosis." *Annals of Internal Medicine*, 79, 551-554, 1973.

ELLINGBOE J. "Effects of alcohol on neurochemical processes." In *Psychopharmacology: A Generation of Progress*, edited by Lipton, M., DiMascio, A., and Killam, K. New York: Raven Press, 1978, pp 1653-1663.

ELLISON, G. and FLYNN, J. "Organized aggressive behavior in cats after surgical isolation of the hypothalamus." *Archives Italiennes de Biologie*, 106, 1-20, 1968.

EVERSON, T. and COLE, W. *Spontaneous Regression of Cancer*. Philadelphia: W. B. Saunders, 1966.

FAHRBACH, S., TRETTER, J., AVARICH, P., McCABE, J., and LEIBOWITZ, S. "Increased carbohydrate preference in the rat after injection of 2-deoxy-D-glucose and clonidine." *Society for Neuroscience*, 6, 784 (Abstract No. 267.6), 1980.

FITZSIMONS, T. and LEMAGNEN, J. "Eating as a regulatory control of drinking in the rat." *Journal of Comparative and Physiological Psychology*, 67, 273-283, 1969.

FONBERG, E. "The relation between alimentary and emotional amygdalar regulation." In *Hunger: Basic Mechanisms and Clinical Implications*, edited by Novin, D., Wyrwicka, W., and Bray, G. New York: Raven Press, 1976, pp 61-75.

FONBERG, E. "Changes in alimentary behavior after medial amygdalar damage in dog, cat, and rat." In *Food Intake and Chemical Senses*, edited by Katsuki, Y., Sato, M., Takagi, S., and Oomura, Y. Baltimore; Tokyo: University Park Press, 1977, pp 437-451.

FRANKENHAEUSER, M. "Behavior and circulating catecholamines." *Brain Research*, 31, 241-262, 1971.

FRENCH, J., PORTER, R., CAVANAUGH, E., and LONGMIRE, R. "Experimental observations on 'psychosomatic' mechanisms." *Archives of Neurology and Psychiatry*, 72, 267-281, 1954.

GASCON, G. and GILLES, F. "Limbic dementia." *Journal of Neurology, Neurosurgery, and Psychiatry*, 36, 421-430, 1973.

GESCHWIND, N. "Disconnection syndromes in animals and man." *Brain*, 88, 237-294, 585-644, 1965.

GIACHETTI, I. and MACLEOD, P. "Preliminary evidence of a specific thalamo-neocortical olfactory pathway." In *Food Intake and Chemical Senses*, edited by Katsuki, Y., Sato, M., Takagi, S., and Oomura, Y. Baltimore; Tokyo: University Park Press, 1977, pp 45-49.

GILBERT, R. "Caffeine as a drug of abuse." In *Research Advances in Alcohol and Drug Problems, volume 3*, edited by Gibbons, R., Israel, Y., Kalant, H., Popham, R., Schmidt, W., and Smart, R. New York: John Wiley & Sons, 1976, pp 49-176.

GOLD, R., JONES, A., SAWCHENKO, P., and KAPATOS, G. "Paraventricular area: critical focus of a longitudinal neurocircuitry mediating food intake." *Physiology and Behavior*, 18, 1111-1119, 1977.

GOLD, W. "Anticholinergic drugs." In *Allergy. Principles and Practice*, edited by Middleton, E., Reed, C., and Ellis, E. St. Louis: C. V. Mosby Co., 1978, pp 499-530.

GOLDSTEIN, D. and JUDSON, B. "Alcohol dependence and opiate dependence: lack of relationship in mice." *Science*, 172, 290-292, 1971.

GRACE, W. and GRAHAM, D. "Relationship of specific attitudes and emotions to certain bodily diseases." *Psychosomatic Medicine*, 14, 243-251, 1952.

GREDEN, J., FONTAINE, P., LUBETSKY, M., and CHAMBERLIN, K. "Anxiety and depression associated with caffeinism among psychiatric inpatients." *American Journal of Psychiatry*, 135, 963-966, 1978.

GRIFFITHS, P., LITTLETON, J., and ORTIZ, A. "Changes in monoamine concentrations in mouse brain associated with ethanol dependence and withdrawal." *British Journal of Pharmacology*, 50, 489-498, 1974.

GROSSMAN, S. "Neuroanatomy of food and water intake." In *Hunger: Basic Mechanisms and Clinical Implications*, edited by Novin, D., Wyrwicka, W., and Bray, G. New York: Raven Press, 1976, pp 51-59.

GROSSMAN, S. "The biology of motivation." *Annual Review of Psychology*, 30, 209-242, 1979.

GROSSMAN, S., DACEY, D., HALARIS, A., COLLIER, T., and ROUTTENBERG, A. "Aphasia and adipsia after preferential destruction of nerve cell bodies in hypothalamus." *Science*, 202, 537-539, 1978.

GROSSMAN, S., and GROSSMAN, L. "Food and water intake following lesions or electrical stimulation of the amygdala." *American Journal of Physiology*, 205, 761-765, 1963.

HALL, G. and MORRISON, C. "New evidence for a relationship between tobacco smoking, nicotine dependence and stress." *Nature*, 243, 199-201, 1973.

HARRIS, G. "Sex hormones, brain development and brain function." *Endocrinology*, 75, 627-648, 1964.

HARTMANN, E. *The Biology of Dreaming*. Springfield, Illinois: Charles C Thomas, 1967.

HENRY, J. "Present concept of stress theory." In *Catecholamines and Stress: Recent Advances*, edited by Usdin, E., Kvetnansky, R., and Kopin, I. New York: Elsevier North-Holland, 1980, pp 557-571.

HENRY, J. and MEEHAN, J. "Psychosocial stimuli, physiological specificity, and cardiovascular disease." In *Brain, Behavior, and Bodily Disease*, edited by Weiner, H., Hofer, M., and Stunkard, A. New York: Raven Press, 1981, pp 305-333.

HERNANDEZ, L. and HOEBEL, B. "Hypothalamic reward and aversion: a link between metabolism and behavior." In *Current Studies of Hypothalamic Function, Volume 2: Metabolism and Behavior*, edited by Veale, W. and Lederis, K. Basel; New York: S. Karger, 1978, pp 72-92.

HERNANDEZ-PEON, R. and STERMAN, M. "Brain functions." *Annual Review of Psychology*, 17, 363-394, 1966.

HERZOG, D. "Anorexia nervosa: a treatment challenge." *Drug Therapy*, 7, 89-96, 1982.

HEYCK, H. and DALAL, N. "Muscle contraction headache." In *Headache and Facial Pain*, by Heyck, H. and Dalal, N. Chicago: Year Book Medical Publishers, 1981, pp 250-262.

HEYMAN, A. "Hyperventilation." In *Cecil's Textbook of Medicine*, edited by Beeson, P., McDermott, W., and Wyngaarden, J. Philadelphia: W. B. Saunders, 1979, pp 745-746.

HIRSCH, H. and SPINELLI, D. "Modification of the distribution of receptive field orientation in cats by selective visual exposure during development." *Experimental Brain Research*, 13, 509-527, 1971.

HOBSON, J. "Sleep and its disorders." In *Cecil's Textbook of Medicine*, edited by Wyngaarden, J. and Smith, L. Philadelphia: W. B. Saunders, 1982, pp 1930-1935.

HOEBEL, B. "Inhibition and disinhibition of self-stimulation and feeding: hypothalamic control and postingestional factors." *Journal of Comparative and Physiological Psychology*, 66, 89-100, 1968.

HOEBEL, B. "Feeding and self-stimulation." *Annals of the New York Academy of Sciences*, 157, 758-778, 1969.

HOEBEL, B. "Hypothalamic self-stimulation and stimulation escape in relation to feeding and mating." *Federation Proceedings*, 38, 2454-2461, 1979.

HOEBEL, B. and LEIBOWITZ, S. "Brain monoamines in the modulation of self-stimulation, feeding, and body weight." In *Brain, Behavior, and Bodily Disease*, edited by Weiner, H., Hofer, M., and Stunkard, A. New York: Raven Press, 1981, pp 103-142.

HOEBEL, B. and THOMPSON, R. "Aversion to lateral hypothalamic stimulation caused by intragastric feeding or obesity." *Journal of Comparative and Physiological Psychology*, 68, 536-543, 1969.

HUBEL, D. and WIESEL, T. "The period of susceptibility to the physiological effects of unilateral eye closure in kittens." *Journal of Physiology*, 206, 419-436, 1970.

HUBEL, D. and WIESEL, T. "Brain mechanisms of vision." *Scientific American*, 241,3, 150-168, 1979.

IMPERATO-MCGINLEY, J., PETERSON, R., GAUTIER, T., and STURLA, E. "Androgens and the evolution of male-gender identity among male pseudohermaphrodites with 5 alpha reductase deficiency." *New England Journal of Medicine*, 300, 1233-1237, 1979.

JONES, G. "The luteal phase defect." *Fertility and Sterility*, 27, 351-356, 1976.

JONES, M. "Conversion reaction: anachronism or evolutionary form? A review of the neurologic, behavioral, and psychoanalytic literature." *Psychological Bulletin*, 87, 427-441, 1980.

JURKOWLANIEC, E. and BIALOWAS, J. "Rewarding effect of noradrenergic stimulation of the amygdala in food deprived rats." *Physiology and Behavior*, 27, 27-31, 1981.

KAADA, B. "Cingulate, posterior orbital, anterior insular and temporal pole cortex." In *Handbook of Physiology, Section I: Neurophysiology, Volume 2*, edited by Field, J., Magoun, H. and Hall, V. Baltimore: Williams & Wilkins, 1960, pp 1345-1372.

KARSCH, F., DIERSCHKE, D., and KNOBIL, E. "Sexual differentiation of pituitary function: apparent difference between primates and rodents." *Science*, 179, 484-486, 1973.

KATZ, P. and FAUCI, A. "Activation of human B lymphocytes." *Journal of Allergy and Clinical Immunology*, 61, 334-338, 1978.

KATZ, P. and FAUCI, A. "The effects of corticosteroids on immunoregulation in sarcoidosis." *Cellular Immunology*, 42, 308-318, 1979.

KIESSLING, R. "Natural killer cells." In *Manipulation of the Immune Response in Cancer*, edited by Mitchison, N. and Landy, M. New York: Academic Press, 1979, pp 131-142.

KING, B. and GROSSMAN, S. "Response to glucoprivic and hydrational challenges by normal and hypothalamic hyperphagic rats." *Physiology and Behavior*, 18, 463-473, 1977.

KISSEN, D. "Psycho-social factors in cigarette smoking motivation." *The Medical Officer*, 104, 365-372, 1960.

KLOPFER, B. "Psychological variables in human cancer." *Journal of Projective Techniques*, 21, 331-340, 1957.

KLUVER, H. and BUCY, P. "Psychic blindness and other symptoms following bilateral temporal lobectomy in rhesus monkeys." *American Journal of Physiology*, 119, 352-353, 1937.

KLUVER, H. and BUCY, P. "An analysis of certain effects of bilateral temporal lobectomy in the rhesus monkey, with special reference to psychic blindness." *Journal of Psychology*, 5, 33-54, 1938.

KLUVER, H. and BUCY, P. "Preliminary analysis of functions of the temporal lobe in monkeys." *Archives of Neurology and Psychiatry*, 42, 979-1000, 1939.

KNAPP, P., MATHE, A., and VACHON, L. "Psychosomatic aspects of bronchial asthma." In *Bronchial Asthma: Mechanisms and Therapeutics*, edited by Weiss, E. and Segal, M. Boston: Little, Brown and Co., 1976, pp 1055-1080.

KUCHARCZYCK, J. and MOGENSON, G. "Separate lateral hypothalamic pathways for extracellular and intracellular thirst." *American Journal of Physiology*, 228, 295-301, 1975.

KUCHARCZYCK, J. and MOGENSON, G. "The role of mesencephalic structures in thirst induced by centrally administered angiotensin II." *Brain Research*, 126, 225-241, 1977.

LACHELIN, G. and YEN, S. "Hypothalamic chronic anovulation." *American Journal of Obstetrics and Gynecology*, 130, 825-831, 1978.

LACEY, J. and LACEY, B. "Verification and extension of the principle of autonomic response-stereotypy." *American Journal of Physiology*, 71, 50-73, 1958.

LANDIS, S. "Development of cholinergic sympathetic neurons: evidence for transmitter plasticity in vivo." *Federation Proceedings*, 42, 1633-1638, 1983.

LAZARE, A. "Current concepts in psychiatry: conversion symptoms." *New England Journal of Medicine*, 305, 745-748, 1981.

LEIBOWITZ, S. and BROWN, L. "Histochemical and pharmacological analysis of noradrenergic projections to the paraventricular hypothalamus in relation to feeding stimulation." *Brain Research*, 201, 289-314, 1980a.

LEIBOWITZ, S. and BROWN, L. "Histochemical and pharmacological analysis of catecholaminergic projections to the perifornical hypothalamus in relation to feeding inhibition." *Brain Research*, 201, 315-345, 1980b.

LIEF, H. "Medical aspects of sexuality." In *Cecil: Textbook of Medicine*, edited by Wyngaarden, J. and Smith, L. Philadelphia: W.B. Saunders, 1982, pp 1998-2004.

LILLY, J. *The Deep Self: Profound Relaxation and the Tank Isolation Technique.* New York: Warner Books, 1978.

LOFTUS, T. "Psychogenic factors in anovulatory women: III. Behavioral and psychoanalytic aspects of anovulatory amenorrhea." *Fertility and Sterility*, 13, 20-28, 1962.

LOMAX, P. and ARY, M. "The hypothalamus in narcotic dependence and withdrawal." In *Metabolism and Behavior, Volume 2*, edited by Veale, W. and Lederis, K. Basel; New York: S. Karger, 1978, pp 149-162.

LUBAR, J., BOYCE, B., and SCHAEFER, C. "Etiology of polydipsia and polyuria in rats with septal lesions." *Physiology and Behavior*, 3, 289-292, 1968.

LUM, L. "The syndrome of habitual chronic hyperventilation." In *Modern Trends in Psychosomatic Medicine, volume 3*, edited by Hill, O. Boston: Butterworths, 1976, pp 196-230.

LUNDBERG, U. "Catecholamine and cortisol excretion under psychologically different laboratory conditions." In *Catecholamines and Stress: Recent Advances*, edited by Usdin, E., Kvetnansky, R., and Kopin, I. New York: Elsevier North-Holland, 1980, pp 455-460.

MAGGI, A., U'PRICHARD, D., and ENNA, S. "Beta-adrenergic regulation of alpha(two)-adrenergic receptors in the central nervous system." *Science*, 207, 645-647, 1980.

MAHER-LOUGHNAN, G. "Hypnosis in bronchial asthma." In *Bronchial Asthma: Mechanisms and Therapeutics*, edited by Weiss, E. and Segal, M. Boston: Little, Brown and Co., 1976, pp 1041-1054.

MARLOWE, W., MANCALL, E., and THOMAS, J. "Complete Kluver-Bucy Syndrome in man." *Cortex*, 11, 53-59, 1975.

MAYER, D. and LIEBESKIND, J. "Pain reduction by focal electrical stimulation of the brain: an anatomical and behavioral analysis." *Brain Research*, 68, 73-93, 1974.

MCARTHUR, C., WALDRON, E., and DICKINSON, J. "The psychology of smoking." *Journal of Abnormal and Social Psychology*, 56, 267-275, 1958.

McHugh, P. "Hysteria." In *Cecil's Textbook of Medicine*, edited by Wyngaarden, J. and Smith, L. Philadelphia: W. B. Saunders, 1982, pp 1995-1997.

Merskey, H. *The Analysis of Hysteria.* London: Bailliere Tindall, 1979.

Milam, J. and Ketcham, K. *Under the Influence: A Guide to Myths and Realities of Alcoholism.* Seattle: Madrona Press, 1981.

Mishkin, M. "Perseveration of central sets after frontal lesions in monkeys." In *The Prefrontal Granular Cortex and Behavior*, edited by Warren, J. and Akert, K. New York: McGraw-Hill, 1964, pp 219-241.

Mogenson, G. "Water deprivation and excesssive water intake during self-stimulation." *Physiology and Behavior*, 4, 393-397, 1969.

Mogenson, G. "Stability and modification of consummatory behaviors elicited by electrical stimulation of the hypothalamus." *Physiology and Behavior*, 6, 255-260, 1971.

Mogenson, G. "Hypothalamic and other neural mechanisms for the control of food and water intake." In *Current Studies of Hypothalamic Function, Volume 2: Metabolism and Behavior*, edited by Veale, W. and Lederis, K. Basel; New York: S. Karger, 1978, pp 93-106.

Mogenson, G. and Morgan, C. "Effects of induced drinking on self-stimulation of the lateral hypothalamus." *Experimental Brain Research*, 3, 111-116, 1967.

Molina, F. and Hunsperger, R. "Organization of the subcortical system governing defence and flight reactions in the cat." *Journal of Physiology (London)*, 160, 200-213, 1962.

Money, J. "Sex hormones and other variables in human eroticism." In *Sex and Internal Secretions, Volume 2*, edited by Young, W. Baltimore: Williams & Wilkins, 1961, pp 1383-1400.

Money, J. "Gender identity and hermaphroditism." *Science*, 191, 872, 1976.

Money, J. and Ehrhardt, A. *Man and Woman, Boy and Girl.* Baltimore: Johns Hopkins University Press, 1972.

Moore, R. and Bloom, F. "Central catecholamine neuron systems: anatomy and physiology of the norepinephrine and epinephrine systems." *Annual Review of Neuroscience*, 2, 113-168, 1979.

Mora, F., Avrith, D., Phillips, A., and Rolls, E. "Effects of satiety on self-stimulation of the orbitofrontal cortex in the rhesus monkey." *Neuroscience Letters*, 13, 141-145, 1979.

Morris, H. and Selner, J. "Endocrine aspects of allergy." In *Allergic Diseases of Infancy, Childhood and Adolescence*, edited by Bierman, C. and Pearlman, D. Philadelphia: W. B. Saunders, 1980, pp 655-674.

Moss, R. "Actions of hypothalamic-hypophysiotropic hormones on the brain." *Annual Review of Physiology*, 41, 617-631, 1979.

Myers, R. and Melchior, C. "Alcohol drinking: abnormal intake caused by tetrahydropapaveroline in brain." *Science*, 196, 554-556, 1977.

Neill, J. "Sexual differences in the hypothalamic regulation of prolactin secretion." *Endocrinology*, 90, 1154-1159, 1979.

Norgren, R., Grill, H., and Pfaffmann C. "CNS projections of taste to the dorsal pons and limbic system with correlated studies of behavior." In *Food Intake and Chemical Senses*, edited by Katsuki, Y., Sato, M., Takagi, S., and Oomura, Y. Baltimore; Tokyo: University Park Press, 1977, pp 233-243.

Novin, D. "The mechanisms of satiety." In *Food Intake and Chemical Senses*, edited by Katsuki, Y., Sato, M., Takagi, S., and Oomura, Y. Baltimore; Tokyo: University Park Press, 1977, pp 399-411.

O'Brien, C., Testa, T., O'Brien, T., Brady, J., and Wells, B. "Conditioned narcotic withdrawal in humans." *Science*, 195, 1000-1002, 1977.

Olds, J., Allen, W., and Briese, E. "Differentiation of hypothalamic drive and reward centers." *American Journal of Physiology*, 221, 368-375, 1971.

Olds, J. and Milner, P. "Positive reinforcement produced by electrical stimulation of septal area and other regions of the rat brain." *Journal of Comparative and Physiological Psychology*, 47, 419-427, 1954.

Olds, M. and Fobes, J. "The central basis of motivation: intracranial self-stimulation studies." *Annual Review of Psychology*, 32, 523-574, 1981.

Oomura, Y. "Significance of glucose, insulin and free fatty acid on the hypothalamus feeding and satiety neurons." In *Hunger: Basic Mechanisms and Clinical Implications*, edited by Novin, D., Wyrwicka, W., and Bray, G. New York: Raven Press, 1976, pp 145-157.

Orr, W. and Stahl, M. "Alimentary function during sleep." In *Physiology in Sleep*, edited by Orem, J. and Barnes, C. New York: Academic Press, 1980, pp 203-212.

Pager, J., Giachetti, I., Holley, A., and LeMagnen, J. "A selective control of olfactory bulb electrical activity in relation to food deprivation and satiety in rats." *Physiology and Behavior*, 9, 573-579, 1972.

Panksepp, J. and Meeker, R. "Effects of insulin and hypothalamic lesions on glucose preference in rats." In *Food Intake and Chemical Senses*, edited by Katsuki, Y., Sato, M., Takagi, S., and Oomura, Y. Baltimore; Tokyo: University Park Press, 1977, 343-355.

Penfield, W. and Faulk, M. "The insula." *Brain*, 78, 445-470, 1955.

Peters, L. and Mason, K. "Influence of stress on experimental cancer." In *Mind and Cancer Prognosis*, edited by Stoll, B. New York: John Wiley & Sons, 1979, pp 103-124.

Plum, F. "Neurological integration of behavioural and metabolic control of breathing." In *Breathing: Hering-Breuer Centenary Symposium (CIBA)*, edited by Porter, R. London: J and A Churchill, 1970, pp 159-181.

Plum, F. "Headache." In *Cecil's Textbook of Medicine*, edited by Wyngaarden, J. and Smith, L. Philadelphia: W. B. Saunders, 1982, pp 1948-1953.

POTTER, D., FURSHPAN, E., and LANDIS, S. "Transmitter status in cultered rat sympathetic neurons: plasticity and multiple function." *Federation Proceedings*, 42, 1626-1632, 1983.

POWLEY, T. and OPSAHL, C. "Autonomic components of the hypothalamic feeding syndromes." In *Hunger: Basic Mechanisms and Clinical Implications*, edited by Novin, D., Wyrwicka, W., and Bray, G. New York: Raven Press, 1976, pp 313-326.

RAKOFF, A. "Psychogenic factors in anovulatory women: I. Hormonal patterns in women with ovarian dysfunctions of psychogenic origin." *Fertility and Sterility*, 13, 1-10, 1962.

RECHTSCHAFFEN, A. and KALES, A. "A manual of standardized terminology, techniques and scoring system for sleep stages of human subjects." *National Institutes of Health*, Publication No. 204, 1968.

REIS, D. "Experimental central neurogenic hypertension from brainstem dysfunction: evidence for a central neural imbalance hypothesis of hypertension." In *Brain, Behavior, and Bodily Disease*, edited by Weiner, H., Hofer, M., and Stunkard, A. New York: Raven Press, 1981, pp 229-257.

REIS, D., DOBA, N., and NATHAN, M. "Predatory attack, grooming, and consummatory behaviors evoked by electrical stimulation of cat cerebellar nuclei." *Science*, 182, 845-847, 1973.

REIS, D., and McHUGH, P. "Hypoxia as a cause of bradycardia during amygdala stimulation in monkey." *American Journal of Physiology*, 214, 601-610, 1968.

RIKLAN, M., HALGIN, L., SHULMAN, M., CULLINAN, T., and COOPER, I. "Behavioral alterations following acute, shorter-term, and longer-term cerebellar stimulation in humans." In *Cerebellar Stimulation in Man*, edited by Cooper, I. New York: Raven Press, 1978, pp 161-183.

RIDEOUT, B. "Non-REM sleep as a source of learning deficits induced by REM sleep deprivation." *Physiology and Behavior*, 22, 1043-1047, 1979.

ROBERTS, W. and KIESS, H. "Motivational properties of hypothalamic aggression in cats." *Journal of Comparative and Physiological Psychology*, 58, 187-193, 1964.

ROBERTS, W. and MOONEY, R. "Brain areas controlling thermoregulatory grooming, prone extension, locomotion, and tail vasodilation in rats." *Journal of Comparative and Physiological Psychology*, 86, 470-480, 1974.

ROBINSON, B. and MISHKIN, M. "Alimentary responses evoked from forebrain structures in Macaca mulatta." *Science*, 136, 260-262, 1962.

ROGERS, M., DUBEY, D., and REICH, P. "The influence of the psyche and the brain on immunity and disease susceptibility: a critical review." *Psychosomatic Medicine*, 41, 147-164, 1979.

ROGERS, M., TRENTHAM, D., and REICH, P. "Modulation of collagen-induced arthritis by different stress protocols (Abstract)." *Psychosomatic Medicine*, 42, 72-73, 1980.

ROLLS, E. and ROLLS, B. "Activity of neurones in sensory, hypothalamic, and motor areas during feeding in the monkey." In *Food Intake and Chemical Senses*, edited by Katsuki, Y., Sato, M., Takagi, S., and Oomura, Y. Baltimore; Tokyo: University Park Press, 1977, pp 525-549.

RUSSELL, G. "Anorexia nervosa." In *Cecil's Textbook of Medicine*, edited by Wyngaarden, J. and Smith, L. Philadelphia: W. B. Saunders, 1982, pp 1379-1382.

RYAN, R. and RYAN, R. "Other types of vascular headache." In *Headache and Head Pain*, by Ryan, R. and Ryan, R. St. Louis: C. V. Mosby, 1978, pp 176-188.

RYMER, M. and FISHMAN, R. "Protective adaptation of brain to water intoxication." *Archives of Neurology*, 28, 49-54, 1973.

SAKSELA, E. "Interferon and natural killer cells." In *Interferon 1981, Volume 3*, edited by Gresser, I. New York: Academic Press, 1981, pp 45-63.

SALASPURO, M., LINDROS, K., and NUUTINEN, H. "Blood acetaldehyde: regulatory factors during ethanol oxidation in man." In *Biological Approach to Alcoholism*, edited by Lieber, C. National Institute on Alcohol Abuse and Alcoholism, research monograph No. 11, Department of Health and Human Services (DHHS) publication No. (ADM) 83-1261, 323-332, 1983.

SATINOFF, E. "Neural organization and evolution of thermal regulation in mammals." *Science*, 201, 16-22, 1978.

SAWA, M., UEKI, Y., ARITA, M., and HARADA, T. "Preliminary report on the amygdaloidectomy on the psychotic patients, with interpretation of oral-emotional manifestation in schizophrenics." *Folia Psychiatrica et Neurologica Japonica*, 7, 309-329, 1954.

SAWYER, C. and EVERETT, J. "Stimulatory and inhibitory effects of progesterone on the release of pituitary ovulating hormone in the rabbit." *Endocrinology*, 65, 644-651, 1959.

SCHOTTSTAEDT, W., GRACE, W., and WOLFF, H. "Life situations, behavior, attitudes, emotions, and renal excretion of fluid and electrolytes." *Journal of Psychosomatic Research*, 1, 203-211, 1956.

SCHWARTZBAUM, J. and DONOVICK, P. "Discrimination reversal and spatial alternation associated with septal and caudate dysfunction in rats." *Journal of Comparative and Physiological Psychology*, 65, 83-92, 1968.

SHIMAZU, T. "Reciprocal functions of the ventromedial and lateral hypothalamic nuclei in regulating carbohydrate metabolism in liver, and their relevance to food intake control." In *Food Intake and Chemical Senses*, edited by Katsuki, Y., Sato, M., Takagi, S., and Oomura, Y. Baltimore; Tokyo: University Park Press, 1977, pp 575-585.

SPRINGER, S. and DEUTSCH, G. *Left Brain, Right Brain.* San Francisco: W. H. Freeman, 1981.

STEFFENS, A. "The relation between the hypothalamus, the islet of Langerhans, and the regulation of food intake." In *Food Intake and Chemical Senses*, edited by Katsuki, Y., Sato, M., Takagi, S., and Oomura, Y.

Baltimore; Tokyo: University Park Press, 1977, pp 367-381.

STEIN, M., KELLER, S., and SCHLEIFER, S. "The hypothalamus and the immune response." In *Brain, Behavior, and Bodily Disease*, edited by Weiner, H., Hofer, M., and Stunkard, A. New York: Raven Press, 1981, pp 45-65.

STERMAN, M. and SHOUSE, M. "Quantitative analysis of training, sleep EEG and clinical response to EEG operant conditioning in epileptics." *Electroencephalography and Clinical Neurophysiology*, 49, 558-576, 1980.

STOLL, B. "Restraint of growth and spontaneous regression of cancer." In *Mind and Cancer Prognosis*, edited by Stoll, B. New York: John Wiley & Sons, 1979, pp 19-29.

SWANSON, L., KUCHARCZYCK, J., and MOGENSON, G. "Autoradiographic evidence for pathways from the medial preoptic area to the midbrain involved in the drinking response to angiotensin II." *Journal of Comparative Neurology*, 178, 645-659, 1978.

SZENTIVANYI, A. and SZEKELY, J. "Effect of injury to, and electrical stimulation of, hypothalamic areas on the anaphylactic and histamine shock of the guinea pig: a preliminary report." *Annals of Allergy*, 14, 259-260, 1956.

SZENTIVANYI, A. and WILLIAMS, J. "The constitutional basis of atopic disease." In *Allergic Diseases of Infancy, Childhood and Adolescence*, edited by Bierman, C. and Pearlman, D. Philadelphia: W. B. Saunders, 1980, pp 173-210.

TAUB, E. and SCHOOL, P. "Some methodological considerations in thermal biofeedback training." *Behavior Research Methods and Instrumentation*, 10, 617-622, 1978.

TELEGDY, G., FEKETE, M., and VARSZEGI, M. "Effect of repeated stress on brain monoamines and plasma corticosterone level." In *Catecholamines and Stress: Recent Advances*, edited by Usdin, E., Kvetnansky, R., and Kopin, I. New York: Elsevier North-Holland, 1980, pp 85-90.

THEODOR, L. and MANDELCORN, M. "Hysterical blindness: a case report and study using a modern psychophysical technique." *Canadian Journal of Ophthalmology*, 8, 353-355, 1973.

TILLEY, A. and EMPSON, J. "REM sleep and memory consolidation." *Biological Psychology*, 6, 293-300, 1978.

TRETTER, J. and LEIBOWITZ, S. "Specific increase in carbohydrate consumption after norepinephrine injection into the paraventricular nucleus." *Society for Neuroscience*, 6, 532 (abstract No. 182.25), 1980.

UNGERSTEDT, U. "Adipsia and aphasia after 6-hydroxydopamine induced degeneration of the nigro-striatal dopamine system." *Acta Physiologica Scandinavica*, 82, Suppl. 367, 95-122, 1971.

U'PRICHARD, D. and KVETNANSKY, R. "Central and peripheral adrenergic receptors in acute and repeated immobilization stress." In *Catecholamines and Stress: Recent Advances*, edited by Usdin, E., Kvetnansky, R., and Kopin, I. New York: Elsevier North-Holland, 1980, pp 299-308.

VAN ZOEREN, J. and STRICKER, M. "Effects of preoptic, lateral hypothalamic, or dopamine-depleting lesions on behavioral thermoregulation in rats exposed to the cold." *Journal of Comparative and Physiological Psychology*, 91, 989-999, 1977.

VERNEY, E. "The antidiuretic hormone and the factors which determine its release." *Proceedings of the Royal Society of London*, Series B, 135, 25-106, 1947.

WALKER, H. "Psychiatric aspects of infertility." In *Aspects of Male Fertility*, edited by White, R. Baltimore: Williams & Wilkins, 1982, pp 250-260.

WARREN, M. "The effects of altered nutritional states, stress, and systemic illness on reproduction in women." In *Clinical Aspects of Neuroendocrinology*, edited by Vaitukaitis, J. New York: Elsevier, 1982, pp 177-206.

WASTERLAIN, C. and POSNER, J. "Cerebral edema in water intoxication." *Archives of Neurology*, 19, 71-78, 1968.

WAYNER, M., GREENBERG, I., CAREY, R., and NOLLEY, D. "Ethanol drinking elicited during electrical stimulation of the lateral hypothalamus." *Physiology and Behavior*, 7, 793-795, 1971.

WEINER, H. *Psychobiology of Essential Hypertension*. New York: Elsevier, 1979.

WEINTRAUB, M. *A Clinician's Manual of Hysterical Conversion Reactions*. New York: Interdisciplinary Communications Media, Inc., 1978.

WEISKRANTZ, L., WARRINGTON, E., SANDERS, M., and MARSHALL, J. "Visual capacity in the hemianoptic field following a restricted occipital ablation." *Brain*, 97, 709-728, 1974.

WIESEL, T. and HUBEL, D. "Effects of visual deprivation on morphology and physiology of cells in the cat's lateral geniculate body." *Journal of Physiology*, 26, 978-993, 1963.

WIESEL, T. and HUBEL, D. "Single-cell responses in striate cortex of kittens deprived of vision in one eye." *Journal of Physiology*, 26, 1003-1017, 1963.

WIKLER, A. "Dynamics of drug dependence: implications of a conditioning theory for research and treatment." In *Classic Contributions in the Addictions*, edited by Shaffer, H. and Burglass, M. New York: Brunner/Mazel, 1981, pp 352-366. (Originally printed in *Archives of General Psychiatry*, 28, 611-616, 1973.)

WISHART, T. and MOGENSON, G. "Reduction of water intake by electrical stimulation of the septal region of the rat brain." *Physiology and Behavior*, 5, 1399-1404, 1970.

WISHART, T. and MOGENSON, G. "Effects of food deprivation on water intake in rats with septal lesions." *Physiology and Behavior*, 5, 1481-1486, 1970.

WOODS, S. "Conditioned insulin secretion." In *Food Intake and Chemical Senses*, edited by Katsuki, Y., Sato, M., Takagi, S., and Oomura, Y. Baltimore; Tokyo: University Park Press, 1977, pp 357-365.

WOOLSEY, C. *Cortical Sensory Organization. Volume 1: Multiple Somatic Areas*, edited by Woolsey, C. Clifton, New Jersey: Humana Press, 1981a, 245 pages.

WOOLSEY, C. *Cortical Sensory Organization. Volume 2: Multiple Visual Areas*, edited by Woolsey, C. Clifton, New Jersey: Humana Press, 1981b, 222 pages.

WOOLSEY, C. *Cortical Sensory Organization. Volume 3: Multiple Auditory Areas*, edited by Woolsey, C. Clifton, New Jersey: Humana Press, 1982, 265 pages.

WURTMAN, J. and WURTMAN, R. "Fenfluramine and fluoxetine spare protein consumption while suppressing caloric intake by rats." *Science*, 198, 1178-1180, 1977.

WURTMAN, R. "Control of the synthesis of neurotransmitters by their circulating precursors." In *Catecholamines and Stress: Recent Advances*, edited by Usdin, E., Kvetnansky, R., and Kopin, I. New York: Elsevier North-Holland, 1980, pp 383-391.

WURTMAN, R. "Nutrients that modify brain function." *Scientific American*, 246,4, 50-59, 1982.

YEN, S. "Neuroendocrine regulation of gonadotropin and prolactin secretion in women: disorders in reproduction." In *Clinical Reproductive Neuroendocrinology*, edited by Vaitukaitis, J. New York: Elsevier, 1982, pp 137-176.

ZANCHETTI, A., BACCELLI, G., MANCIA, G., and ELLISON, G. "Emotion and the cardiovascular system in the cat." In *Physiology, Emotions and Psychosomatic Illness*, edited by Porter, R. and Knight, J. New York: Associated Scientific Publishers, 1972, pp 201-223.

Index